fifth edition

COLLEGE ALGEBRA
A GRAPHING APPROACH

Ron Larson
The Pennsylvania State University
The Behrend College

Robert Hostetler
The Pennsylvania State University
The Behrend College

Bruce H. Edwards
University of Florida

With the assistance of
David C. Falvo
The Pennsylvania State University
The Behrend College

HOUGHTON MIFFLIN HARCOURT PUBLISHING COMPANY   Boston   New York

Publisher: Richard Stratton
Sponsoring Editor: Cathy Cantin
Senior Marketing Manager: Jennifer Jones
Development Editor: Lisa Collette
Supervising Editor: Karen Carter
Senior Project Editor: Patty Bergin
Photo Editor: Jennifer Meyer Dare
Composition Buyer: Chuck Dutton
New Title Project Manager: James Lonergan
Editorial Associate: Jeannine Lawless
Marketing Associate: Mary Legere
Editorial Assistant: Jill Clark
Composition and Art: Larson Texts, Inc.

We have included examples and exercises that use real-life data as well as technology output from a variety of software. This would not have been possible without the help of many people and organizations. Our wholehearted thanks go to all for their time and effort.

Custom Publishing Editor: Heidi Johnson
Custom Publishing Production Manager: Christina Battista
Project Coordinator: Sara Abbott
Cover Design: Sorae Lee
Cover Image: PhotoDisc

This book contains select works from existing Houghton Mifflin Harcourt Publishing Company resources and was produced by Houghton Mifflin Harcourt Custom Publishing for collegiate use. As such, those adopting and/or contributing to this work are responsible for editorial content, accuracy, continuity and completeness.

Printed in the United States of America.

ISBN-13: 978-0-547-19905-4
ISBN-10: 0-547-19905-8
1058411

1 2 3 4 5 6 7 8 9 – CM – 10 09 08

 Houghton Mifflin
                   Custom Publishing

222 Berkeley Street • Boston, MA 02116

Address all correspondence and order information to the above address.

Contents

A Word from the Authors   vi

Features Highlights   xi

Chapter P   **Prerequisites**   1

P.1   Real Numbers   2

P.2   Exponents and Radicals   12

P.3   Polynomials and Factoring   24

P.4   Rational Expressions   37

P.5   The Cartesian Plane   48

P.6   Representing Data Graphically   59

Chapter Summary   68   **Review Exercises**   69

Chapter Test   73   **Proofs in Mathematics**   74

Chapter 1   **Functions and Their Graphs**   75

Introduction to Library of Parent Functions   76

1.1   Graphs of Equations   77

1.2   Lines in the Plane   88

1.3   Functions   101

1.4   Graphs of Functions   115

1.5   Shifting, Reflecting, and Stretching Graphs   127

1.6   Combinations of Functions   136

1.7   Inverse Functions   147

Chapter Summary   158   **Review Exercises**   159

Chapter Test   163   **Proofs in Mathematics**   164

Chapter 2   **Solving Equations and Inequalities**   165

2.1   Linear Equations and Problem Solving   166

2.2   Solving Equations Graphically   176

2.3   Complex Numbers   187

2.4   Solving Quadratic Equations Algebraically   195

2.5   Solving Other Types of Equations Algebraically   209

2.6   Solving Inequalities Algebraically and Graphically   219

2.7   Linear Models and Scatter Plots   232

Chapter Summary   241   **Review Exercises**   242

Chapter Test   246   **Cumulative Test P–2**   247

Proofs in Mathematics   249

Progressive Summary P–2   250

Chapter 3   Polynomial and Rational Functions   251

    3.1   Quadratic Functions   252

    3.2   Polynomial Functions of Higher Degree   263

    3.3   Real Zeros of Polynomial Functions   276

    3.4   The Fundamental Theorem of Algebra   291

    3.5   Rational Functions and Asymptotes   298

    3.6   Graphs of Rational Functions   308

    3.7   Quadratic Models   317

       Chapter Summary   324   **Review Exercises**   325

       Chapter Test   330   **Proofs in Mathematics**   331

Chapter 4   Exponential and Logarithmic Functions   333

    4.1   Exponential Functions and Their Graphs   334

    4.2   Logarithmic Functions and Their Graphs   346

    4.3   Properties of Logarithms   357

    4.4   Solving Exponential and Logarithmic Equations   364

    4.5   Exponential and Logarithmic Models   375

    4.6   Nonlinear Models   387

       Chapter Summary   396   **Review Exercises**   397

       Chapter Test   402   **Proofs in Mathematics**   403

       Progressive Summary P–4   404

Chapter 5   Linear Systems and Matrices   405

    5.1   Solving Systems of Equations   406

    5.2   Systems of Linear Equations in Two Variables   417

    5.3   Multivariable Linear Systems   427

    5.4   Matrices and Systems of Equations   443

    5.5   Operations with Matrices   458

    5.6   The Inverse of a Square Matrix   473

    5.7   The Determinant of a Square Matrix   483

    5.8   Applications of Matrices and Determinants   491

       Chapter Summary   501   **Review Exercises**   502

       Chapter Test   508   **Cumulative Test 3–5**   509

       Proofs in Mathematics   511

Chapter 6   Sequences, Series, and Probabilty   513

  6.1   Sequences and Series   514
  6.2   Arithmetic Sequences and Partial Sums   526
  6.3   Geometric Sequences and Series   535
  6.4   Mathematical Induction   545
  6.5   The Binomial Theorem   553
  6.6   Counting Principles   561
  6.7   Probability   571
      Chapter Summary   584   **Review Exercises**   585
      Chapter Test   589   **Proofs in Mathematics**   590

Appendices   Appendix A   Technology Support Guide   A1

  Appendix B   Concepts in Statistics   A25
  B.1   Measures of Central Tendency and Dispersion   A25
  B.2   Least Squares Regression   A34

  Appendix C   Variation   A36

  Appendix D   Solving Linear Equations and Inequalities   A43

  Appendix E   Systems of Inequalities   A46
  E.1   Solving Systems of Inequalities   A46
  E.2   Linear Programming   A56

  Appendix F   Study Capsules   A65

      Answers to Odd-Numbered Exercises and Tests   A73
      Index of Selected Applications   A181
      Index   A183

Welcome to *College Algebra: A Graphing Approach*, Fifth Edition. We are pleased to present this new edition of our textbook in which we focus on making the mathematics accessible, supporting student success, and offering instructors flexible teaching options.

Accessible to Students

We have taken care to write this text with the student in mind. Paying careful attention to the presentation, we use precise mathematical language and a clear writing style to develop an effective learning tool. We believe that every student can learn mathematics, and we are committed to providing a text that makes the mathematics of the college algebra course accessible to all students.

Throughout the text, solutions to many examples are presented from multiple perspectives—algebraically, graphically, and numerically. The side-by-side format of this pedagogical feature helps students to see that a problem can be solved in more than one way and to see that different methods yield the same result. The side-by-side format also addresses many different learning styles.

We have found that many college algebra students grasp mathematical concepts more easily when they work with them in the context of real-life situations. Students have numerous opportunities to do this throughout this text. The *Make a Decision* feature further connects real-life data and applications and motivates students. It also offers students the opportunity to generate and analyze mathematical models from large data sets. To reinforce the concept of functions, we have compiled all the elementary functions as a *Library of Parent Functions*, presented in a summary on the endpapers of the text for convenient reference. Each function is introduced at the first point of use in the text with a definition and description of basic characteristics.

We have carefully written and designed each page to make the book more readable and accessible to students. For example, to avoid unnecessary page turning and disruptions to students' thought processes, each example and corresponding solution begins and ends on the same page.

Supports Student Success

During more than 30 years of teaching and writing, we have learned many things about the teaching and learning of mathematics. We have found that students are most successful when they know what they are expected to learn and why it is important to learn the concepts. With that in mind, we have incorporated a thematic study thread throughout this textbook.

Each chapter begins with a list of applications that are covered in the chapter and serve as a motivational tool by connecting section content to real-life situations. Using the same pedagogical theme, each section begins with a set of section learning objectives—*What You Should Learn*. These are followed by an engaging real-life application—*Why You Should Learn It*—that motivates students and illustrates an area where the mathematical concepts will be applied in an example or exercise in the section. *The Chapter Summary—What Did You Learn?*—at the end of each chapter includes *Key Terms* with page references and *Key Concepts*, organized by section, that were covered throughout the chapter. The *Chapter Summary* serves as a useful study aid for students.

Throughout the text, other features further improve accessibility. *Study Tips* are provided throughout the text at point-of-use to reinforce concepts and to help students learn how to study mathematics. *Explorations* reinforce mathematical concepts. Each example with worked-out solution is followed by a *Checkpoint*, which directs the student to work a similar exercise from the exercise set. The *Section Exercises* begin with a *Vocabulary Check*, which gives the students an opportunity to test their understanding of the important terms in the section. A *Prerequisites Skills* is offered in margin notes throughout the textbook exposition. Reviewing the prerequisite skills will enable students to master new concepts more quickly. *Synthesis Exercises* check students' conceptual understanding of the topics in each section. *Skills Review Exercises* provide additional practice with the concepts in the chapter or previous chapters. *Review Exercises*, *Chapter Tests*, and periodic *Cumulative Tests* offer students frequent opportunities for self-assessment and to develop strong study and test-taking skills. The *Progressive Summaries* and the *Study Capsules* serve as a quick reference when working on homework or as a cumulative study aid.

The use of technology also supports students with different learning styles, and graphing calculators are fully integrated into the text presentation. The *Technology Support Appendix* makes it easier for students to use technology. *Technology Support* notes are provided throughout the text at point-of-use. These notes guide students to the *Technology Support Appendix*, where they can learn how to use specific graphing calculator features to enhance their understanding of the concepts presented in the text. These notes also direct students to the *Graphing Technology Guide*, in the *Online Study Center*, for keystroke support that is available for numerous calculator models. *Technology Tips* are provided in the text at point-of-use to call attention to the strengths and weaknesses of graphing technology, as well as to offer alternative methods for solving or checking a problem using technology. Because students are often misled by the limitations of graphing calculators, we have, where appropriate, used color to enhance the graphing calculator displays in the textbook. This enables students to visualize the mathematical concepts clearly and accurately and avoid common misunderstandings.

Numerous additional text-specific resources are available to help students succeed in the college algebra course. These include "live" online tutoring, instructional DVDs, and a variety of other resources, such as tutorial support and self-assessment, which are available on the Web and in Eduspace®. In addition, the *Online Notetaking Guide* is a notetaking guide that helps students organize their class notes and create an effective study and review tool.

Flexible Options for Instructors

From the time we first began writing textbooks in the early 1970s, we have always considered it a critical part of our role as authors to provide instructors with flexible programs. In addition to addressing a variety of learning styles, the optional features within the text allow instructors to design their courses to meet their instructional needs and the needs of their students. For example, the *Explorations* throughout the text can be used as a quick introduction to concepts or as a way to reinforce student understanding.

Our goal when developing the exercise sets was to address a wide variety of learning styles and teaching preferences. The *Vocabulary Check* questions are provided at the beginning of every exercise set to help students learn proper mathematical terminology. In each exercise set we have included a variety of exercise types, including questions requiring writing and critical thinking, as well as real-data applications. The problems are carefully graded in difficulty from mastery of basic skills to more challenging exercises. Some of the more challenging exercises include the *Synthesis Exercises* that combine skills and are used to check for conceptual understanding, and the *Make a Decision* exercises that further connect real-life data and applications and motivate students. *Skills Review Exercises*, placed at the end of each exercise set, reinforce previously learned skills. The *Proofs in Mathematics*, at the end of each chapter, are proofs of important mathematical properties and theorems and illustrate various proof techniques. This feature gives the instructors the opportunity to incorporate more rigor into their course. In addition, Houghton Mifflin's Eduspace® website offers instructors the option to assign homework and tests online—and also includes the ability to grade these assignments automatically.

Several other print and media resources are available to support instructors. The *Online Instructor Success Organizer* includes suggested lesson plans and is an especially useful tool for larger departments that want all sections of a course to follow the same outline. The *Instructor's Edition* of the *Online Student Notetaking Guide* can be used as a lecture outline for every section of the text and includes additional examples for classroom discussion and important definitions. This is another valuable resource for schools trying to have consistent instruction and it can be used as a resource to support less experienced instructors. When used in conjunction with the *Online Student Notetaking Guide* these resources can save instructors preparation time and help students concentrate on important concepts.

Instructors who stress applications and problem solving and integrate technology into their course will be able to use this text successfully.

We hope you enjoy the Fifth Edition.

Ron Larson

Robert Hostetler

Bruce H. Edwards

Acknowledgments

We would like to thank the many people who have helped us prepare the text and supplements package, including all those reviewers who have contributed to this and previous editions of the text. Their encouragement, criticisms, and suggestions have been invaluable to us.

Reviewers

Tony Homayoon Akhlaghi
Bellevue Community College

Daniel D. Anderson
University of Iowa

Bruce Armbrust
Lake Tahoe Community College

Jamie Whitehead Ashby
Texarkana College

Teresa Barton
Western New England College

Kimberly Bennekin
Georgia Perimeter College

Charles M. Biles
Humboldt State University

Phyllis Barsch Bolin
Oklahoma Christian University

Khristo Boyadzhiev
Ohio Northern University

Dave Bregenzer
Utah State University

Anne E. Brown
Indiana University-South Bend

Diane Burleson
Central Piedmont Community College

Alexander Burstein
University of Rhode Island

Marilyn Carlson
University of Kansas

Victor M. Cornell
Mesa Community College

John Dersh
Grand Rapids Community College

Jennifer Dollar
Grand Rapids Community College

Marcia Drost
Texas A & M University

Cameron English
Rio Hondo College

Susan E. Enyart
Otterbein College

Patricia J. Ernst
St. Cloud State University

Eunice Everett
Seminole Community College

Kenny Fister
Murray State University

Susan C. Fleming
Virginia Highlands Community College

Jeff Frost
Johnson County Community College

James R. Fryxell
College of Lake County

Khadiga H. Gamgoum
Northern Virginia Community College

Nicholas E. Geller
Collin County Community College

Betty Givan
Eastern Kentucky University

Patricia K. Gramling
Trident Technical College

Michele Greenfield
Middlesex County College

Bernard Greenspan
University of Akron

Zenas Hartvigson
University of Colorado at Denver

Rodger Hergert
Rock Valley College

Allen Hesse
Rochester Community College

Rodney Holke-Farnam
Hawkeye Community College

Lynda Hollingsworth
Northwest Missouri State University

Jean M. Horn
Northern Virginia Community College

Spencer Hurd
The Citadel

Bill Huston
Missouri Western State College

Deborah Johnson
Cambridge South Dorchester High School

Francine Winston Johnson
Howard Community College

Luella Johnson
State University of New York, College at Buffalo

Susan Kellicut
Seminole Community College

John Kendall
Shelby State Community College

Donna M. Krawczyk
University of Arizona

Peter A. Lappan
Michigan State University

Charles G. Laws
Cleveland State Community College

JoAnn Lewin
Edison Community College

Richard J. Maher
Loyola University

Carl Main
Florida College

Marilyn McCollum
North Carolina State University

Judy McInerney
Sandhills Community College

David E. Meel
Bowling Green University

Beverly Michael
University of Pittsburgh

Roger B. Nelsen
Lewis and Clark College

Jon Odell
Richland Community College

Paul Oswood
Ridgewater College

Wing M. Park
College of Lake County

Rupa M. Patel
University of Portland

Robert Pearce
South Plains College

David R. Peterson
University of Central Arkansas

James Pommersheim
Reed College

Antonio Quesada
University of Akron

Laura Reger
Milwaukee Area Technical College

Jennifer Rhinehart
Mars Hill College

Lila F. Roberts
Georgia Southern University

Keith Schwingendorf
Purdue University North Central

George W. Shultz
St. Petersburg Junior College

Stephen Slack
Kenyon College

Judith Smalling
St. Petersburg Junior College

Pamela K. M. Smith
Fort Lewis College

Cathryn U. Stark
Collin County Community College

Craig M. Steenberg
Lewis-Clark State College

Mary Jane Sterling
Bradley University

G. Bryan Stewart
Tarrant County Junior College

Mahbobeh Vezvaei
Kent State University

Ellen Vilas
York Technical College

Hayat Weiss
Middlesex Community College

Howard L. Wilson
Oregon State University

Joel E. Wilson
Eastern Kentucky University

Michelle Wilson
Franklin University

Fred Worth
Henderson State University

Karl M. Zilm
Lewis and Clark Community College

We would like to thank the staff of Larson Texts, Inc. who assisted in preparing the manuscript, rendering the art package, and typesetting and proofreading the pages and supplements.

On a personal level, we are grateful to our wives, Deanna Gilbert Larson, Eloise Hostetler, and Consuelo Edwards for their love, patience, and support. Also, a special thanks goes to R. Scott O'Neil.

If you have suggestions for improving this text, please feel free to write us. Over the past two decades we have received many useful comments from both instructors and students, and we value these very much.

Ron Larson
Robert Hostetler
Bruce H. Edwards

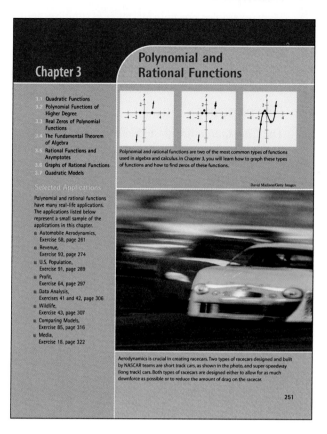

Chapter 3

3.1 Quadratic Functions
3.2 Polynomial Functions of Higher Degree
3.3 Real Zeros of Polynomial Functions
3.4 The Fundamental Theorem of Algebra
3.5 Rational Functions and Asymptotes
3.6 Graphs of Rational Functions
3.7 Quadratic Models

Polynomial and Rational Functions

Polynomial and rational functions are two of the most common types of functions used in algebra and calculus. In Chapter 3, you will learn how to graph these types of functions and how to find zeros of these functions.

David Madison/Getty Images

Selected Applications

Polynomial and rational functions have many real-life applications. The applications listed below represent a small sample of the applications in this chapter.

- Automobile Aerodynamics, Exercise 58, page 261
- Revenue, Exercise 93, page 274
- U.S. Population, Exercise 91, page 289
- Profit, Exercise 64, page 297
- Data Analysis, Exercises 41 and 42, page 306
- Wildlife, Exercise 43, page 307
- Comparing Models, Exercise 85, page 316
- Media, Exercise 18, page 322

Aerodynamics is crucial in creating racecars. Two types of racecars designed and built by NASCAR teams are short track cars, as shown in the photo, and super-speedway (long track) cars. Both types of racecars are designed either to allow for as much downforce as possible or to reduce the amount of drag on the racecar.

251

Chapter Opener

Each chapter begins with a comprehensive overview of the chapter concepts. The photograph and caption illustrate a real-life application of a key concept. Section references help students prepare for the chapter.

Applications List

An abridged list of applications, covered in the chapter, serve as a motivational tool by connecting section content to real-life situations.

"What You Should Learn" and "Why You Should Learn It"

Sections begin with *What You Should Learn*, an outline of the main concepts covered in the section, and *Why You Should Learn It*, a real-life application or mathematical reference that illustrates the relevance of the section content.

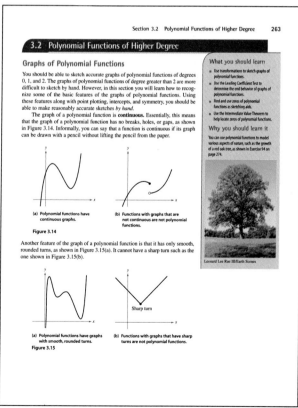

Section 3.2 Polynomial Functions of Higher Degree   263

3.2 Polynomial Functions of Higher Degree

Graphs of Polynomial Functions

You should be able to sketch accurate graphs of polynomial functions of degrees 0, 1, and 2. The graphs of polynomial functions of degree greater than 2 are more difficult to sketch by hand. However, in this section you will learn how to recognize some of the basic features of the graphs of polynomial functions. Using these features along with point plotting, intercepts, and symmetry, you should be able to make reasonably accurate sketches *by hand*.

The graph of a polynomial function is **continuous**. Essentially, this means that the graph of a polynomial function has no breaks, holes, or gaps, as shown in Figure 3.14. Informally, you can say that a graph is continuous if its graph can be drawn with a pencil without lifting the pencil from the paper.

What you should learn

- Use transformations to sketch graphs of polynomial functions.
- Use the Leading Coefficient Test to determine the end behavior of graphs of polynomial functions.
- Find and use zeros of polynomial functions as sketching aids.
- Use the Intermediate Value Theorem to help locate zeros of polynomial functions.

Why you should learn it

You can use polynomial functions to model various aspects of nature, such as the growth of a red oak tree, as shown in Exercise 94 on page 274.

Leonard Lee Rue III/Earth Scenes

(a) Polynomial functions have continuous graphs.

(b) Functions with graphs that are not continuous are not polynomial functions.

Figure 3.14

Another feature of the graph of a polynomial function is that it has only smooth, rounded turns, as shown in Figure 3.15(a). It cannot have a sharp turn such as the one shown in Figure 3.15(b).

Sharp turn

(a) Polynomial functions have graphs with smooth, rounded turns.

(b) Functions with graphs that have sharp turns are not polynomial functions.

Figure 3.15

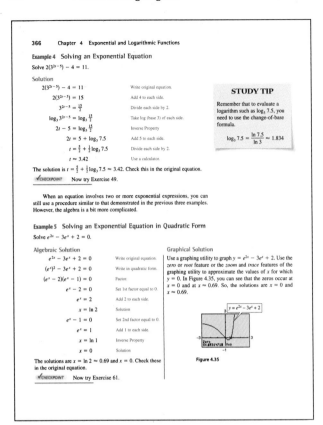

Examples

Many examples present side-by-side solutions with multiple approaches—algebraic, graphical, and numerical. This format addresses a variety of learning styles and shows students that different solution methods yield the same result.

Checkpoint

The *Checkpoint* directs students to work a similar problem in the exercise set for extra practice.

Study Tips

Study Tips reinforce concepts and help students learn how to study mathematics.

Library of Parent Functions

The *Library of Parent Functions* feature defines each elementary function and its characteristics at first point of use. The *Study Capsules* are also referenced for further review of each elementary function.

Explorations

The *Explorations* engage students in active discovery of mathematical concepts, strengthen critical thinking skills, and help them to develop an intuitive understanding of theoretical concepts.

New! Prerequisite Skills

A review of algebra skills needed to complete the examples is offered to the students at point of use throughout the text.

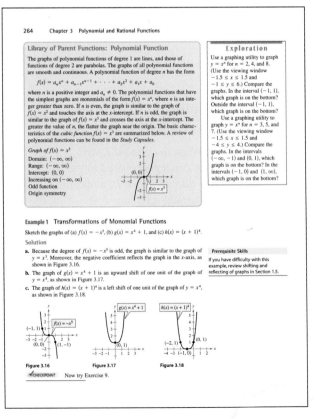

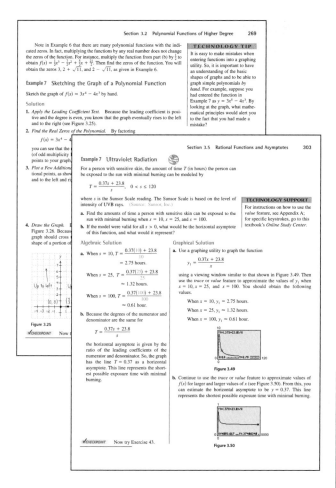

Technology Tip

Technology Tips point out the pros and cons of technology use in certain mathematical situations. *Technology Tips* also provide alternative methods of solving or checking a problem by the use of a graphing calculator.

Technology Support

The *Technology Support* feature guides students to the *Technology Support Appendix* if they need to reference a specific calculator feature. These notes also direct students to the *Graphing Technology Guide*, in the *Online Study Center*, for keystroke support that is available for numerous calculator models.

Real-Life Applications

A wide variety of real-life applications, many using current real data, are integrated throughout the examples and exercises. The 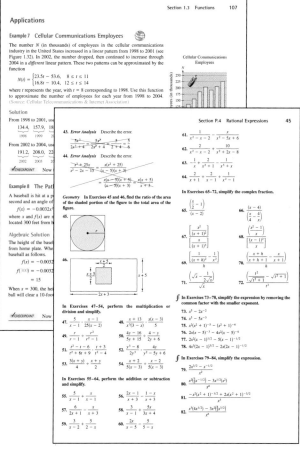 indicates an example that involves a real-life application.

Algebra of Calculus

Throughout the text, special emphasis is given to the algebraic techniques used in calculus. *Algebra of Calculus* examples and exercises are integrated throughout the text and are identified by the symbol $\int$.

FEATURES

xiv   Features Highlights

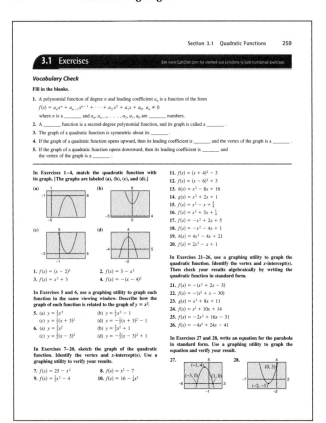

Section Exercises

The section exercise sets consist of a variety of computational, conceptual, and applied problems.

Vocabulary Check

Section exercises begin with a *Vocabulary Check* that serves as a review of the important mathematical terms in each section.

New! Calc Chat

The worked-out solutions to the odd-numbered text exercises are now available at *www.CalcChat.com*.

Synthesis and Skills Review Exercises

Each exercise set concludes with three types of exercises.

Synthesis exercises promote further exploration of mathematical concepts, critical thinking skills, and writing about mathematics. The exercises require students to show their understanding of the relationships between many concepts in the section.

Skills Review Exercises reinforce previously learned skills and concepts.

New! *Make a Decision* exercises, found in selected sections, further connect real-life data and applications and motivate students. They also offer students the opportunity to generate and analyze mathematical models from large data sets.

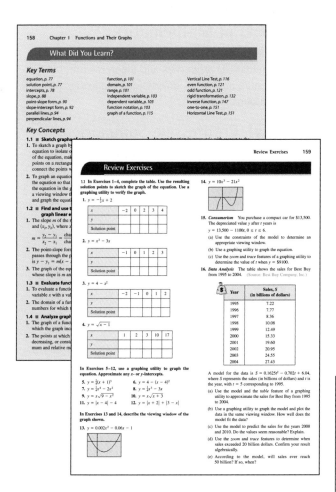

Chapter Summary

The *Chapter Summary* "*What Did You Learn?*" includes *Key Terms* with page references and *Key Concepts*, organized by section, that were covered throughout the chapter.

Review Exercises

The chapter *Review Exercises* provide additional practice with the concepts covered in the chapter.

Chapter Tests and Cumulative Tests

Chapter Tests, at the end of each chapter, and periodic *Cumulative Tests* offer students frequent opportunities for self-assessment and to develop strong study and test-taking skills.

FEATURES

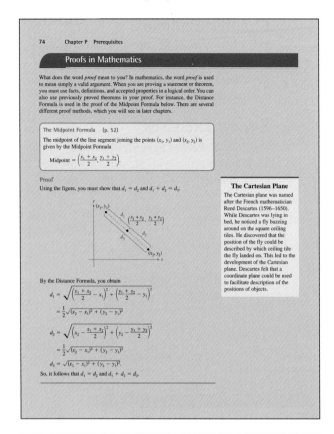

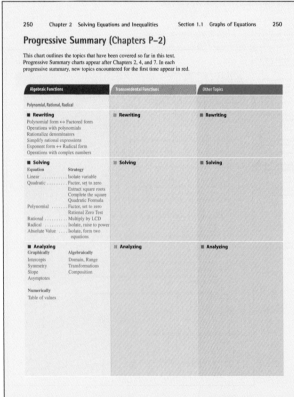

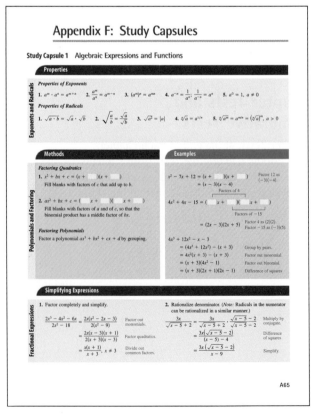

Proofs in Mathematics

At the end of every chapter, proofs of important mathematical properties and theorems are presented as well as discussions of various proof techniques.

New! Progressive Summaries

The *Progressive Summaries* are a series of charts that are usually placed at the end of every third chapter. Each *Progressive Summary* is completed in a gradual manner as new concepts are covered. Students can use the *Progressive Summaries* as a cumulative study aid and to see the connection between concepts and skills.

New! Study Capsules

Each *Study Capsule* in Appendix F summarizes many of the key concepts covered in previous chapters. A *Study Capsule* provides definitions, examples, and procedures for solving, simplifying, and graphing functions. Students can use this appendix as a quick reference when working on homework or studying for a test.

Supplements for the Instructor

Instructor's Annotated Edition (IAE)

Online Complete Solutions Guide

Online Instructor Success Organizer

 **Online Teaching Center**

This free companion website contains an abundance of instructors resources. Visit **college.hmco.com/pic/larsonCAAGA5e** and click on the Online Teaching Center icon.

HM Testing™ (Powered by Diploma™) *"Testing the way you want it"*

HM Testing provides instructors all the tools they need to **create, author/edit, customize,** and **deliver** multiple types of tests. Instructors can use existing test bank content, edit the content, and author new static or algorithmic questions—all within Diploma's powerful electronic platform.

Supplements for the Student

Study and Solutions Guide

Written by the author, this manual offers step-by-step solutions for all odd-numbered text exercises as well as Chapter and Cumulative Tests. The manual also provides practice tests that are accompanied by a solution key. In addition, these worked-out solutions are available at *www.CalcChat.com*.

 Online Study Center

This free companion website contains an abundance of student resources including the *Online Student Notetaking Guide*. Visit the website **college.hmco.com/pic/larsonCAAGA5e** and click on the Online Study Center icon.

Instructional DVDs

Hosted by Dana Mosely, these text-specific DVDs cover all sections of the text and provide key explanations of key concepts, examples, exercises, and applications in a lecture-based format. New to this edition, the DVDs will now include Captioning for the Hearing Impaired.

Eduspace®: Houghton Mifflin's Online Learning Tool (Powered by Blackboard™)

Eduspace is a web-based learning system that provides instructors and students with powerful course management tools and text-specific content to support all of their online teaching and learning needs. By pairing the widely recognized tools of Blackboard with customizable content from Houghton Mifflin, Eduspace makes it easy to deliver all or part of a course online. Instructors can use Eduspace to offer a combination of ready-to-use resources to students. These resources include algorithmic and non-algorithmic homework, quizzes, tests, tutorials, instructional videos, interactive textbooks, live online tutoring with **SMARTHINKING**®, and additional study materials. Instructors can choose to use the content as is, modify it, or even add their own content. Visit *www.eduspace.com* for more information.

SMARTHINKING®: Houghton Mifflin has partnered with SMARTHINKING to provide an easy-to-use, effective, online tutorial service. Through state-of-the-art tools and a two-way whiteboard, students communicate in real-time with qualified e-structors. Three levels of service are offered to students that include live tutorial help, question submission, and access to independent study resources.

Visit *smarthinking.college.hmco.com* for more information.

Online Course Content for Blackboard™, WebCT®, and eCollege®

Deliver program or text-specific Houghton Mifflin content online using your institution's local course management system. Houghton Mifflin offers homework, tutorials, videos, and other resources formatted for Blackboard™, WebCT®, eCollege®, and other course management systems. Add to an existing online course or create a new one by selecting from a wide range of powerful learning and instructional materials.

SUPPLEMENTS

Chapter P

P.1 Real Numbers
P.2 Exponents and Radicals
P.3 Polynomials and Factoring
P.4 Rational Expressions
P.5 The Cartesian Plane
P.6 Representing Data Graphically

Selected Applications

Prealgebra concepts have many real-life applications. The applications listed below represent a small sample of the applications in this chapter.

- Budget Variance,
  Exercises 79–82, page 10
- Erosion,
  Exercise 115, page 23
- Stopping Distance,
  Exercise 157, page 34
- Resistance,
  Exercise 95, page 46
- Meteorology,
  Exercise 22, page 56
- Sports,
  Exercise 88, page 58
- Agriculture,
  Exercise 5, page 64
- Cellular Phones,
  Exercises 21 and 22, page 67

Prerequisites

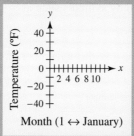
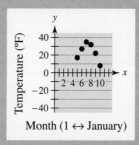
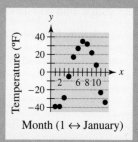

Algebra can be used to model real-life situations. Representing real-life situations as expressions, equations, or inequalities or in a graph increases our understanding of the world around us. In Chapter P, you will review the concepts that form the foundation for algebra: real numbers, exponents, radicals, polynomials, and graphical representation of data sets.

© Karl Weatherly/Corbis

Meteorology is the study of weather and weather forecasting. It involves collecting and analyzing climatic data for geographical regions. Mathematics plays a crucial role in the study of meteorology. Mathematical equations are used to model meteorological concepts such as temperature, wind chill, and precipitation.

P.1 Real Numbers

Real Numbers

Real numbers are used in everyday life to describe quantities such as age, miles per gallon, and population. Real numbers are represented by symbols such as

$$-5, 9, 0, \tfrac{4}{3}, 0.666\ldots, 28.21, \sqrt{2}, \pi, \text{ and } \sqrt[3]{-32}.$$

Here are some important **subsets** (each member of subset B is also a member of set A) of the set of real numbers.

$$\{1, 2, 3, 4, \ldots\} \qquad \text{Set of natural numbers}$$

$$\{0, 1, 2, 3, 4, \ldots\} \qquad \text{Set of whole numbers}$$

$$\{\ldots, -3, -2, -1, 0, 1, 2, 3, \ldots\} \qquad \text{Set of integers}$$

A real number is **rational** if it can be written as the ratio p/q of two integers, where $q \neq 0$. For instance, the numbers

$$\frac{1}{3} = 0.3333\ldots = 0.\overline{3}, \frac{1}{8} = 0.125, \text{ and } \frac{125}{111} = 1.126126\ldots = 1.\overline{126}$$

are rational. The decimal representation of a rational number either *repeats* (as in $\frac{173}{55} = 3.1\overline{45}$) or *terminates* (as in $\frac{1}{2} = 0.5$). A real number that cannot be written as the ratio of two integers is called **irrational.** Irrational numbers have infinite nonrepeating decimal representations. For instance, the numbers

$$\sqrt{2} = 1.4142135\ldots \approx 1.41 \quad \text{and} \quad \pi = 3.1415926\ldots \approx 3.14$$

are irrational. (The symbol $\approx$ means "is approximately equal to.") Figure P.1 shows subsets of real numbers and their relationships to each other.

Real numbers are represented graphically by a **real number line.** The point 0 on the real number line is the **origin.** Numbers to the right of 0 are positive and numbers to the left of 0 are negative, as shown in Figure P.2. The term **nonnegative** describes a number that is either positive or zero.

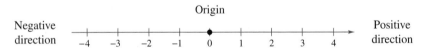

Figure P.2   The Real Number Line

There is a *one-to-one correspondence* between real numbers and points on the real number line. That is, every point on the real number line corresponds to exactly one real number, called its **coordinate,** and every real number corresponds to exactly one point on the real number line, as shown in Figure P.3.

 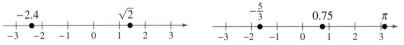

Every point on the real number line corresponds to exactly one real number.

Every real number corresponds to exactly one point on the real number line.

Figure P.3   One-to-One Correspondence

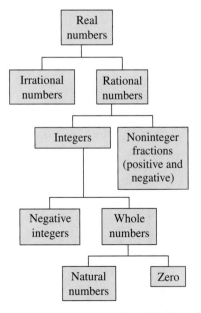

© Alan Schein Photography/Corbis

Figure P.1   Subsets of Real Numbers

Absolute V[...]

The **absolute va[...]
origin and the p[...]

Definition of [...]

If a is a real nu[...]

$$|a| = \begin{cases} a, \\ - \end{cases}$$

Notice from
negative. For ins
of a real numbe
whose absolute

Example 4   Ev

Evaluate $\dfrac{|x|}{x}$ for

Solution

a. If $x > 0$, the

b. If $x < 0$, the

✓CHECKPOINT

Properties of

   1. $|a| \geq$ (

   3. $|ab| =$

Absolute v
the real numbe

$$|-3 - 4|$$

as shown in Fig

Distance Bet

Let a and b b

$$d(a, b)$$

Ordering Real Numbers

One important property of real numbers is that they are **ordered.**

Definition of Order on the Real Number Line

If a and b are real numbers, a is **less than** b if $b - a$ is positive. This order is denoted by the **inequality** $a < b$. This relationship can also be described by saying that b is **greater than** a and writing $b > a$. The inequality $a \leq b$ means that a is **less than or equal to** b, and the inequality $b \geq a$ means that b is **greater than or equal to** a. The symbols $<$, $>$, $\leq$, and $\geq$, are **inequality symbols.**

Geometrically, this definition implies that $a < b$ if and only if a lies to the *left* of b on the real number line, as shown in Figure P.4.

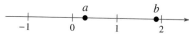

Figure P.4 $a < b$ if and only if a lies to the left of b.

Example 1   Interpreting Inequalities

Describe the subset of real numbers represented by each inequality.

a. $x \leq 2$ **b.** $x > -1$ **c.** $-2 \leq x < 3$

Solution

a. The inequality $x \leq 2$ denotes all real numbers less than or equal to 2, as shown in Figure P.5.

b. The inequality $x > -1$ denotes all real numbers greater than -1, as shown in Figure P.6.

c. The inequality $-2 \leq x < 3$ means that $x \geq -2$ *and* $x < 3$. The "double inequality" denotes all real numbers between -2 and 3, including -2 but not including 3, as shown in Figure P.7.

✓CHECKPOINT   Now try Exercise 31(a).

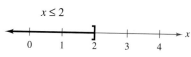

Figure P.5

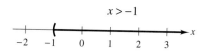

Figure P.6

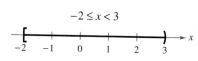

Figure P.7

Inequalities can be used to describe subsets of real numbers called **intervals.** In the bounded intervals below, the real numbers a and b are the **endpoints** of each interval.

Bounded Intervals on the Real Number Line

Notation	Interval Type	Inequality	Graph
$[a, b]$	Closed	$a \leq x \leq b$	
(a, b)	Open	$a < x < b$	
$[a, b)$		$a \leq x < b$	
$(a, b]$		$a < x \leq b$	

STUDY TIP

The endpoints of a closed interval are included in the interval. The endpoints of an open interval are *not* included in the interval.

4   Chapt

The symbols
represent real num
unboundedness of

Unbounded Int

Notation
$[a, \infty)$
(a, ∞)
$(-\infty, b]$
$(-\infty, b)$
$(-\infty, \infty)$

P.2 Exponents and Radicals

Integer Exponents

Repeated *multiplication* can be written in **exponential form.**

Repeated Multiplication	Exponential Form
$a \cdot a \cdot a \cdot a \cdot a$	a^5
$(-4)(-4)(-4)$	$(-4)^3$
$(2x)(2x)(2x)(2x)$	$(2x)^4$

In general, if a is a real number, variable, or algebraic expression and n is a positive integer, then

$$a^n = \underbrace{a \cdot a \cdot a \cdots a}_{n \text{ factors}}$$

where n is the **exponent** and a is the **base.** The expression a^n is read "a to the nth **power.**" An exponent can be negative as well. Property 3 below shows how to use a negative exponent.

What you should learn

- Use properties of exponents.
- Use scientific notation to represent real numbers.
- Use properties of radicals.
- Simplify and combine radicals.
- Rationalize denominators and numerators.
- Use properties of rational exponents.

Why you should learn it

Real numbers and algebraic expressions are often written with exponents and radicals. For instance, in Exercise 115 on page 23, you will use an expression involving a radical to find the size of a particle that can be carried by a stream moving at a certain velocity.

SuperStock

Example 2   Usi

Use inequality n

a. c is at most 2.

Solution

a. The statemen

b. "All x in the i

✓CHECKPOINT

Example 3   In

Give a verbal de

a. $(-1, 0)$

Solution

a. This interval
than 0.

b. This interval

c. This interval

✓CHECKPOINT

The **Law**
precisely one c

$a = b$, a

Properties of Exponents

Let a and b be real numbers, variables, or algebraic expressions, and let m and n be integers. (All denominators and bases are nonzero.)

Property	Example
1. $a^m a^n = a^{m+n}$	$3^2 \cdot 3^4 = 3^{2+4} = 3^6 = 729$
2. $\dfrac{a^m}{a^n} = a^{m-n}$	$\dfrac{x^7}{x^4} = x^{7-4} = x^3$
3. $a^{-n} = \dfrac{1}{a^n} = \left(\dfrac{1}{a}\right)^n$	$y^{-4} = \dfrac{1}{y^4} = \left(\dfrac{1}{y}\right)^4$
4. $a^0 = 1, \quad a \neq 0$	$(x^2 + 1)^0 = 1$
5. $(ab)^m = a^m b^m$	$(5x)^3 = 5^3 x^3 = 125x^3$
6. $(a^m)^n = a^{mn}$	$(y^3)^{-4} = y^{3(-4)} = y^{-12} = \dfrac{1}{y^{12}}$
7. $\left(\dfrac{a}{b}\right)^m = \dfrac{a^m}{b^m}$	$\left(\dfrac{2}{x}\right)^3 = \dfrac{2^3}{x^3} = \dfrac{8}{x^3}$
8. $\lvert a^2 \rvert = \lvert a \rvert^2 = a^2$	$\lvert (-2)^2 \rvert = \lvert -2 \rvert^2 = 2^2 = 4$

It is important to recognize the difference between expressions such as $(-2)^4$ and -2^4. In $(-2)^4$, the parentheses indicate that the exponent applies to the negative sign as well as to the 2, but in $-2^4 = -(2^4)$, the exponent applies only to the 2. So, $(-2)^4 = 16$, whereas $-2^4 = -16$. It is also important to know when to use parentheses when evaluating exponential expressions using a graphing calculator. Figure P.9 shows that a graphing calculator follows the order of operations.

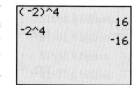

Figure P.9

The properties of exponents listed on the preceding page apply to *all* integers m and n, not just positive integers. For instance, by Property 2, you can write

$$\frac{3^4}{3^{-5}} = 3^{4-(-5)} = 3^{4+5} = 3^9.$$

Example 1 Using Properties of Exponents

a. $(-3ab^4)(4ab^{-3}) = -12(a)(a)(b^4)(b^{-3}) = -12a^2b$

b. $(2xy^2)^3 = 2^3(x)^3(y^2)^3 = 8x^3y^6$

c. $3a(-4a^2)^0 = 3a(1) = 3a, \ a \neq 0$

✓CHECKPOINT   Now try Exercise 15.

Example 2 Rewriting with Positive Exponents

a. $x^{-1} = \dfrac{1}{x}$ Property 3

b. $\dfrac{1}{3x^{-2}} = \dfrac{1(x^2)}{3} = \dfrac{x^2}{3}$ The exponent -2 does not apply to 3.

c. $\dfrac{1}{(3x)^{-2}} = (3x)^2 = 9x^2$ The exponent -2 does apply to 3.

d. $\dfrac{12a^3b^{-4}}{4a^{-2}b} = \dfrac{12a^3 \cdot a^2}{4b \cdot b^4} = \dfrac{3a^5}{b^5}$ Properties 3 and 1

e. $\left(\dfrac{3x^2}{y}\right)^{-2} = \dfrac{3^{-2}(x^2)^{-2}}{y^{-2}}$ Properties 5 and 7

$\qquad = \dfrac{3^{-2}x^{-4}}{y^{-2}}$ Property 6

$\qquad = \dfrac{y^2}{3^2x^4} = \dfrac{y^2}{9x^4}$ Property 3, and simplify.

✓CHECKPOINT   Now try Exercise 19.

Example 3 Calculators and Exponents

Expression	Graphing Calculator Keystrokes	Display
a. $3^{-2} + 4^{-1}$	3 ^ (−) 2 + 4 ^ (−) 1 ENTER	.3611111111
b. $\dfrac{3^5 + 1}{3^5 - 1}$	(3 ^ 5 + 1) ÷	
	(3 ^ 5 − 1) ENTER	1.008264463

✓CHECKPOINT   Now try Exercise 23.

TECHNOLOGY TIP   The graphing calculator keystrokes given in this text may not be the same as the keystrokes for your graphing calculator. Be sure you are familiar with the use of the keys on your own calculator.

STUDY TIP

Rarely in algebra is there only one way to solve a problem. Don't be concerned if the steps you use to solve a problem are not exactly the same as the steps presented in this text. The important thing is to use steps that you understand *and*, of course, that are justified by the rules of algebra. For instance, you might prefer the following steps for Example 2(e).

$$\left(\frac{3x^2}{y}\right)^{-2} = \left(\frac{y}{3x^2}\right)^2 = \frac{y^2}{9x^4}$$

Scientific Notation

Exponents provide an efficient way of writing and computing with very large (or very small) numbers. For instance, there are about 359 billion billion gallons of water on Earth—that is, 359 followed by 18 zeros.

359,000,000,000,000,000,000

It is convenient to write such numbers in **scientific notation.** This notation has the form $\pm c \times 10^n$, where $1 \leq c < 10$ and n is an integer. So, the number of gallons of water on Earth can be written in scientific notation as

$3.59 \times 100{,}000{,}000{,}000{,}000{,}000{,}000 = 3.59 \times 10^{20}.$

The *positive* exponent 20 indicates that the number is *large* (10 or more) and that the decimal point has been moved 20 places. A *negative* exponent indicates that the number is *small* (less than 1). For instance, the mass (in grams) of one electron is approximately

$9.0 \times 10^{-28} = 0.0000000000000000000000000009.$

28 decimal places

Example 4   Scientific Notation

a. $1.345 \times 10^2 = 134.5$ **b.** $0.0000782 = 7.82 \times 10^{-5}$

c. $-9.36 \times 10^{-6} = -0.00000936$ **d.** $836{,}100{,}000 = 8.361 \times 10^8$

✓CHECKPOINT   Now try Exercise 31.

TECHNOLOGY TIP   Most calculators automatically switch to scientific notation when they are showing large or small numbers that exceed the display range. Try evaluating $86{,}500{,}000 \times 6000$. If your calculator follows standard conventions, its display should be

$\boxed{5.19\ 11}$ or $\boxed{5.19\ E\ 11}$

which is 5.19×10^{11}.

Example 5   Using Scientific Notation with a Calculator

Use a calculator to evaluate $65{,}000 \times 3{,}400{,}000{,}000$.

Solution

Because $65{,}000 = 6.5 \times 10^4$ and $3{,}400{,}000{,}000 = 3.4 \times 10^9$, you can multiply the two numbers using the following graphing calculator keystrokes.

6.5 $\boxed{\text{EE}}$ 4 $\boxed{\times}$ 3.4 $\boxed{\text{EE}}$ 9 $\boxed{\text{ENTER}}$

After entering these keystrokes, the calculator display should read $\boxed{2.21\ E\ 14}$. So, the product of the two numbers is

$(6.5 \times 10^4)(3.4 \times 10^9) = 2.21 \times 10^{14} = 221{,}000{,}000{,}000{,}000.$

✓CHECKPOINT   Now try Exercise 53.

Radicals and Their Properties

A **square root** of a number is one of its two equal factors. For example, 5 is a square root of 25 because 5 is one of the two equal factors of $25 = 5 \cdot 5$. In a similar way, a **cube root** of a number is one of its three equal factors, as in $125 = 5^3$.

Definition of the nth Root of a Number

Let a and b be real numbers and let $n \geq 2$ be a positive integer. If

$$a = b^n$$

then b is an **nth root of a**. If $n = 2$, the root is a **square root.** If $n = 3$, the root is a **cube root.**

Some numbers have more than one nth root. For example, both 5 and -5 are square roots of 25. The *principal square root* of 25, written as $\sqrt{25}$, is the positive root, 5. The **principal nth root** of a number is defined as follows.

Principal nth Root of a Number

Let a be a real number that has at least one nth root. The **principal nth root of a** is the nth root that has the same sign as a. It is denoted by a **radical symbol**

$$\sqrt[n]{a}. \qquad \text{Principal } n\text{th root}$$

The positive integer n is the **index** of the radical, and the number a is the **radicand.** If $n = 2$, omit the index and write $\sqrt{a}$ rather than $\sqrt[2]{a}$. (The plural of index is *indices*.)

A common misunderstanding when taking square roots of real numbers is that the square root sign implies both negative and positive roots. This is not correct. The square root sign implies only a positive root. When a negative root is needed, you must use the negative sign with the square root sign.

Incorrect: $\sqrt{4} = \pm 2$ Correct: $-\sqrt{4} = -2$ and $\sqrt{4} = 2$

Example 6   Evaluating Expressions Involving Radicals

a. $\sqrt{36} = 6$ because $6^2 = 36$.

b. $-\sqrt{36} = -6$ because $-\left(\sqrt{36}\right) = -\left(\sqrt{6^2}\right) = -(6) = -6$.

c. $\sqrt[3]{\dfrac{125}{64}} = \dfrac{5}{4}$ because $\left(\dfrac{5}{4}\right)^3 = \dfrac{5^3}{4^3} = \dfrac{125}{64}$.

d. $\sqrt[5]{-32} = -2$ because $(-2)^5 = -32$.

e. $\sqrt[4]{-81}$ is not a real number because there is no real number that can be raised to the fourth power to produce -81.

✓**CHECKPOINT**   Now try Exercise 59.

Here are some generalizations about the *n*th roots of a real number.

Generalizations About *n*th Roots of Real Numbers

Real number *a*	Integer *n*	Root(s) of *a*	Example
$a > 0$	$n > 0$, *n* is even.	$\sqrt[n]{a},\ -\sqrt[n]{a}$	$\sqrt[4]{81} = 3,\ -\sqrt[4]{81} = -3$
$a > 0$ or $a < 0$	*n* is odd.	$\sqrt[n]{a}$	$\sqrt[3]{-8} = -2$
$a < 0$	*n* is even.	No real roots	$\sqrt{-4}$ is not a real number.
$a = 0$	*n* is even or odd.	$\sqrt[n]{0} = 0$	$\sqrt[5]{0} = 0$

Integers such as 1, 4, 9, 16, 25, and 36 are called **perfect squares** because they have integer square roots. Similarly, integers such as 1, 8, 27, 64, and 125 are called **perfect cubes** because they have integer cube roots.

Properties of Radicals

Let *a* and *b* be real numbers, variables, or algebraic expressions such that the indicated roots are real numbers, and let *m* and *n* be positive integers.

Property	Example
1. $\sqrt[n]{a^m} = \left(\sqrt[n]{a}\right)^m$	$\sqrt[3]{8^2} = \left(\sqrt[3]{8}\right)^2 = (2)^2 = 4$
2. $\sqrt[n]{a} \cdot \sqrt[n]{b} = \sqrt[n]{ab}$	$\sqrt{5} \cdot \sqrt{7} = \sqrt{5 \cdot 7} = \sqrt{35}$
3. $\dfrac{\sqrt[n]{a}}{\sqrt[n]{b}} = \sqrt[n]{\dfrac{a}{b}},\ b \neq 0$	$\dfrac{\sqrt[4]{27}}{\sqrt[4]{9}} = \sqrt[4]{\dfrac{27}{9}} = \sqrt[4]{3}$
4. $\sqrt[m]{\sqrt[n]{a}} = \sqrt[mn]{a}$	$\sqrt[3]{\sqrt{10}} = \sqrt[6]{10}$
5. $\left(\sqrt[n]{a}\right)^n = a$	$\left(\sqrt{3}\right)^2 = 3$
6. For *n* even, $\sqrt[n]{a^n} = |a|$.	$\sqrt{(-12)^2} = |-12| = 12$
For *n* odd, $\sqrt[n]{a^n} = a$.	$\sqrt[3]{(-12)^3} = -12$

TECHNOLOGY TIP

There are three methods of evaluating radicals on most graphing calculators. For square roots, you can use the *square root key* ⬛. For cube roots, you can use the *cube root key* ⬛ (or menu choice). For other roots, you can use the *xth root key* ⬛ (or menu choice). For example, the screen below shows you how to evaluate $\sqrt{36}$, $\sqrt[3]{-8}$, and $\sqrt[5]{32}$ using one of the three methods described.

```
√(36)
              6
3√(-8)
             -2
5×√32
              2
```

Example 7 Using Properties of Radicals

Use the properties of radicals to simplify each expression.

a. $\sqrt{8} \cdot \sqrt{2}$ **b.** $\left(\sqrt[3]{5}\right)^3$ **c.** $\sqrt[3]{x^3}$ **d.** $\sqrt[6]{y^6}$

Solution

a. $\sqrt{8} \cdot \sqrt{2} = \sqrt{8 \cdot 2} = \sqrt{16} = 4$

b. $\left(\sqrt[3]{5}\right)^3 = 5$

c. $\sqrt[3]{x^3} = x$

d. $\sqrt[6]{y^6} = |y|$

✓CHECKPOINT   Now try Exercise 79.

Simplifying Radicals

An expression involving radicals is in **simplest form** when the following conditions are satisfied.

1. All possible factors have been removed from the radical.
2. All fractions have radical-free denominators (accomplished by a process called *rationalizing the denominator*).
3. The index of the radical is reduced.

   To simplify a radical, factor the radicand into factors whose exponents are multiples of the index. The roots of these factors are written outside the radical, and the "leftover" factors make up the new radicand.

Example 8   Simplifying Even Roots

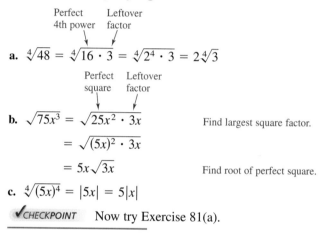

a. $\sqrt[4]{48} = \sqrt[4]{16 \cdot 3} = \sqrt[4]{2^4 \cdot 3} = 2\sqrt[4]{3}$

b. $\sqrt{75x^3} = \sqrt{25x^2 \cdot 3x}$ Find largest square factor.

$= \sqrt{(5x)^2 \cdot 3x}$

$= 5x\sqrt{3x}$ Find root of perfect square.

c. $\sqrt[4]{(5x)^4} = |5x| = 5|x|$

✓**CHECKPOINT**   Now try Exercise 81(a).

Example 9   Simplifying Odd Roots

a. $\sqrt[3]{24} = \sqrt[3]{8 \cdot 3} = \sqrt[3]{2^3 \cdot 3} = 2\sqrt[3]{3}$

b. $\sqrt[3]{-40x^6} = \sqrt[3]{(-8x^6) \cdot 5}$ Find largest cube factor.

$= \sqrt[3]{(-2x^2)^3 \cdot 5}$

$= -2x^2\sqrt[3]{5}$ Find root of perfect cube.

✓**CHECKPOINT**   Now try Exercise 81(b).

   Radical expressions can be combined (added or subtracted) if they are **like radicals**—that is, if they have the same index and radicand. For instance, $\sqrt{2}$, $3\sqrt{2}$, and $\frac{1}{2}\sqrt{2}$ are like radicals, but $\sqrt{3}$ and $\sqrt{2}$ are unlike radicals. To determine whether two radicals can be combined, you should first simplify each radical.

Example 10   Combining Radicals

a. $2\sqrt{48} - 3\sqrt{27} = 2\sqrt{16 \cdot 3} - 3\sqrt{9 \cdot 3}$ Find square factors.

                    $= 8\sqrt{3} - 9\sqrt{3}$ Find square roots and multiply by coefficients.

                    $= (8 - 9)\sqrt{3}$ Combine like terms.

                    $= -\sqrt{3}$ Simplify.

b. $\sqrt[3]{16x} - \sqrt[3]{54x^4} = \sqrt[3]{8 \cdot 2x} - \sqrt[3]{27 \cdot x^3 \cdot 2x}$ Find cube factors.

                    $= 2\sqrt[3]{2x} - 3x\sqrt[3]{2x}$ Find cube roots.

                    $= (2 - 3x)\sqrt[3]{2x}$ Combine like terms.

✓**CHECKPOINT**   Now try Exercise 85.

Try using your calculator to check the result of Example 10(a). You should obtain -1.732050808, which is the same as the calculator's approximation for $-\sqrt{3}$.

Rationalizing Denominators and Numerators

To rationalize a denominator or numerator of the form $a - b\sqrt{m}$ or $a + b\sqrt{m}$, multiply both numerator and denominator by a **conjugate:** $a + b\sqrt{m}$ and $a - b\sqrt{m}$ are conjugates of each other. If $a = 0$, then the rationalizing factor for $\sqrt{m}$ is itself, $\sqrt{m}$. Note that the product of a number and its conjugate is a rational number.

Example 11   Rationalizing Denominators

Rationalize the denominator of each expression.

a. $\dfrac{5}{2\sqrt{3}}$ **b.** $\dfrac{2}{\sqrt[3]{5}}$

Solution

a. $\dfrac{5}{2\sqrt{3}} = \dfrac{5}{2\sqrt{3}} \cdot \dfrac{\sqrt{3}}{\sqrt{3}}$ $\sqrt{3}$ is rationalizing factor.

     $= \dfrac{5\sqrt{3}}{2(3)}$ Multiply.

     $= \dfrac{5\sqrt{3}}{6}$ Simplify.

b. $\dfrac{2}{\sqrt[3]{5}} = \dfrac{2}{\sqrt[3]{5}} \cdot \dfrac{\sqrt[3]{5^2}}{\sqrt[3]{5^2}}$ $\sqrt[3]{5^2}$ is rationalizing factor.

     $= \dfrac{2\sqrt[3]{5^2}}{\sqrt[3]{5^3}} = \dfrac{2\sqrt[3]{25}}{5}$ Multiply and simplify.

✓**CHECKPOINT**   Now try Exercise 91.

STUDY TIP

Notice in Example 11(b) that the numerator and denominator are multiplied by $\sqrt[3]{5^2}$ to produce a perfect cube radicand.

Example 12   Rationalizing a Denominator with Two Terms

Rationalize the denominator of $\dfrac{2}{3 + \sqrt{7}}$.

Solution

$$\frac{2}{3 + \sqrt{7}} = \frac{2}{3 + \sqrt{7}} \cdot \frac{3 - \sqrt{7}}{3 - \sqrt{7}}$$

Multiply numerator and denominator by conjugate of denominator.

$$= \frac{2(3 - \sqrt{7})}{(3)^2 - (\sqrt{7})^2}$$

Find products. In denominator,
$(a + b)(a - b) = a^2 - ab + ab - b^2$
$\qquad\qquad = a^2 - b^2.$

$$= \frac{2(3 - \sqrt{7})}{2} = 3 - \sqrt{7}$$

Simplify and divide out common factors.

✓CHECKPOINT   Now try Exercise 93.

In calculus, sometimes it is necessary to rationalize the numerator of an expression.

Example 13   Rationalizing a Numerator

Rationalize the numerator of $\dfrac{\sqrt{5} - \sqrt{7}}{2}$.

Solution

$$\frac{\sqrt{5} - \sqrt{7}}{2} = \frac{\sqrt{5} - \sqrt{7}}{2} \cdot \frac{\sqrt{5} + \sqrt{7}}{\sqrt{5} + \sqrt{7}}$$

Multiply numerator and denominator by conjugate of numerator.

$$= \frac{(\sqrt{5})^2 - (\sqrt{7})^2}{2(\sqrt{5} + \sqrt{7})}$$

Find products. In numerator,
$(a + b)(a - b) = a^2 - ab + ab - b^2$
$\qquad\qquad = a^2 - b^2.$

$$= \frac{-2}{2(\sqrt{5} + \sqrt{7})} = \frac{-1}{\sqrt{5} + \sqrt{7}}$$

Simplify and divide out common factors.

✓CHECKPOINT   Now try Exercise 97.

Rational Exponents

Definition of Rational Exponents

If a is a real number and n is a positive integer such that the principal nth root of a exists, then $a^{1/n}$ is defined as

$a^{1/n} = \sqrt[n]{a}$ where $1/n$ is the **rational exponent** of a.

Moreover, if m is a positive integer that has no common factor with n, then

$$a^{m/n} = (a^{1/n})^m = \left(\sqrt[n]{a}\right)^m \quad \text{and} \quad a^{m/n} = (a^m)^{1/n} = \sqrt[n]{a^m}.$$

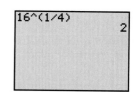
The symbol $\int$ indicates an example or exercise that highlights algebraic techniques specifically used in calculus.

The numerator of a rational exponent denotes the *power* to which the base is raised, and the denominator denotes the *index* or the *root* to be taken.

$$\begin{array}{c} \overbrace{}^{\text{Power}} \\ b^{m/n} = \left(\sqrt[n]{b}\right)^{m} = \sqrt[n]{b^m} \end{array}$$

When you are working with rational exponents, the properties of integer exponents still apply. For instance,

$$2^{1/2}2^{1/3} = 2^{(1/2)+(1/3)} = 2^{5/6}.$$

Example 14   Changing from Radical to Exponential Form

a. $\sqrt{3} = 3^{1/2}$

b. $\sqrt{(3xy)^5} = \sqrt[2]{(3xy)^5} = (3xy)^{(5/2)}$

c. $2x\sqrt[4]{x^3} = (2x)(x^{3/4}) = 2x^{1+(3/4)} = 2x^{7/4}$

✓CHECKPOINT   Now try Exercise 99.

Example 15   Changing from Exponential to Radical Form

a. $(x^2 + y^2)^{3/2} = \left(\sqrt{x^2 + y^2}\right)^3 = \sqrt{(x^2 + y^2)^3}$

b. $2y^{3/4}z^{1/4} = 2(y^3z)^{1/4} = 2\sqrt[4]{y^3z}$

c. $a^{-3/2} = \dfrac{1}{a^{3/2}} = \dfrac{1}{\sqrt{a^3}}$

d. $x^{0.2} = x^{1/5} = \sqrt[5]{x}$

✓CHECKPOINT   Now try Exercise 101.

Rational exponents are useful for evaluating roots of numbers on a calculator, reducing the index of a radical, and simplifying calculus expressions.

Example 16   Simplifying with Rational Exponents

a. $(-32)^{-4/5} = \left(\sqrt[5]{-32}\right)^{-4} = (-2)^{-4} = \dfrac{1}{(-2)^4} = \dfrac{1}{16}$

b. $(-5x^{5/3})(3x^{-3/4}) = -15x^{(5/3)-(3/4)} = -15x^{11/12}, \qquad x \neq 0$

c. $\sqrt[9]{a^3} = a^{3/9} = a^{1/3} = \sqrt[3]{a}$

d. $\sqrt[3]{\sqrt{125}} = \sqrt[6]{125} = \sqrt[6]{(5)^3} = 5^{3/6} = 5^{1/2} = \sqrt{5}$

e. $(2x - 1)^{4/3}(2x - 1)^{-1/3} = (2x - 1)^{(4/3)-(1/3)} = 2x - 1, \qquad x \neq \dfrac{1}{2}$

✓CHECKPOINT   Now try Exercise 107.

STUDY TIP

Rational exponents can be tricky, and you must remember that the expression $b^{m/n}$ is not defined unless $\sqrt[n]{b}$ is a real number. This restriction produces some unusual-looking results. For instance, the number $(-8)^{1/3}$ is defined because $\sqrt[3]{-8} = -2$, but the number $(-8)^{2/6}$ is undefined because $\sqrt[6]{-8}$ is not a real number.

STUDY TIP

The expression in Example 16(e) is not defined when $x = \frac{1}{2}$ because

$$\left(2 \cdot \tfrac{1}{2} - 1\right)^{-1/3} = (0)^{-1/3}$$

is not a real number.

P.2 Exercises

See www.CalcChat.com for worked-out solutions to odd-numbered exercises.

Vocabulary Check

Fill in the blanks.

1. In the exponential form a^n, n is the _____ and a is the _____ .

2. A convenient way of writing very large or very small numbers is called _____ .

3. One of the two equal factors of a number is called a _____ of the number.

4. The _____ of a number is the nth root that has the same sign as a, and is denoted by $\sqrt[n]{a}$.

5. In the radical form $\sqrt[n]{a}$, the positive integer n is called the _____ of the radical and the number a is called the _____ .

6. When an expression involving radicals has all possible factors removed, radical-free denominators, and a reduced index, it is in _____ .

7. The expressions $a + b\sqrt{m}$ and $a - b\sqrt{m}$ are _____ of each other.

8. The process used to create a radical-free denominator is known as _____ the denominator.

9. In the expression $b^{m/n}$, m denotes the _____ to which the base is raised and n denotes the _____ or root to be taken.

In Exercises 1–8, evaluate each expression.

1. (a) $4^2 \cdot 3$ (b) $3 \cdot 3^3$

2. (a) $\dfrac{5^5}{5^2}$ (b) $\dfrac{3^2}{3^4}$

3. (a) $(3^3)^2$ (b) -3^2

4. (a) $(2^3 \cdot 3^2)^2$ (b) $\left(-\frac{3}{5}\right)^3\left(\frac{5}{3}\right)^2$

5. (a) $\dfrac{3}{3^{-4}}$ (b) $24(-2)^{-5}$

6. (a) $\dfrac{4 \cdot 3^{-2}}{2^{-2} \cdot 3^{-1}}$ (b) $(-2)^0$

7. (a) $2^{-1} + 3^{-1}$ (b) $(2^{-1})^{-2}$

8. (a) $3^{-1} + 2^{-2}$ (b) $(3^{-2})^2$

In Exercises 9–14, evaluate the expression for the value of x.

Expression	Value
9. $7x^{-2}$	2
10. $6x^0 - (6x)^0$	7
11. $2x^3$	-3
12. $-3x^4$	-2
13. $4x^2$	$-\frac{1}{2}$
14. $5(-x)^3$	$\frac{1}{3}$

In Exercises 15–20, simplify each expression.

15. (a) $(-5z)^3$ (b) $5x^4(x^2)$

16. (a) $(3x)^2$ (b) $(4x^3)^2$

17. (a) $\dfrac{7x^2}{x^3}$ (b) $\dfrac{12(x + y)^3}{9(x + y)}$

18. (a) $\dfrac{r^4}{r^6}$ (b) $\left(\dfrac{4}{y}\right)^3\left(\dfrac{3}{y}\right)^4$

19. (a) $[(x^2y^{-2})^{-1}]^{-1}$ (b) $\left(\dfrac{a^{-2}}{b^{-2}}\right)\left(\dfrac{b}{a}\right)^3$

20. (a) $(2x^5)^0, \quad x \neq 0$ (b) $(5x^2z^6)^3(5x^2z^6)^{-3}$

In Exercises 21–24, use a calculator to evaluate the expression. (Round your answer to three decimal places.)

21. $(-4)^3(5^2)$ 22. $(8^{-4})(10^3)$

23. $\dfrac{3^6}{7^3}$ 24. $\dfrac{4^3}{3^{-4}}$

In Exercises 25–34, write the number in scientific notation.

25. 852.25   26. 28,022.2

27. 10,252.484   28. 525,252,118

29. -1110.25 30. $-5,222,145$

31. 0.0002485   32. 0.0000025

33. -0.0000025 34. -0.000125005

In Exercises 35–42, write the number in decimal notation.

35. 1.25×10^5

36. 1.08×10^4

37. -4.816×10^8

38. -3.785×10^{10}

39. 3.25×10^{-8}

40. 5.05×10^{-10}

41. -9.001×10^{-3}

42. -8.098×10^{-6}

In Exercises 43–46, write the number in scientific notation.

43. Land area of Earth: 57,300,000 square miles

44. Light year: 9,460,000,000,000 kilometers

45. Relative density of hydrogen: 0.0000899 gram per cubic centimeter

46. One micron (millionth of a meter): 0.00003937 inch

In Exercises 47–50, write the number in decimal notation.

47. Daily consumption of Coca-Cola products worldwide: 5.71×10^8 drinks   (Source: The Coca-Cola Company)

48. Interior temperature of sun: 1.5×10^7 degrees Celsius

49. Charge of electron: 1.6022×10^{-19} coulomb

50. Width of human hair: 9.0×10^{-5} meter

In Exercises 51 and 52, evaluate the expression without using a calculator.

51. $\sqrt{25 \times 10^8}$

52. $\sqrt[3]{8 \times 10^{15}}$

In Exercises 53–56, use a calculator to evaluate each expression. (Round your answer to three decimal places.)

53. (a) $(9.3 \times 10^6)^3(6.1 \times 10^{-4})$

(b) $\dfrac{(2.414 \times 10^4)^6}{(1.68 \times 10^5)^5}$

54. (a) $750\left(1 + \dfrac{0.11}{365}\right)^{800}$

(b) $\dfrac{67,000,000 + 93,000,000}{0.0052}$

55. (a) $\sqrt{4.5 \times 10^9}$ (b) $\sqrt[3]{6.3 \times 10^4}$

56. (a) $(2.65 \times 10^{-4})^{1/3}$ (b) $\sqrt{9 \times 10^{-4}}$

In Exercises 57–66, evaluate the expression without using a calculator.

57. $\sqrt{121}$ **58.** $\sqrt{16}$

59. $-\sqrt[3]{-27}$ **60.** $\dfrac{\sqrt[4]{81}}{3}$

61. $\left(\sqrt[3]{-125}\right)^3$ **62.** $\sqrt[4]{562^4}$

63. $32^{-3/5}$ **64.** $\left(\frac{9}{4}\right)^{-1/2}$

65. $\left(-\dfrac{1}{64}\right)^{-1/3}$ **66.** $-\left(\dfrac{1}{125}\right)^{-4/3}$

In Exercises 67–78, use a calculator to approximate the value of the expression. (Round your answer to three decimal places.)

67. $\sqrt[5]{-27^3}$ **68.** $\sqrt[3]{45^2}$

69. $(3.4)^{2.5}$ **70.** $(6.1)^{-2.9}$

71. $(1.2^{-2})\sqrt{75} + 3\sqrt{8}$ **72.** $\dfrac{-5 + \sqrt{33}}{5}$

73. $\sqrt{\pi + 1}$ **74.** $\sqrt{10 - \pi}$

75. $\dfrac{3.14}{\pi} + \sqrt[3]{5}$ **76.** $\dfrac{\sqrt{10}}{2.5} - \pi^2$

77. $(2.8)^{-2} + 1.01 \times 10^6$

78. $2.12 \times 10^{-2} + \sqrt{15}$

In Exercises 79 and 80, use the properties of radicals to simplify each expression.

79. (a) $\left(\sqrt[4]{3}\right)^4$ (b) $\sqrt[5]{96x^5}$

80. (a) $\sqrt{12} \cdot \sqrt{3}$ (b) $\sqrt[4]{x^4}$

In Exercises 81–86, simplify each expression.

81. (a) $\sqrt{54xy^4}$ (b) $\sqrt[3]{\dfrac{32a^2}{b^2}}$

82. (a) $\sqrt[3]{54}$ (b) $\sqrt{32x^3y^4}$

83. (a) $2\sqrt{50} + 12\sqrt{8}$ (b) $10\sqrt{32} - 6\sqrt{18}$

84. (a) $5\sqrt{x} - 3\sqrt{x}$

(b) $-2\sqrt{9y} + 10\sqrt{y}$

85. (a) $3\sqrt{x+1} + 10\sqrt{x+1}$

(b) $7\sqrt{80x} - 2\sqrt{125x}$

86. (a) $5\sqrt{10x^2} - \sqrt{90x^2}$

(b) $8\sqrt[3]{27x} - \frac{1}{2}\sqrt[3]{64x}$

In Exercises 87–90, complete the statement with <, =, or >.

87. $\sqrt{5} + \sqrt{3}$ ____ $\sqrt{5+3}$ **88.** $\sqrt{\dfrac{3}{11}}$ ____ $\dfrac{\sqrt{3}}{\sqrt{11}}$

89. 5 ____ $\sqrt{3^2 + 2^2}$ **90.** 5 ____ $\sqrt{3^2 + 4^2}$

In Exercises 91–94, rationalize the denominator of the expression. Then simplify your answer.

91. $\dfrac{1}{\sqrt{3}}$ **92.** $\dfrac{8}{\sqrt[3]{2}}$

93. $\dfrac{5}{\sqrt{14} - 2}$ **94.** $\dfrac{3}{\sqrt{5} + \sqrt{6}}$

∫ **In Exercises 95–98, rationalize the numerator of the expression. Then simplify your answer.**

95. $\dfrac{\sqrt{8}}{2}$ **96.** $\dfrac{\sqrt{2}}{3}$

97. $\dfrac{\sqrt{5} + \sqrt{3}}{3}$ **98.** $\dfrac{\sqrt{7} - 3}{4}$

The symbol ∫ indicates an example or exercise that highlights algebraic techniques specifically used in calculus.

In Exercises 99–106, fill in the missing form of the expression.

Radical Form	*Rational Exponent Form*
99. $\sqrt[3]{64}$	
100.	$-(144^{1/2})$
101.	$32^{1/5}$
102. $\sqrt[3]{614.125}$	
103. $\sqrt[3]{-216}$	
104.	$(-243)^{1/5}$
105. $\sqrt[4]{81^3}$	
106.	$16^{5/4}$

In Exercises 107–110, perform the operations and simplify.

107. $\dfrac{(2x^2)^{3/2}}{2^{1/2}x^4}$

108. $\dfrac{x^{4/3}y^{2/3}}{(xy)^{1/3}}$

109. $\dfrac{x^{-3} \cdot x^{1/2}}{x^{3/2} \cdot x^{-1}}$

110. $\dfrac{5^{-1/2} \cdot 5x^{5/2}}{(5x)^{3/2}}$

In Exercises 111 and 112, reduce the index of each radical and rewrite in radical form.

111. (a) $\sqrt[4]{3^2}$ (b) $\sqrt[6]{(x+1)^4}$

112. (a) $\sqrt[6]{x^3}$ (b) $\sqrt[4]{(3x^2)^4}$

In Exercises 113 and 114, write each expression as a single radical. Then simplify your answer.

113. (a) $\sqrt{\sqrt{32}}$ (b) $\sqrt{\sqrt[4]{2x}}$

114. (a) $\sqrt{\sqrt{243(x+1)}}$ (b) $\sqrt{\sqrt[3]{10a^7b}}$

115. *Erosion*   A stream of water moving at the rate of v feet per second can carry particles of size $0.03\sqrt{v}$ inches. Find the size of the particle that can be carried by a stream flowing at the rate of $\frac{3}{4}$ foot per second.

116. *Environment*   There was 2.362×10^8 tons of municipal waste generated in 2003. Find the number of tons for each of the categories in the graph. (Source: Franklin Associates, a Division of ERG)

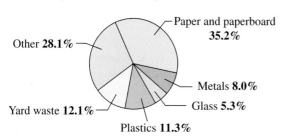

Paper and paperboard **35.2%**

Other **28.1%**

Metals **8.0%**

Glass **5.3%**

Plastics **11.3%**

Yard waste **12.1%**

117. *Tropical Storms*   The table shows the number of Atlantic tropical storms and hurricanes per year from 1995 to 2005. Find the average number of tropical storms and hurricanes from 1995 to 2005. Is your answer an *integer*, a *rational number*, or an *irrational number*? Explain. (Source: NOAA)

Year	Number of tropical storms and hurricanes
1995	19
1996	13
1997	8
1998	14
1999	12
2000	15
2001	15
2002	12
2003	16
2004	15
2005	27

118. *Mathematical Modeling*   A funnel is filled with water to a height of h centimeters. The formula

$$t = 0.03[12^{5/2} - (12 - h)^{5/2}], \quad 0 \le h \le 12$$

represents the amount of time t (in seconds) it will take for the funnel to empty. Find t for $h = 7$ centimeters.

Synthesis

True or False? **In Exercises 119 and 120, determine whether the statement is true or false. Justify your answer.**

119. $\dfrac{x^{k+1}}{x} = x^k$

120. $(a^n)^k = a^{(n^k)}$

121. *Think About It*   Verify that $a^0 = 1$, $a \ne 0$. (*Hint:* Use the property of exponents $a^m/a^n = a^{m-n}$.)

122. *Think About It*   Is the real number 52.7×10^5 written in scientific notation? Explain.

123. *Exploration*   List all possible digits that occur in the units place of the square of a positive integer. Use that list to determine whether $\sqrt{5233}$ is an integer.

124. *Think About It*   Square the real number $2/\sqrt{5}$ and note that the radical is eliminated from the denominator. Is this equivalent to rationalizing the denominator? Why or why not?

P.3 Polynomials and Factoring

Polynomials

An algebraic expression is a collection of variables and real numbers. The most common type of algebraic expression is the **polynomial.** Some examples are

$$2x + 5, \quad 3x^4 - 7x^2 + 2x + 4, \quad \text{and} \quad 5x^2y^2 - xy + 3.$$

The first two are *polynomials in x* and the third is a *polynomial in x and y*. The terms of a polynomial in x have the form ax^k, where a is the **coefficient** and k is the **degree** of the term. For instance, the polynomial

$$2x^3 - 5x^2 + 1 = 2x^3 + (-5)x^2 + (0)x + 1$$

has coefficients 2, -5, 0, and 1.

Definition of a Polynomial in x

Let $a_0, a_1, a_2, \ldots, a_n$ be *real numbers* and let n be a *nonnegative integer.* A **polynomial in x** is an expression of the form

$$a_n x^n + a_{n-1}x^{n-1} + \cdots + a_1 x + a_0$$

where $a_n \neq 0$. The polynomial is of **degree** n, a_n is the **leading coefficient,** and a_0 is the **constant term.**

In **standard form,** a polynomial in x is written with descending powers of x. Polynomials with one, two, and three terms are called **monomials, binomials,** and **trinomials,** respectively.

A polynomial that has all zero coefficients is called the **zero polynomial,** denoted by 0. No degree is assigned to this particular polynomial. For polynomials in more than one variable, the degree of a *term* is the sum of the exponents of the variables in the term. The degree of the *polynomial* is the highest degree of its terms. For instance, the degree of the polynomial $-2x^3y^6 + 4xy - x^7y^4$ is 11 because the sum of the exponents in the last term is the greatest. Expressions such as the following are not polynomials.

$$x^3 - \sqrt{3x} = x^3 - (3x)^{1/2} \qquad \text{The exponent } 1/2 \text{ is not an integer.}$$

$$x^2 + \frac{5}{x} = x^2 + 5x^{-1} \qquad \text{The exponent } -1 \text{ is not a nonnegative integer.}$$

Example 1 Writing Polynomials in Standard Form

Polynomial	Standard Form	Degree
a. $4x^2 - 5x^7 - 2 + 3x$	$-5x^7 + 4x^2 + 3x - 2$	7
b. $4 - 9x^2$	$-9x^2 + 4$	2
c. 8	$8 \ (8 = 8x^0)$	0

✓CHECKPOINT Now try Exercise 15.

What you should learn

- Write polynomials in standard form.
- Add, subtract, and multiply polynomials.
- Use special products to multiply polynomials.
- Remove common factors from polynomials.
- Factor special polynomial forms.
- Factor trinomials as the product of two binomials.
- Factor by grouping.

Why you should learn it

Polynomials can be used to model and solve real-life problems. For instance, in Exercise 157 on page 34, a polynomial is used to model the total distance an automobile travels when stopping.

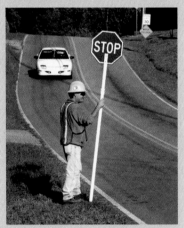

© Robert W. Ginn/age fotostock

STUDY TIP

Expressions are not polynomials if:

1. A variable is underneath a radical.

2. A polynomial expression (with degree greater than 0) is in the denominator of a term.

Operations with Polynomials

You can add and subtract polynomials in much the same way you add and subtract real numbers. Simply add or subtract the *like terms* (terms having exactly the same variables to exactly the same powers) by adding their coefficients. For instance, $-3xy^2$ and $5xy^2$ are like terms and their sum is

$$-3xy^2 + 5xy^2 = (-3 + 5)xy^2 = 2xy^2.$$

Example 2   Sums and Differences of Polynomials

Perform the indicated operation.

a. $(5x^3 - 7x^2 - 3) + (x^3 + 2x^2 - x + 8)$
b. $(7x^4 - x^2 - 4x + 2) - (3x^4 - 4x^2 + 3x)$

Solution

a. $(5x^3 - 7x^2 - 3) + (x^3 + 2x^2 - x + 8)$

$$= (5x^3 + x^3) + (-7x^2 + 2x^2) - x + (-3 + 8) \qquad \text{Group like terms.}$$
$$= 6x^3 - 5x^2 - x + 5 \qquad \text{Combine like terms.}$$

b. $(7x^4 - x^2 - 4x + 2) - (3x^4 - 4x^2 + 3x)$

$$= 7x^4 - x^2 - 4x + 2 - 3x^4 + 4x^2 - 3x \qquad \text{Distributive Property}$$
$$= (7x^4 - 3x^4) + (-x^2 + 4x^2) + (-4x - 3x) + 2 \qquad \text{Group like terms.}$$
$$= 4x^4 + 3x^2 - 7x + 2 \qquad \text{Combine like terms.}$$

✓CHECKPOINT   Now try Exercise 23.

> **STUDY TIP**
>
> When a negative sign precedes an expression within parentheses, treat it like the coefficient (-1) and distribute the negative sign to each term inside the parentheses.
>
> $$-(x^2 - x + 3) = -x^2 + x - 3$$

To find the product of two polynomials, use the left and right Distributive Properties.

Example 3   Multiplying Polynomials: The FOIL Method

$$(3x - 2)(5x + 7) = 3x(5x + 7) - 2(5x + 7)$$
$$= (3x)(5x) + (3x)(7) - (2)(5x) - (2)(7)$$
$$= 15x^2 + 21x - 10x - 14$$

Product of **First terms**   Product of **Outer terms**   Product of **Inner terms**   Product of **Last terms**

$$= 15x^2 + 11x - 14$$

Note that when using the **FOIL Method** (which can be used only to multiply two binomials), the outer (O) and inner (I) terms may be like terms that can be combined into one term.

✓CHECKPOINT   Now try Exercise 39.

Example 4   The Product of Two Trinomials

Find the product of $4x^2 + x - 2$ and $-x^2 + 3x + 5$.

Solution

When multiplying two polynomials, be sure to multiply *each* term of one polynomial by *each* term of the other. A vertical format is helpful.

$$
\begin{array}{r}
4x^2 + x - 2 \\
\times \quad -x^2 + 3x + 5 \\
\hline
20x^2 + 5x - 10 \\
12x^3 + 3x^2 - 6x \\
-4x^4 - x^3 + 2x^2 \\
\hline
-4x^4 + 11x^3 + 25x^2 - x - 10
\end{array}
$$

Write in standard form.

Write in standard form.

$5(4x^2 + x - 2)$

$3x(4x^2 + x - 2)$

$-x^2(4x^2 + x - 2)$

Combine like terms.

✓*CHECKPOINT*   Now try Exercise 59.

Special Products

Special Products

Let u and v be real numbers, variables, or algebraic expressions.

Special Product	*Example*
Sum and Difference of Same Terms	
$(u + v)(u - v) = u^2 - v^2$	$(x + 4)(x - 4) = x^2 - 4^2 = x^2 - 16$
Square of a Binomial	
$(u + v)^2 = u^2 + 2uv + v^2$	$(x + 3)^2 = x^2 + 2(x)(3) + 3^2 = x^2 + 6x + 9$
$(u - v)^2 = u^2 - 2uv + v^2$	$(3x - 2)^2 = (3x)^2 - 2(3x)(2) + 2^2 = 9x^2 - 12x + 4$
Cube of a Binomial	
$(u + v)^3 = u^3 + 3u^2v + 3uv^2 + v^3$	$(x + 2)^3 = x^3 + 3x^2(2) + 3x(2^2) + 2^3 = x^3 + 6x^2 + 12x + 8$
$(u - v)^3 = u^3 - 3u^2v + 3uv^2 - v^3$	$(x - 1)^3 = x^3 - 3x^2(1) + 3x(1^2) - 1^3 = x^3 - 3x^2 + 3x - 1$

Example 5   The Product of Two Trinomials

Find the product of $x + y - 2$ and $x + y + 2$.

Solution

By grouping $x + y$ in parentheses, you can write the product of the trinomials as a special product.

$$(x + y - 2)(x + y + 2) = [(x + y) - 2][(x + y) + 2]$$

$$= (x + y)^2 - 2^2 = x^2 + 2xy + y^2 - 4$$

✓*CHECKPOINT*   Now try Exercise 61.

Factoring

The process of writing a polynomial as a product is called **factoring.** It is an important tool for solving equations and for simplifying rational expressions.

Unless noted otherwise, when you are asked to factor a polynomial, you can assume that you are looking for factors with integer coefficients. If a polynomial cannot be factored using integer coefficients, it is **prime** or **irreducible over the integers.** For instance, the polynomial $x^2 - 3$ is irreducible over the integers. Over the real numbers, this polynomial can be factored as

$$x^2 - 3 = (x + \sqrt{3})(x - \sqrt{3}).$$

A polynomial is **completely factored** when each of its factors is prime. So,

$$x^3 - x^2 + 4x - 4 = (x - 1)(x^2 + 4)$$ Completely factored

is completely factored, but

$$x^3 - x^2 - 4x + 4 = (x - 1)(x^2 - 4)$$ Not completely factored

is not completely factored. Its complete factorization is

$$x^3 - x^2 - 4x + 4 = (x - 1)(x + 2)(x - 2).$$

The simplest type of factoring involves a polynomial that can be written as the product of a monomial and another polynomial. The technique used here is the Distributive Property, $a(b + c) = ab + ac$, in the *reverse* direction. For instance, the polynomial $5x^2 + 15x$ can be factored as follows.

$$5x^2 + 15x = 5x(x) + 5x(3)$$ $5x$ is a common factor.

$$= 5x(x + 3)$$

The first step in completely factoring a polynomial is to remove (factor out) any common factors, as shown in the next example.

Example 6 Removing Common Factors

Factor each expression.

a. $6x^3 - 4x$ **b.** $3x^4 + 9x^3 + 6x^2$ **c.** $(x - 2)(2x) + (x - 2)(3)$

Solution

a. $6x^3 - 4x = 2x(3x^2) - 2x(2) = 2x(3x^2 - 2)$ $2x$ is a common factor.

b. $3x^4 + 9x^3 + 6x^2 = 3x^2(x^2) + 3x^2(3x) + 3x^2(2)$ $3x^2$ is a common factor.

$$= 3x^2(x^2 + 3x + 2)$$

$$= 3x^2(x + 1)(x + 2)$$

c. $(x - 2)(2x) + (x - 2)(3) = (x - 2)(2x + 3)$ $x - 2$ is a common factor.

✓CHECKPOINT   Now try Exercise 73.

Factoring Special Polynomial Forms

Some polynomials have special forms that arise from the special product forms on page 26. You should learn to recognize these forms so that you can factor such polynomials easily.

Factoring Special Polynomial Forms

Factored Form	*Example*

Difference of Two Squares

$$u^2 - v^2 = (u + v)(u - v)$$
$$9x^2 - 4 = (3x)^2 - 2^2 = (3x + 2)(3x - 2)$$

Perfect Square Trinomial

$$u^2 + 2uv + v^2 = (u + v)^2$$
$$x^2 + 6x + 9 = x^2 + 2(x)(3) + 3^2 = (x + 3)^2$$
$$u^2 - 2uv + v^2 = (u - v)^2$$
$$x^2 - 6x + 9 = x^2 - 2(x)(3) + 3^2 = (x - 3)^2$$

Sum or Difference of Two Cubes

$$u^3 + v^3 = (u + v)(u^2 - uv + v^2)$$
$$x^3 + 8 = x^3 + 2^3 = (x + 2)(x^2 - 2x + 4)$$
$$u^3 - v^3 = (u - v)(u^2 + uv + v^2)$$
$$27x^3 - 1 = (3x)^3 - 1^3 = (3x - 1)(9x^2 + 3x + 1)$$

One of the easiest special polynomial forms to factor is the difference of two squares. Think of this form as follows.

$$u^2 - v^2 = (u + v)(u - v)$$

Difference   Opposite signs

To recognize perfect square terms, look for coefficients that are squares of integers and variables raised to *even powers*.

Example 7   Removing a Common Factor First

$3 - 12x^2 = 3(1 - 4x^2)$	3 is a common factor.
$= 3[1^2 - (2x)^2]$	Difference of two squares
$= 3(1 + 2x)(1 - 2x)$	Factored form

✓CHECKPOINT   Now try Exercise 77.

Example 8   Factoring the Difference of Two Squares

a. $(x + 2)^2 - y^2 = [(x + 2) + y][(x + 2) - y]$
$= (x + 2 + y)(x + 2 - y)$

b.
$16x^4 - 81 = (4x^2)^2 - 9^2$	Difference of two squares
$= (4x^2 + 9)(4x^2 - 9)$	
$= (4x^2 + 9)[(2x)^2 - 3^2]$	Difference of two squares
$= (4x^2 + 9)(2x + 3)(2x - 3)$	Factored form

✓CHECKPOINT   Now try Exercise 81.

STUDY TIP

In Example 7, note that the first step in factoring a polynomial is to check for a common factor. Once the common factor is removed, it is often possible to recognize patterns that were not immediately obvious.

A perfect square trinomial is the square of a binomial, as shown below.

$$u^2 + 2uv + v^2 = (u + v)^2 \qquad \text{or} \qquad u^2 - 2uv + v^2 = (u - v)^2$$

Like signs   Like signs

Note that the first and last terms are squares and the middle term is twice the product of u and v.

Example 9   Factoring Perfect Square Trinomials

Factor each trinomial.

a. $x^2 - 10x + 25$ **b.** $16x^2 + 8x + 1$

Solution

a. $x^2 - 10x + 25 = x^2 - 2(x)(5) + 5^2$ Rewrite in $u^2 - 2uv + v^2$ form.

$\qquad\qquad\qquad\quad = (x - 5)^2$

b. $16x^2 + 8x + 1 = (4x)^2 + 2(4x)(1) + 1^2$ Rewrite in $u^2 + 2uv + v^2$ form.

$\qquad\qquad\qquad\quad = (4x + 1)^2$

✔**CHECKPOINT**   Now try Exercise 87.

The next two formulas show the sums and differences of cubes. Pay special attention to the signs of the terms.

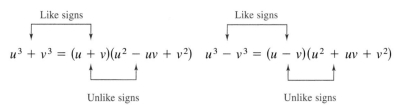

Like signs   Like signs

$$u^3 + v^3 = (u + v)(u^2 - uv + v^2) \quad u^3 - v^3 = (u - v)(u^2 + uv + v^2)$$

Unlike signs   Unlike signs

Exploration

Rewrite $u^6 - v^6$ as the difference of two squares. Then find a formula for completely factoring $u^6 - v^6$. Use your formula to factor completely $x^6 - 1$ and $x^6 - 64$.

Example 10   Factoring the Difference of Cubes

Factor $x^3 - 27$.

Solution

$\qquad x^3 - 27 = x^3 - 3^3$ Rewrite 27 as 3^3.

$\qquad\qquad\qquad = (x - 3)(x^2 + 3x + 9)$ Factor.

✔**CHECKPOINT**   Now try Exercise 92.

Example 11   Factoring the Sum of Cubes

$3x^3 + 192 = 3(x^3 + 64)$ 3 is a common factor.

$\qquad\qquad = 3(x^3 + 4^3)$ Rewrite 64 as 4^3.

$\qquad\qquad = 3(x + 4)(x^2 - 4x + 16)$ Factor.

✔**CHECKPOINT**   Now try Exercise 93.

Trinomials with Binomial Factors

To factor a trinomial of the form $ax^2 + bx + c$, use the following pattern.

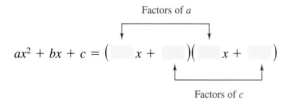

Factors of a

$$ax^2 + bx + c = (\quad x + \quad)(\quad x + \quad)$$

Factors of c

The goal is to find a combination of factors of a and c such that the outer and inner products add up to the middle term bx. For instance, in the trinomial $6x^2 + 17x + 5$, you can write all possible factorizations and determine which one has outer and inner products that add up to $17x$.

$(6x + 5)(x + 1), (6x + 1)(x + 5), (2x + 1)(3x + 5), (2x + 5)(3x + 1)$

You can see that $(2x + 5)(3x + 1)$ is the correct factorization because the outer (O) and inner (I) products add up to $17x$.

$$\begin{array}{cccccc} \text{F} & \text{O} & \text{I} & \text{L} & & \text{O + I} \\ (2x + 5)(3x + 1) &=& 6x^2 &+& 2x + 15x + 5 &=& 6x^2 + 17x + 5. \end{array}$$

Example 12   Factoring a Trinomial: Leading Coefficient Is 1

Factor $x^2 - 7x + 12$.

Solution

The possible factorizations are

$$(x - 2)(x - 6), \quad (x - 1)(x - 12), \quad \text{and} \quad (x - 3)(x - 4).$$

Testing the middle term, you will find the correct factorization to be

$$x^2 - 7x + 12 = (x - 3)(x - 4). \qquad \text{O + I} = -4x + (-3x) = -7x$$

✓CHECKPOINT   Now try Exercise 103.

Example 13   Factoring a Trinomial: Leading Coefficient Is Not 1

Factor $2x^2 + x - 15$.

Solution

The eight possible factorizations are as follows.

$$(2x - 1)(x + 15), (2x + 1)(x - 15), (2x - 3)(x + 5), (2x + 3)(x - 5),$$

$$(2x - 5)(x + 3), (2x + 5)(x - 3), (2x - 15)(x + 1), (2x + 15)(x - 1)$$

Testing the middle term, you will find the correct factorization to be

$$2x^2 + x - 15 = (2x - 5)(x + 3). \qquad \text{O + I} = 6x - 5x = x$$

✓CHECKPOINT   Now try Exercise 111.

> **STUDY TIP**
>
> Factoring a trinomial can involve trial and error. However, once you have produced the factored form, it is an easy matter to check your answer. For instance, you can verify the factorization in Example 12 by multiplying out the expression $(x - 3)(x - 4)$ to see that you obtain the original trinomial, $x^2 - 7x + 12$.

Factoring by Grouping

Sometimes polynomials with more than three terms can be factored by a method called **factoring by grouping.**

Example 14   Factoring by Grouping

Use factoring by grouping to factor $x^3 - 2x^2 - 3x + 6$.

Solution

$$
\begin{aligned}
x^3 - 2x^2 - 3x + 6 &= (x^3 - 2x^2) - (3x - 6) && \text{Group terms.}\\
&= x^2(x - 2) - 3(x - 2) && \text{Factor groups.}\\
&= (x - 2)(x^2 - 3) && (x - 2) \text{ is a common factor.}
\end{aligned}
$$

✓CHECKPOINT   Now try Exercise 115.

> **STUDY TIP**
>
> When grouping terms be sure to strategically group terms that have a common factor.

Factoring a trinomial can involve quite a bit of trial and error. Some of this trial and error can be lessened by using factoring by grouping. The key to this method of factoring is knowing how to rewrite the middle term. In general, to factor a trinomial $ax^2 + bx + c$ by grouping, choose factors of the product ac that add up to b and use these factors to rewrite the middle term.

Example 15   Factoring a Trinomial by Grouping

Use factoring by grouping to factor $2x^2 + 5x - 3$.

Solution

In the trinomial $2x^2 + 5x - 3$, $a = 2$ and $c = -3$, which implies that the product ac is -6. Now, because -6 factors as $(6)(-1)$ and $6 - 1 = 5 = b$, rewrite the middle term as $5x = 6x - x$. This produces the following.

$$
\begin{aligned}
2x^2 + 5x - 3 &= 2x^2 + 6x - x - 3 && \text{Rewrite middle term.}\\
&= (2x^2 + 6x) - (x + 3) && \text{Group terms.}\\
&= 2x(x + 3) - (x + 3) && \text{Factor groups.}\\
&= (x + 3)(2x - 1) && (x + 3) \text{ is a common factor.}
\end{aligned}
$$

So, the trinomial factors as $2x^2 + 5x - 3 = (x + 3)(2x - 1)$.

✓CHECKPOINT   Now try Exercise 117.

Guidelines for Factoring Polynomials

1. Factor out any common factors using the Distributive Property.

2. Factor according to one of the special polynomial forms.

3. Factor as $ax^2 + bx + c = (mx + r)(nx + s)$.

4. Factor by grouping.

P.3 Exercises

See www.CalcChat.com for worked-out solutions to odd-numbered exercises.

Vocabulary Check

Fill in the blanks.

1. For the polynomial $a_n x^n + a_{n-1} x^{n-1} + \cdots + a_1 x + a_0$, the degree is _____ and the leading coefficient is _____ .

2. A polynomial that has all zero coefficients is called the _____ .

3. A polynomial with one term is called a _____ .

4. The letters in "FOIL" stand for the following. F _____   O _____   I _____   L _____

5. If a polynomial cannot be factored using integer coefficients, it is called _____ .

6. The polynomial $u^2 + 2uv + v^2$ is called a _____ .

In Exercises 1–6, match the polynomial with its description. [The polynomials are labeled (a), (b), (c), (d), (e), and (f).]

(a) $6x$

(b) $1 - 4x^3$

(c) $x^3 + 2x^2 - 4x + 1$

(d) 7

(e) $-3x^5 + 2x^3 + x$

(f) $\frac{3}{4}x^4 + x^2 + 14$

1. A polynomial of degree zero

2. A trinomial of degree five

3. A binomial with leading coefficient -4

4. A monomial of positive degree

5. A trinomial with leading coefficient $\frac{3}{4}$

6. A third-degree polynomial with leading coefficient 1

In Exercises 7–10, write a polynomial that fits the description. (There are many correct answers.)

7. A third-degree polynomial with leading coefficient -2

8. A fifth-degree polynomial with leading coefficient 8

9. A fourth-degree polynomial with a negative leading coefficient

10. A third-degree trinomial with an even leading coefficient

In Exercises 11–16, write the polynomial in standard form. Then identify the degree and leading coefficient of the polynomial.

11. $3x + 4x^2 + 2$

12. $x^2 - 4 - 3x^4$

13. $5 - x^6$

14. $-13 + x^2$

15. $1 - x + 6x^4 - 2x^5$

16. $7 + 8x$

In Exercises 17–20, determine whether the expression is a polynomial. If so, write the polynomial in standard form.

17. $3x + 4x^3 - 5$

18. $5x^4 - 2x^2 + x^{-2}$

19. $\sqrt{x^2 - x^4}$

20. $\dfrac{x^2 + 2x - 3}{6}$

In Exercises 21–36, perform the operations and write the result in standard form.

21. $(6x + 5) - (8x + 15)$

22. $(2x^2 + 1) - (x^2 - 2x + 1)$

23. $-(t^3 - 1) + (6t^3 - 5t)$

24. $-(5x^2 - 1) - (-3x^2 + 5)$

25. $(15x^2 - 6) - (-8.1x^3 - 14.7x^2 - 17)$

26. $(15.6w - 14w - 17.4) - (16.9w^4 - 9.2w + 13)$

27. $3x(x^2 - 2x + 1)$

28. $y^2(4y^2 + 2y - 3)$

29. $-5z(3z - 1)$

30. $(-3x)(5x + 2)$

31. $(1 - x^3)(4x)$

32. $-4x(3 - x^3)$

33. $(2.5x^2 + 5)(-3x)$

34. $(2 - 3.5y)(4y^3)$

35. $-2x\left(\frac{1}{8}x + 3\right)$

36. $6y\left(4 - \frac{3}{8}y\right)$

In Exercises 37–68, multiply or find the special product.

37. $(x + 3)(x + 4)$

38. $(x - 5)(x + 10)$

39. $(3x - 5)(2x + 1)$

40. $(7x - 2)(4x - 3)$

41. $(2x - 5y)^2$

42. $(5 - 8x)^2$

43. $(x + 10)(x - 10)$

44. $(2x + 3)(2x - 3)$

45. $(x + 2y)(x - 2y)$

46. $(4a + 5b)(4a - 5b)$

47. $(2r^2 - 5)(2r^2 + 5)$

48. $(3a^3 - 4b^2)(3a^3 + 4b^2)$

49. $(x + 1)^3$

50. $(y - 4)^3$

51. $(2x - y)^3$

52. $(3x + 2y)^3$

53. $\left(\frac{1}{2}x - 5\right)^2$

54. $\left(\frac{3}{5}t + 4\right)^2$

55. $\left(\frac{1}{4}x - 3\right)\left(\frac{1}{4}x + 3\right)$

56. $\left(2x + \frac{1}{6}\right)\left(2x - \frac{1}{6}\right)$

57. $(2.4x + 3)^2$ **58.** $(1.8y - 5)^2$

59. $(-x^2 + x - 5)(3x^2 + 4x + 1)$

60. $(x^2 + 3x + 2)(2x^2 - x + 4)$

61. $[(x + 2z) + 5][(x + 2z) - 5]$

62. $[(x - 3y) + z][(x - 3y) - z]$

63. $[(x - 3) + y]^2$ **64.** $[(x + 1) - y]^2$

65. $5x(x + 1) - 3x(x + 1)$

66. $(2x - 1)(x + 3) + 3(x + 3)$

67. $(u + 2)(u - 2)(u^2 + 4)$

68. $(x + y)(x - y)(x^2 + y^2)$

In Exercises 69–74, factor out the common factor.

69. $4x + 16$ **70.** $5y - 30$

71. $2x^3 - 6x$ **72.** $3z^3 - 6z^2 + 9z$

73. $3x(x - 5) + 8(x - 5)$

74. $(5x - 4)^2 + (5x - 4)$

In Exercises 75–82, factor the difference of two squares.

75. $x^2 - 64$ **76.** $x^2 - 81$

77. $48y^2 - 27$ **78.** $50 - 98z^2$

79. $4x^2 - \frac{1}{9}$ **80.** $\frac{25}{36}y^2 - 49$

81. $(x - 1)^2 - 4$ **82.** $25 - (z + 5)^2$

In Exercises 83–90, factor the perfect square trinomial.

83. $x^2 - 4x + 4$ **84.** $x^2 + 10x + 25$

85. $x^2 + x + \frac{1}{4}$ **86.** $x^2 - \frac{4}{3}x + \frac{4}{9}$

87. $4x^2 - 12x + 9$ **88.** $25z^2 - 10z + 1$

89. $4x^2 - \frac{4}{3}x + \frac{1}{9}$ **90.** $9y^2 - \frac{3}{2}y + \frac{1}{16}$

In Exercises 91–100, factor the sum or difference of cubes.

91. $x^3 + 64$ **92.** $x^3 - 1$

93. $y^3 + 216$ **94.** $z^3 - 125$

95. $x^3 - \frac{8}{27}$ **96.** $x^3 + \frac{8}{125}$

97. $8x^3 - 1$ **98.** $27x^3 + 8$

99. $(x + 2)^3 - y^3$ **100.** $(x - 3y)^3 - 8z^3$

In Exercises 101–114, factor the trinomial.

101. $x^2 + x - 2$ **102.** $x^2 + 5x + 6$

103. $s^2 - 5s + 6$ **104.** $t^2 - t - 6$

105. $20 - y - y^2$ **106.** $24 + 5z - z^2$

107. $3x^2 - 5x + 2$ **108.** $3x^2 + 13x - 10$

109. $2x^2 - x - 1$ **110.** $2x^2 - x - 21$

111. $5x^2 + 26x + 5$ **112.** $8x^2 - 45x - 18$

113. $-5u^2 - 13u + 6$ **114.** $-6x^2 + 23x + 4$

In Exercises 115–120, factor by grouping.

115. $x^3 - x^2 + 2x - 2$

116. $x^3 + 5x^2 - 5x - 25$

117. $6x^2 + x - 2$

118. $3x^2 + 10x + 8$

119. $x^3 - 5x^2 + x - 5$

120. $x^3 - x^2 + 3x - 3$

In Exercises 121–152, completely factor the expression.

121. $x^3 - 16x$ **122.** $12x^2 - 48$

123. $x^3 - x^2$ **124.** $6x^2 - 54$

125. $x^2 - 2x + 1$ **126.** $9x^2 - 6x + 1$

127. $1 - 4x + 4x^2$ **128.** $16 - 6x - x^2$

129. $2x^2 + 4x - 2x^3$ **130.** $7y^2 + 15y - 2y^3$

131. $9x^2 + 10x + 1$ **132.** $13x + 6 + 5x^2$

133. $\frac{1}{8}x^2 - \frac{1}{96}x - \frac{1}{16}$ **134.** $\frac{1}{81}x^2 + \frac{2}{9}x - 8$

135. $3x^3 + x^2 + 15x + 5$ **136.** $5 - x + 5x^2 - x^3$

137. $3u - 2u^2 + 6 - u^3$

138. $x^4 - 4x^3 + x^2 - 4x$

139. $2x^3 + x^2 - 8x - 4$

140. $3x^3 + x^2 - 27x - 9$

141. $(x^2 + 1)^2 - 4x^2$

142. $(x^2 + 8)^2 - 36x^2$

143. $2t^3 - 16$

144. $5x^3 + 40$

145. $4x(2x - 1) + 2(2x - 1)^2$

146. $5(3 - 4x)^2 - 8(3 - 4x)(5x - 1)$

147. $2(x + 1)(x - 3)^2 - 3(x + 1)^2(x - 3)$

148. $7(3x + 2)^2(1 - x)^2 + (3x + 2)(1 - x)^3$

149. $(2x + 1)^4(2)(3x - 1)(3) + (3x - 1)^2(4)(2x + 1)^3(2)$

150. $(2x + 5)^3(4)(3x + 2)^3(3) + (3x + 2)^4(3)(2x + 5)^2(2)$

151. $(x^2 + 5)^4(2)(3x - 1)(3) + (3x - 1)^2(4)(x^2 + 5)^3(2x)$

152. $(x^2 - 1)^3(2)(4x + 5)(4) + (4x + 5)^2(3)(x^2 - 1)^2(2x)$

153. *Compound Interest* After 2 years, an investment of $500 compounded annually at an interest rate r will yield an amount of $500(1 + r)^2$.

(a) Write this polynomial in standard form.

(b) Use a calculator to evaluate the polynomial for the values of r shown in the table.

r	$2\frac{1}{2}\%$	3%	4%	$4\frac{1}{2}\%$	5%
$500(1 + r)^2$					

(c) What conclusion can you make from the table?

154. *Compound Interest* After 3 years, an investment of $1200 compounded annually at an interest rate r will yield an amount of $1200(1 + r)^3$.

(a) Write this polynomial in standard form.

(b) Use a calculator to evaluate the polynomial for the values of r shown in the table.

r	2%	3%	$3\frac{1}{2}\%$	4%	$4\frac{1}{2}\%$
$1200(1 + r)^3$					

(c) What conclusion can you make from the table?

155. *Geometry* An overnight shipping company is designing a closed box by cutting along the solid lines and folding along the broken lines on the rectangular piece of corrugated cardboard shown in the figure. The length and width of the rectangle are 45 centimeters and 15 centimeters, respectively. Find the volume of the box in terms of x. Find the volume when $x = 3$, $x = 5$, and $x = 7$.

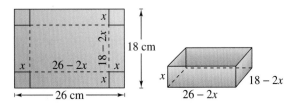

156. *Geometry* A take-out fast food restaurant is constructing an open box made by cutting squares out of the corners of a piece of cardboard that is 18 centimeters by 26 centimeters (see figure). The edge of each cut-out square is x centimeters. Find the volume of the box in terms of x. Find the volume when $x = 1$, $x = 2$, and $x = 3$.

157. *Stopping Distance* The stopping distance of an automobile is the distance traveled during the driver's reaction time plus the distance traveled after the brakes are applied. In an experiment, these distances were measured (in feet) when the automobile was traveling at a speed of x miles per hour on dry, level pavement, as shown in the bar graph. The distance traveled during the reaction time R was

$$R = 1.1x$$

and the braking distance B was

$$B = 0.0475x^2 - 0.001x + 0.23.$$

(a) Determine the polynomial that represents the total stopping distance T.

(b) Use the result of part (a) to estimate the total stopping distance when $x = 30$, $x = 40$, and $x = 55$.

(c) Use the bar graph to make a statement about the total stopping distance required for increasing speeds.

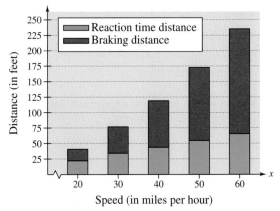

Figure for 157

158. *Engineering* A uniformly distributed load is placed on a one-inch-wide steel beam. When the span of the beam is x feet and its depth is 6 inches, the safe load S (in pounds) is approximated by

$$S_6 = (0.06x^2 - 2.42x + 38.71)^2.$$

When the depth is 8 inches, the safe load is approximated by

$$S_8 = (0.08x^2 - 3.30x + 51.93)^2.$$

(a) Use the bar graph to estimate the difference in the safe loads for these two beams when the span is 12 feet.

(b) How does the difference in safe load change as the span increases?

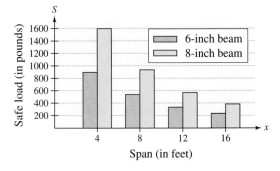

Geometric Modeling In Exercises 159–162, match the factoring formula with the correct geometric factoring model. [The models are labeled (a), (b), (c), and (d).] For instance, a factoring model for

$$2x^2 + 3x + 1 = (2x + 1)(x + 1)$$

is shown in the figure.

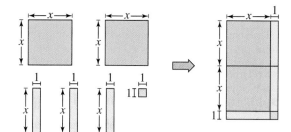

(a)

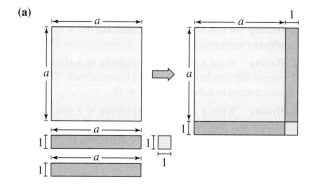

(b)

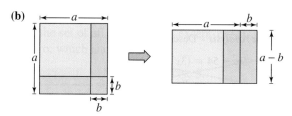

(c)

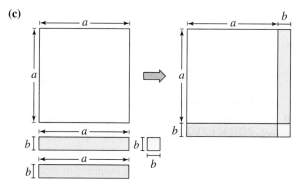

(d)

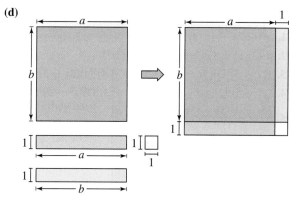

159. $a^2 - b^2 = (a + b)(a - b)$

160. $a^2 + 2ab + b^2 = (a + b)^2$

161. $a^2 + 2a + 1 = (a + 1)^2$

162. $ab + a + b + 1 = (a + 1)(b + 1)$

Geometric Modeling In Exercises 163–166, draw a geometric factoring model to represent the factorization.

163. $3x^2 + 7x + 2 = (3x + 1)(x + 2)$

164. $x^2 + 4x + 3 = (x + 3)(x + 1)$

165. $2x^2 + 7x + 3 = (2x + 1)(x + 3)$

166. $x^2 + 3x + 2 = (x + 2)(x + 1)$

Geometry In Exercises 167–170, write an expression in factored form for the area of the shaded portion of the figure.

167.

168.

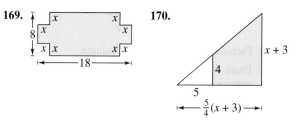

169.

170.

The key to success in simplifying rational expressions lies in your ability to *factor* polynomials. When simplifying rational expressions, be sure to factor each polynomial completely before concluding that the numerator and denominator have no factors in common.

Example 2 Simplifying a Rational Expression

Write $\dfrac{x^2 + 4x - 12}{3x - 6}$ in simplest form.

Solution

$$\frac{x^2 + 4x - 12}{3x - 6} = \frac{(x + 6)(x - 2)}{3(x - 2)}$$ Factor completely.

$$= \frac{x + 6}{3}, \quad x \neq 2$$ Divide out common factors.

Note that the original expression is undefined when $x = 2$ (because division by zero is undefined). To make sure that the simplified expression is *equivalent* to the original expression, you must restrict the domain of the simplified expression by excluding the value $x = 2$.

✔CHECKPOINT   Now try Exercise 27.

It may sometimes be necessary to change the sign of a factor by factoring out (-1) to simplify a rational expression, as shown in Example 3.

Example 3 Simplifying a Rational Expression

Write $\dfrac{12 + x - x^2}{2x^2 - 9x + 4}$ in simplest form.

Solution

$$\frac{12 + x - x^2}{2x^2 - 9x + 4} = \frac{(4 - x)(3 + x)}{(2x - 1)(x - 4)}$$ Factor completely.

$$= \frac{-(x - 4)(3 + x)}{(2x - 1)(x - 4)}$$ $(4 - x) = -(x - 4)$

$$= -\frac{3 + x}{2x - 1}, \quad x \neq 4$$ Divide out common factors.

✔CHECKPOINT   Now try Exercise 35.

STUDY TIP

In this text, when a rational expression is written, the domain is usually not listed with the expression. It is *implied* that the real numbers that make the denominator zero are excluded from the expression. Also, when performing operations with rational expressions, this text follows the convention of listing *beside the simplified expression* all values of x that must be specifically excluded from the domain in order to make the domains of the simplified and original expressions agree. In Example 3, for instance, the restriction $x \neq 4$ is listed beside the simplified expression to make the two domains agree. Note that the value $x = \frac{1}{2}$ is excluded from *both* domains, so it is not necessary to list this value.

Operations with Rational Expressions

To multiply or divide rational expressions, you can use the properties of fractions discussed in Section P.1. Recall that to divide fractions you invert the divisor and multiply.

Example 4   Multiplying Rational Expressions

$$\frac{2x^2 + x - 6}{x^2 + 4x - 5} \cdot \frac{x^3 - 3x^2 + 2x}{4x^2 - 6x} = \frac{(2x-3)(x + 2)}{(x + 5)(x-1)} \cdot \frac{x(x - 2)(x-1)}{2x(2x-3)}$$

$$= \frac{(x + 2)(x - 2)}{2(x + 5)}, \quad x \neq 0, x \neq 1, x \neq \frac{3}{2}$$

✔CHECKPOINT   Now try Exercise 51.

Example 5   Dividing Rational Expressions

Divide $\frac{x^3 - 8}{x^2 - 4}$ by $\frac{x^2 + 2x + 4}{x^3 + 8}$.

Solution

$$\frac{x^3 - 8}{x^2 - 4} \div \frac{x^2 + 2x + 4}{x^3 + 8} = \frac{x^3 - 8}{x^2 - 4} \cdot \frac{x^3 + 8}{x^2 + 2x + 4} \qquad \text{Invert and multiply.}$$

$$= \frac{(x-2)(x^2 + 2x + 4)}{(x+2)(x-2)} \cdot \frac{(x+2)(x^2 - 2x + 4)}{(x^2 + 2x + 4)}$$

$$= x^2 - 2x + 4, \quad x \neq \pm 2 \qquad \text{Divide out common factors.}$$

✔CHECKPOINT   Now try Exercise 53.

To add or subtract rational expressions, you can use the LCD (least common denominator) method or the basic definition

$$\frac{a}{b} \pm \frac{c}{d} = \frac{ad \pm bc}{bd}, \qquad b \neq 0 \text{ and } d \neq 0. \qquad \text{Basic definition}$$

This definition provides an efficient way of adding or subtracting *two* fractions that have no common factors in their denominators.

Example 6   Subtracting Rational Expressions

Subtract $\frac{2}{3x + 4}$ from $\frac{x}{x - 3}$.

Solution

$$\frac{x}{x - 3} - \frac{2}{3x + 4} = \frac{x(3x + 4) - 2(x - 3)}{(x - 3)(3x + 4)} \qquad \text{Basic definition}$$

$$= \frac{3x^2 + 4x - 2x + 6}{(x - 3)(3x + 4)} \qquad \text{Distributive Property}$$

$$= \frac{3x^2 + 2x + 6}{(x - 3)(3x + 4)} \qquad \text{Combine like terms.}$$

✔CHECKPOINT   Now try Exercise 57.

STUDY TIP

When subtracting rational expressions, remember to distribute the negative sign to *all* the terms in the quantity that is being subtracted.

The next four examples illustrate some methods for simplifying rational expressions involving negative exponents and radicals. These types of expressions occur frequently in calculus.

To simplify an expression with negative exponents, one method is to begin by factoring out the common factor with the smaller exponent. Remember that when factoring, you subtract exponents. For instance, in $3x^{-5/2} + 2x^{-3/2}$ the smaller exponent is $-\frac{5}{2}$ and the common factor is $x^{-5/2}$.

$$3x^{-5/2} + 2x^{-3/2} = x^{-5/2}[3(1) + 2x^{-3/2-(-5/2)}]$$

$$= x^{-5/2}(3 + 2x^1) = \frac{3 + 2x}{x^{5/2}}$$

Example 9   Simplifying an Expression with Negative Exponents

Simplify $x(1 - 2x)^{-3/2} + (1 - 2x)^{-1/2}$.

Solution

Begin by factoring out the common factor with the smaller exponent.

$$x(1 - 2x)^{-3/2} + (1 - 2x)^{-1/2} = (1 - 2x)^{-3/2}[x + (1 - 2x)^{(-1/2)-(-3/2)}]$$

$$= (1 - 2x)^{-3/2}[x + (1 - 2x)^1]$$

$$= \frac{1 - x}{(1 - 2x)^{3/2}}$$

✓CHECKPOINT   Now try Exercise 75.

A second method for simplifying this type of expression involves multiplying the numerator and denominator by a term to eliminate the negative exponent.

Example 10   Simplifying an Expression with Negative Exponents

Simplify $\dfrac{(4 - x^2)^{1/2} + x^2(4 - x^2)^{-1/2}}{4 - x^2}$.

Solution

$$\frac{(4 - x^2)^{1/2} + x^2(4 - x^2)^{-1/2}}{4 - x^2}$$

$$= \frac{(4 - x^2)^{1/2} + x^2(4 - x^2)^{-1/2}}{4 - x^2} \cdot \frac{(4 - x^2)^{1/2}}{(4 - x^2)^{1/2}}$$

$$= \frac{(4 - x^2)^1 + x^2(4 - x^2)^0}{(4 - x^2)^{3/2}}$$

$$= \frac{4 - x^2 + x^2}{(4 - x^2)^{3/2}} = \frac{4}{(4 - x^2)^{3/2}}$$

✓CHECKPOINT   Now try Exercise 79.

Mathematical models for the data are

Endangered plants: $E = \dfrac{2342.52t^2 + 565}{3.91t^2 + 1}$

and

Threatened plants: $T = \dfrac{243.48t^2 + 139}{1.65t^2 + 1}$

where t represents the year, with $t = 0$ corresponding to 2000.

(a) Using the models, create a table to estimate the numbers of endangered plant species and the numbers of threatened plant species for the given years. Compare these estimates with the actual data.

(b) Determine a model for the ratio of the number of threatened plant species to the number of endangered plant species. Use the model to find this ratio for each of the given years.

98. Marriages and Divorces   The table shows the rates (per 1000 of the total population) of marriages and divorces in the United States for the years 1990 through 2004. (Source: U.S. National Center for Health Statistics)

Year	Marriages, M	Divorces, D
1990	9.8	4.7
1991	9.4	4.7
1992	9.3	4.8
1993	9.0	4.6
1994	9.1	4.6
1995	8.9	4.4
1996	8.8	4.3
1997	8.9	4.3
1998	8.4	4.2
1999	8.6	4.1
2000	8.3	4.2
2001	8.2	4.0
2002	7.8	4.0
2003	7.5	3.8
2004	7.4	3.7

Mathematical models for the data are

Marriages: $M = \dfrac{8686.635t^2 - 191{,}897.18t - 9.8}{774.364t^2 - 20{,}427.65t - 1}$

and

Divorces: $D = -0.001t^2 - 0.06t + 4.8$

where t represents the year, with $t = 0$ corresponding to 1990.

Example 11   Rewriting a Difference Quotient

The following expression from calculus is an example of a *difference quotient*.

$$\frac{\sqrt{x + h} - \sqrt{x}}{h}$$

Rewrite this expression by rationalizing its numerator.

Solution

$$\frac{\sqrt{x + h} - \sqrt{x}}{h} = \frac{\sqrt{x + h} - \sqrt{x}}{h} \cdot \frac{\sqrt{x + h} + \sqrt{x}}{\sqrt{x + h} + \sqrt{x}}$$

$$= \frac{\left(\sqrt{x + h}\right)^2 - \left(\sqrt{x}\right)^2}{h\left(\sqrt{x + h} + \sqrt{x}\right)}$$

$$= \frac{h}{h\left(\sqrt{x + h} + \sqrt{x}\right)}$$

$$= \frac{1}{\sqrt{x + h} + \sqrt{x}}, \qquad h \neq 0$$

Notice that the original expression is undefined when $h = 0$. So, you must exclude $h = 0$ from the domain of the simplified expression so that the expressions are equivalent.

✔**CHECKPOINT**   Now try Exercise 85.

Difference quotients, like that in Example 11, occur frequently in calculus. Often, they need to be rewritten in an equivalent form that can be evaluated when $h = 0$. Note that the equivalent form is not simpler than the original form, but it has the advantage that it is defined when $h = 0$.

Example 12   Rewriting a Difference Quotient

Rewrite the expression by rationalizing its numerator.

$$\frac{\sqrt{x - 4} - \sqrt{x}}{4}$$

Solution

$$\frac{\sqrt{x - 4} - \sqrt{x}}{4} = \frac{\sqrt{x - 4} - \sqrt{x}}{4} \cdot \frac{\sqrt{x - 4} + \sqrt{x}}{\sqrt{x - 4} + \sqrt{x}}$$

$$= \frac{\left(\sqrt{x - 4}\right)^2 - \left(\sqrt{x}\right)^2}{4\left(\sqrt{x - 4} + \sqrt{x}\right)}$$

$$= \frac{-4}{4\left(\sqrt{x - 4} + \sqrt{x}\right)}$$

$$= -\frac{1}{\sqrt{x - 4} + \sqrt{x}}$$

✔**CHECKPOINT**   Now try Exercise 86.

83. $\dfrac{(x^2 + 5)(\frac{1}{2})(4x + 3)^{-1/2}(4) - (4x + 3)^{1/2}(2x)}{(x^2 + 5)^2}$

84. $\dfrac{(2x + 1)^{1/2}(3)(x - 5)^2 - (x - 5)^3(\frac{1}{2})(2x + 1)^{-1/2}(2)}{2x + 1}$

∫ **In Exercises 85–90, rationalize the numerator of the expression.**

85. $\dfrac{\sqrt{x + 2} - \sqrt{x}}{2}$

86. $\dfrac{\sqrt{z - 3} - \sqrt{z}}{3}$

87. $\dfrac{\sqrt{x + 2} - \sqrt{2}}{x}$

88. $\dfrac{\sqrt{x + 5} - \sqrt{5}}{x}$

89. $\dfrac{\sqrt{x + 9} - 3}{x}$

90. $\dfrac{\sqrt{x + 4} - 2}{x}$

Probability   **In Exercises 91 and 92, consider an experiment in which a marble is tossed into a box whose base is shown in the figure. The probability that the marble will come to rest in the shaded portion of the box is equal to the ratio of the shaded area to the total area of the figure. Find the probability.**

91.
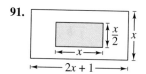

92.
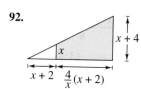

93. *Rate*   A photocopier copies at a rate of 16 pages per minute.

(a) Find the time required to copy 1 page.

(b) Find the time required to copy x pages.

(c) Find the time required to copy 60 pages.

94. *Monthly Payment*   The formula that approximates the annual interest rate r of a monthly installment loan is given by

$$r = \dfrac{\left[\dfrac{24(NM - P)}{N}\right]}{\left(P + \dfrac{NM}{12}\right)}$$

where N is the total number of payments, M is the monthly payment, and P is the amount financed.

(a) Approximate the annual interest rate for a five-year car loan of $20,000 that has monthly payments of $400.

(b) Simplify the expression for the annual interest rate r, and then rework part (a).

You can use a graphing utility to graph the scatter plot in Example 2. First, enter the data into the graphing utility's *list editor* as shown in Figure P.14. Then use the *statistical plotting* feature to set up the scatter plot, as shown in Figure P.15. Finally, display the scatter plot (use a viewing window in which $1998 \le x \le 2005$ and $0 \le y \le 300$), as shown in Figure P.16.

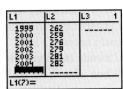

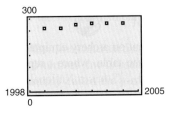

Figure P.14   **Figure P.15**   **Figure P.16**

Some graphing utilities have a *ZoomStat* feature, as shown in Figure P.17. This feature automatically selects an appropriate viewing window that displays all the data in the list editor, as shown in Figure P.18.

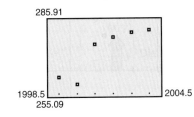

Figure P.17   **Figure P.18**

The Distance Formula

Recall from the Pythagorean Theorem that, for a right triangle with hypotenuse of length c and sides of lengths a and b, you have $a^2 + b^2 = c^2$, as shown in Figure P.19. (The converse is also true. That is, if $a^2 + b^2 = c^2$, then the triangle is a right triangle.)

Suppose you want to determine the distance d between two points (x_1, y_1) and (x_2, y_2) in the plane. With these two points, a right triangle can be formed, as shown in Figure P.20. The length of the vertical side of the triangle is $|y_2 - y_1|$, and the length of the horizontal side is $|x_2 - x_1|$. By the Pythagorean Theorem,

$$d^2 = |x_2 - x_1|^2 + |y_2 - y_1|^2$$
$$d = \sqrt{|x_2 - x_1|^2 + |y_2 - y_1|^2}$$
$$d = \sqrt{(x_2 - x_1)^2 + (y_2 - y_1)^2}.$$

This result is called the **Distance Formula.**

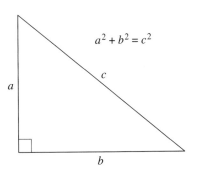

Figure P.19

The Distance Formula

The distance d between the points (x_1, y_1) and (x_2, y_2) in the plane is

$$d = \sqrt{(x_2 - x_1)^2 + (y_2 - y_1)^2}.$$

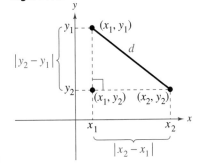

Figure P.20

Example 3 Finding a Distance

Find the distance between the points $(-2, 1)$ and $(3, 4)$.

Algebraic Solution

Let $(x_1, y_1) = (-2, 1)$ and $(x_2, y_2) = (3, 4)$. Then apply the Distance Formula as follows.

$$d = \sqrt{(x_2 - x_1)^2 + (y_2 - y_1)^2} \quad \text{Distance Formula}$$

$$= \sqrt{[3 - (-2)]^2 + (4 - 1)^2} \quad \begin{array}{l}\text{Substitute for}\\ x_1, y_1, x_2, \text{ and } y_2.\end{array}$$

$$= \sqrt{(5)^2 + (3)^2} \quad \text{Simplify.}$$

$$= \sqrt{34} \approx 5.83 \quad \text{Simplify.}$$

So, the distance between the points is about 5.83 units.

You can use the Pythagorean Theorem to check that the distance is correct.

$$d^2 \overset{?}{=} 3^2 + 5^2 \quad \text{Pythagorean Theorem}$$

$$\left(\sqrt{34}\right)^2 \overset{?}{=} 3^2 + 5^2 \quad \text{Substitute for } d.$$

$$34 = 34 \quad \text{Distance checks.} \checkmark$$

Graphical Solution

Use centimeter graph paper to plot the points $A(-2, 1)$ and $B(3, 4)$. Carefully sketch the line segment from A to B. Then use a centimeter ruler to measure the length of the segment.

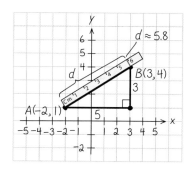

Figure P.21

The line segment measures about 5.8 centimeters, as shown in Figure P.21. So, the distance between the points is about 5.8 units.

 CHECKPOINT   Now try Exercise 23.

Example 4 Verifying a Right Triangle

Show that the points $(2, 1)$, $(4, 0)$, and $(5, 7)$ are the vertices of a right triangle.

Solution

The three points are plotted in Figure P.22. Using the Distance Formula, you can find the lengths of the three sides as follows.

$$d_1 = \sqrt{(5 - 2)^2 + (7 - 1)^2} = \sqrt{9 + 36} = \sqrt{45}$$

$$d_2 = \sqrt{(4 - 2)^2 + (0 - 1)^2} = \sqrt{4 + 1} = \sqrt{5}$$

$$d_3 = \sqrt{(5 - 4)^2 + (7 - 0)^2} = \sqrt{1 + 49} = \sqrt{50}$$

Because $(d_1)^2 + (d_2)^2 = 45 + 5 = 50 = (d_3)^2$, you can conclude that the triangle must be a right triangle.

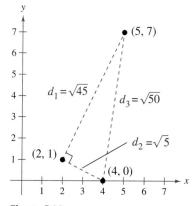

Figure P.22

 **CHECKPOINT**   Now try Exercise 37.

The Midpoint Formula

To find the **midpoint** of the line segment that joins two points in a coordinate plane, find the average values of the respective coordinates of the two endpoints using the **Midpoint Formula.**

Example 8   Translating Points in the Plane

The triangle in Figure P.27 has vertices at the points $(-1, 2)$, $(1, -4)$, and $(2, 3)$. Shift the triangle three units to the right and two units upward and find the vertices of the shifted triangle, as shown in Figure P.28.

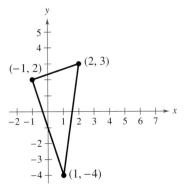

Figure P.27

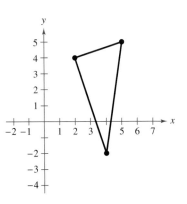

Figure P.28

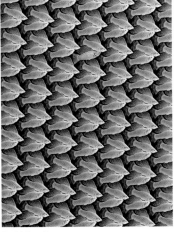

Paul Morrell

Much of computer graphics, including this computer-generated goldfish tessellation, consists of transformations of points in a coordinate plane. One type of transformation, a translation, is illustrated in Example 8. Other types of transformations include reflections, rotations, and stretches.

Solution

To shift the vertices three units to the right, add 3 to each of the x-coordinates. To shift the vertices two units upward, add 2 to each of the y-coordinates.

Original Point	Translated Point
$(-1, 2)$	$(-1 + 3, 2 + 2) = (2, 4)$
$(1, -4)$	$(1 + 3, -4 + 2) = (4, -2)$
$(2, 3)$	$(2 + 3, 3 + 2) = (5, 5)$

Plotting the translated points and sketching the line segments between them produces the shifted triangle shown in Figure P.28.

✓CHECKPOINT   Now try Exercise 79.

Example 8 shows how to translate points in a coordinate plane. The following transformed points are related to the original points as follows.

Original Point	Transformed Point	
(x, y)	$(-x, y)$	$(-x, y)$ is a reflection of the original point in the y-axis.
(x, y)	$(x, -y)$	$(x, -y)$ is a reflection of the original point in the x-axis.
(x, y)	$(-x, -y)$	$(-x, -y)$ is a reflection of the original point through the origin.

The figures provided with Example 8 were not really essential to the solution. Nevertheless, it is strongly recommended that you develop the habit of including sketches with your solutions, even if they are not required, because they serve as useful problem-solving tools.

P.5   Exercises

See www.CalcChat.com for worked-out solutions to odd-numbered exercises.

Vocabulary Check

1. Match each term with its definition.

(a) x-axis

(b) y-axis

(c) origin

(d) quadrants

(e) x-coordinate

(f) y-coordinate

(i) point of intersection of vertical axis and horizontal axis

(ii) directed distance from the x-axis

(iii) horizontal real number line

(iv) four regions of the coordinate plane

(v) directed distance from the y-axis

(vi) vertical real number line

In Exercises 2–5, fill in the blanks.

2. An ordered pair of real numbers can be represented in a plane called the rectangular coordinate system or the _____ plane.

3. The _____ is a result derived from the Pythagorean Theorem.

4. Finding the average values of the respective coordinates of the two endpoints of a line segment in a coordinate plane is also known as using the _____ .

5. The standard form of the equation of a circle is _____ , where the point (h, k) is the _____ of the circle and the positive number r is the _____ of the circle.

In Exercises 1 and 2, approximate the coordinates of the points.

1.

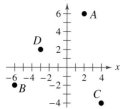

2.

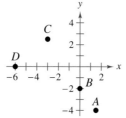

In Exercises 3–6, plot the points in the Cartesian plane.

3. $(-4, 2), (-3, -6), (0, 5), (1, -4)$

4. $(4, -2), (0, 0), (-4, 0), (-5, -5)$

5. $(3, 8), (0.5, -1), (5, -6), (-2, -2.5)$

6. $\left(1, -\frac{1}{2}\right), \left(-\frac{3}{4}, 2\right), (3, -3), \left(\frac{3}{2}, \frac{4}{3}\right)$

In Exercises 7–10, find the coordinates of the point.

7. The point is located five units to the left of the y-axis and four units above the x-axis.

8. The point is located three units below the x-axis and two units to the right of the y-axis.

9. The point is located six units below the x-axis and the coordinates of the point are equal.

10. The point is on the x-axis and 10 units to the left of the y-axis.

In Exercises 11–20, determine the quadrant(s) in which (x, y) is located so that the condition(s) is (are) satisfied.

11. $x > 0$ and $y < 0$

12. $x < 0$ and $y < 0$

13. $x = -4$ and $y > 0$

14. $x > 2$ and $y = 3$

15. $y < -5$

16. $x > 4$

17. $x < 0$ and $-y > 0$

18. $-x > 0$ and $y < 0$

19. $xy > 0$

20. $xy < 0$

In Exercises 21 and 22, sketch a scatter plot of the data shown in the table.

21. *Sales*   The table shows the sales y (in millions of dollars) for Apple Computer, Inc. for the years 1997–2006. (Source: Value Line)

Year	Sales, y (in millions of dollars)
1997	7,081
1998	5,941
1999	6,134
2000	7,983
2001	5,363
2002	5,742
2003	6,207
2004	8,279
2005	13,900
2006	16,600

22. *Meteorology* The table shows the lowest temperature on record y (in degrees Fahrenheit) in Duluth, Minnesota for each month x, where $x = 1$ represents January. (Source: NOAA)

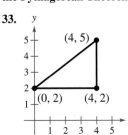

Month, x	Temperature, y
1	-39
2	-39
3	-29
4	-5
5	17
6	27
7	35
8	32
9	22
10	8
11	-23
12	-34

In Exercises 23–32, find the distance between the points algebraically and verify graphically by using centimeter graph paper and a centimeter ruler.

23. $(6, -3), (6, 5)$

24. $(1, 4), (8, 4)$

25. $(-3, -1), (2, -1)$

26. $(-3, -4), (-3, 6)$

27. $(-2, 6), (3, -6)$

28. $(8, 5), (0, 20)$

29. $\left(\frac{1}{2}, \frac{4}{3}\right), (2, -1)$

30. $\left(-\frac{2}{3}, 3\right), \left(-1, \frac{5}{4}\right)$

31. $(-4.2, 3.1), (-12.5, 4.8)$

32. $(9.5, -2.6), (-3.9, 8.2)$

In Exercises 33–36, (a) find the length of each side of the right triangle and (b) show that these lengths satisfy the Pythagorean Theorem.

33.

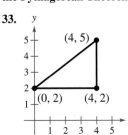

34.

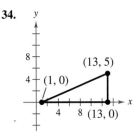

35.

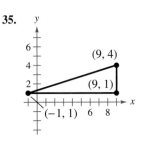

36.

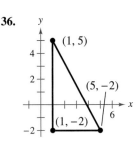

In Exercises 37–44, show that the points form the vertices of the polygon.

37. Right triangle: $(4, 0), (2, 1), (-1, -5)$

38. Right triangle: $(-1, 3), (3, 5), (5, 1)$

39. Isosceles triangle: $(1, -3), (3, 2), (-2, 4)$

40. Isosceles triangle: $(2, 3), (4, 9), (-2, 7)$

41. Parallelogram: $(2, 5), (0, 9), (-2, 0), (0, -4)$

42. Parallelogram: $(0, 1), (3, 7), (4, 4), (1, -2)$

43. Rectangle: $(-5, 6), (0, 8), (-3, 1), (2, 3)$ (*Hint:* Show that the diagonals are of equal length.)

44. Rectangle: $(2, 4), (3, 1), (1, 2), (4, 3)$ (*Hint:* Show that the diagonals are of equal length.)

In Exercises 45–54, (a) plot the points, (b) find the distance between the points, and (c) find the midpoint of the line segment joining the points.

45. $(1, 1), (9, 7)$ **46.** $(1, 12), (6, 0)$

47. $(-4, 10), (4, -5)$

48. $(-7, -4), (2, 8)$

49. $(-1, 2), (5, 4)$

50. $(2, 10), (10, 2)$

51. $\left(\frac{1}{2}, 1\right), \left(-\frac{5}{2}, \frac{4}{3}\right)$

52. $\left(-\frac{1}{3}, -\frac{1}{3}\right), \left(-\frac{1}{6}, -\frac{1}{2}\right)$

53. $(6.2, 5.4), (-3.7, 1.8)$

54. $(-16.8, 12.3), (5.6, 4.9)$

Revenue **In Exercises 55 and 56, use the Midpoint Formula to estimate the annual revenues (in millions of dollars) for Wendy's Intl., Inc. and Papa John's Intl. in 2003. The revenues for the two companies in 2000 and 2006 are shown in the tables. Assume that the revenues followed a linear pattern.** (Source: Value Line)

55. Wendy's Intl., Inc.

Year	Annual revenue (in millions of dollars)
2000	2237
2006	3950

56. Papa John's Intl.

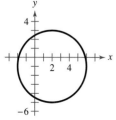

Year	Annual revenue (in millions of dollars)
2000	945
2006	1005

57. *Exploration*   A line segment has (x_1, y_1) as one endpoint and (x_m, y_m) as its midpoint. Find the other endpoint (x_2, y_2) of the line segment in terms of $x_1, y_1, x_m,$ and y_m. Use the result to find the coordinates of the endpoint of a line segment if the coordinates of the other endpoint and midpoint are, respectively,

(a) $(1, -2), (4, -1)$

(b) $(-5, 11), (2, 4)$

58. *Exploration*   Use the Midpoint Formula three times to find the three points that divide the line segment joining (x_1, y_1) and (x_2, y_2) into four parts. Use the result to find the points that divide the line segment joining the given points into four equal parts.

(a) $(1, -2), (4, -1)$

(b) $(-2, -3), (0, 0)$

In Exercises 59–72, write the standard form of the equation of the specified circle.

59. Center: $(0, 0)$; radius: 3

60. Center: $(0, 0)$; radius: 6

61. Center: $(2, -1)$; radius: 4

62. Center: $\left(0, \frac{1}{3}\right)$; radius: $\frac{1}{3}$

63. Center: $(-1, 2)$; solution point: $(0, 0)$

64. Center: $(3, -2)$; solution point: $(-1, 1)$

65. Endpoints of a diameter: $(0, 0), (6, 8)$

66. Endpoints of a diameter: $(-4, -1), (4, 1)$

67. Center: $(-2, 1)$; tangent to the x-axis

68. Center: $(3, -2)$; tangent to the y-axis

69. The circle inscribed in the square with vertices $(7, -2)$, $(-1, -2), (-1, -10),$ and $(7, -10)$

70. The circle inscribed in the square with vertices $(-12, 10)$, $(8, 10), (8, -10),$ and $(-12, -10)$

71.

72.

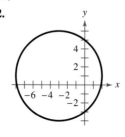

In Exercises 73–78, find the center and radius, and sketch the circle.

73. $x^2 + y^2 = 25$

74. $x^2 + y^2 = 16$

75. $(x - 1)^2 + (y + 3)^2 = 4$

76. $x^2 + (y - 1)^2 = 49$

77. $\left(x - \frac{1}{2}\right)^2 + \left(y - \frac{1}{2}\right)^2 = \frac{9}{4}$

78. $\left(x - \frac{2}{3}\right)^2 + \left(y + \frac{1}{4}\right)^2 = \frac{25}{9}$

In Exercises 79–82, the polygon is shifted to a new position in the plane. Find the coordinates of the vertices of the polygon in the new position.

79.

80.

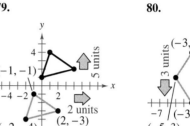

81. Original coordinates of vertices:

$(0, 2), (3, 5), (5, 2), (2, -1)$

Shift: three units upward, one unit to the left

82. Original coordinates of vertices:

$(1, -1), (3, 2), (1, -2)$

Shift: two units downward, three units to the left

Analyzing Data   **In Exercises 83 and 84, refer to the scatter plot, which shows the mathematics entrance test scores x and the final examination scores y in an algebra course for a sample of 10 students.**

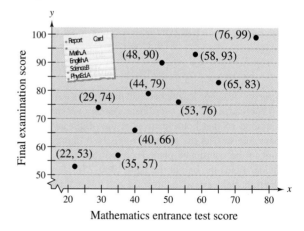

83. Find the entrance exam score of any student with a final exam score in the 80s.

84. Does a higher entrance exam score necessarily imply a higher final exam score? Explain.

Histograms and Frequency Distributions

When you want to organize large sets of data, it is useful to group the data into intervals and plot the frequency of the data in each interval. A **frequency distribution** can be used to construct a **histogram.** A histogram uses a portion of a real number line as its horizontal axis. The bars of a histogram are not separated by spaces.

Example 2   Constructing a Histogram

The table at the right shows the percent of the resident population of each state and the District of Columbia that was at least 65 years old in 2004. Construct a frequency distribution and a histogram for the data.   (Source: U.S. Census Bureau)

Solution

To begin constructing a frequency distribution, you must first decide on the number of intervals. There are several ways to group the data. However, because the smallest number is 6.4 and the largest is 16.8, it seems that six intervals would be appropriate. The first would be the interval $[6, 8)$, the second would be $[8, 10)$, and so on. By tallying the data into the six intervals, you obtain the frequency distribution shown below. You can construct the histogram by drawing a vertical axis to represent the number of states and a horizontal axis to represent the percent of the population 65 and older. Then, for each interval, draw a vertical bar whose height is the total tally, as shown in Figure P.30.

Interval	Tally
$[6, 8)$		
$[8, 10)$	||||
$[10, 12)$	⍫⍫ ||
$[12, 14)$	⍫⍫ ⍫⍫ ⍫⍫ ⍫⍫ ⍫⍫ ⍫⍫ ||
$[14, 16)$	⍫⍫ |
$[16, 18)$		

AK	6.4	MT	13.7
AL	13.2	NC	12.1
AR	13.8	ND	14.7
AZ	12.7	NE	13.3
CA	10.7	NH	12.1
CO	9.8	NJ	12.9
CT	13.5	NM	12.1
DC	12.1	NV	11.2
DE	13.1	NY	13.0
FL	16.8	OH	13.3
GA	9.6	OK	13.2
HI	13.6	OR	12.8
IA	14.7	PA	15.3
ID	11.4	RI	13.9
IL	12.0	SC	12.4
IN	12.4	SD	14.2
KS	13.0	TN	12.5
KY	12.5	TX	9.9
LA	11.7	UT	8.7
MA	13.3	VA	11.4
MD	11.4	VT	13.0
ME	14.4	WA	11.3
MI	12.3	WI	13.0
MN	12.1	WV	15.3
MO	13.3	WY	12.1
MS	12.2		

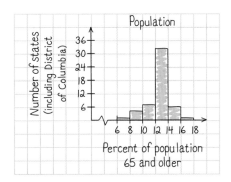

Figure P.30

 CHECKPOINT   Now try Exercise 5.

Example 3   Constructing a Histogram

A company has 48 sales representatives who sold the following numbers of units during the first quarter of 2008. Construct a frequency distribution for the data.

107	162	184	170	177	102	145	141
105	193	167	149	195	127	193	191
150	153	164	167	171	163	141	129
109	171	150	138	100	164	147	153
171	163	118	142	107	144	100	132
153	107	124	162	192	134	187	177

Interval	Tally
100–109	⊪ |||
110–119		
120–129	|||
130–139	|||
140–149	⊪ ||
150–159	⊪
160–169	⊪ |||
170–179	⊪	
180–189	||
190–199	⊪

Solution

To begin constructing a frequency distribution, you must first decide on the number of intervals. There are several ways to group the data. However, because the smallest number is 100 and the largest is 195, it seems that 10 intervals would be appropriate. The first interval would be 100–109, the second would be 110–119, and so on. By tallying the data into the 10 intervals, you obtain the distribution shown at the right above. A histogram for the distribution is shown in Figure P.31.

✓**CHECKPOINT**   Now try Exercise 6.

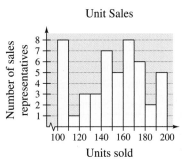

Figure P.31

Bar Graphs

A **bar graph** is similar to a histogram, except that the bars can be either horizontal or vertical and the labels of the bars are not necessarily numbers. Another difference between a bar graph and a histogram is that the bars in a bar graph are usually separated by spaces.

Example 4   Constructing a Bar Graph

The data below show the monthly normal precipitation (in inches) in Houston, Texas. Construct a bar graph for the data. What can you conclude?   (Source: National Climatic Data Center)

January	3.7	February	3.0	March	3.4
April	3.6	May	5.2	June	5.4
July	3.2	August	3.8	September	4.3
October	4.5	November	4.2	December	3.7

Solution

To create a bar graph, begin by drawing a vertical axis to represent the precipitation and a horizontal axis to represent the month. The bar graph is shown in Figure P.32. From the graph, you can see that Houston receives a fairly consistent amount of rain throughout the year—the driest month tends to be February and the wettest month tends to be June.

✓**CHECKPOINT**   Now try Exercise 7.

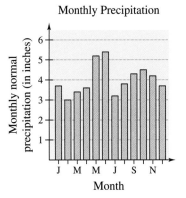

Figure P.32

Example 5   **Constructing a Double Bar Graph**

The table shows the percents of associate degrees awarded to males and females for selected fields of study in the United States in 2003. Construct a double bar graph for the data.   (Source: U.S. National Center for Education Statistics)

Field of Study	% Female	% Male
Agriculture and Natural Resources	36.4	63.6
Biological Sciences/ Life Sciences	70.4	29.6
Business and Management	66.8	33.2
Education	80.5	19.5
Engineering	16.5	83.5
Law and Legal Studies	89.6	10.4
Liberal/General Sciences	63.1	36.9
Mathematics	36.5	63.5
Physical Sciences	44.7	55.3
Social Sciences	65.3	34.7

Solution

For the data, a horizontal bar graph seems to be appropriate. This makes it easier to label and read the bars. Such a graph is shown in Figure P.33.

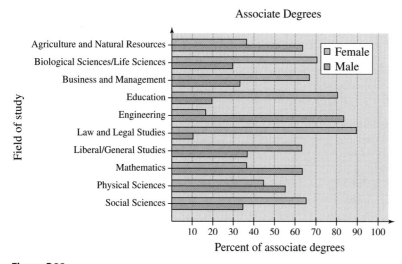

Figure P.33

✓CHECKPOINT   Now try Exercise 11.

Line Graphs

A **line graph** is similar to a standard coordinate graph. Line graphs are usually used to show trends over periods of time.

Example 6   Constructing a Line Graph

The table at the right shows the number of immigrants (in thousands) entering the United States for each decade from 1901 to 2000. Construct a line graph for the data. What can you conclude?   (Source: U.S. Immigration and Naturalization Service)

Solution

Begin by drawing a vertical axis to represent the number of immigrants in thousands. Then label the horizontal axis with decades and plot the points shown in the table. Finally, connect the points with line segments, as shown in Figure P.34. From the line graph, you can see that the number of immigrants hit a low point during the depression of the 1930s. Since then the number has steadily increased.

Decade	Number
1901–1910	8795
1911–1920	5736
1921–1930	4107
1931–1940	528
1941–1950	1035
1951–1960	2515
1961–1970	3322
1971–1980	4493
1981–1990	7338
1991–2000	9095

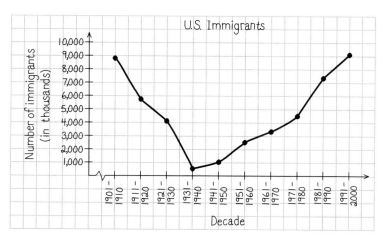

Figure P.34

✓CHECKPOINT   Now try Exercise 17.

TECHNOLOGY TIP   You can use a graphing utility to create different types of graphs, such as line graphs. For instance, the table at the right shows the numbers N (in thousands) of women on active duty in the United States military for selected years. To use a graphing utility to create a line graph of the data, first enter the data into the graphing utility's *list editor*, as shown in Figure P.35. Then use the *statistical plotting* feature to set up the line graph, as shown in Figure P.36. Finally, display the line graph (use a viewing window in which $1970 \leq x \leq 2010$ and $0 \leq y \leq 250$), as shown in Figure P.37.   (Source: U.S. Department of Defense)

Year	Number
1975	97
1980	171
1985	212
1990	227
1995	196
2000	203
2005	203

Figure P.35   **Figure P.36**

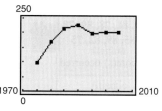

Figure P.37

In Exercises 47–52, simplify by removing all possible factors from the radical.

47. $\sqrt{25a^2}$ **48.** $\sqrt[5]{64x^6}$

49. $\sqrt{\frac{81}{144}}$ **50.** $\sqrt[3]{\frac{125}{216}}$

51. $\sqrt[3]{\frac{2x^3}{27}}$ **52.** $\sqrt{\frac{75x^2}{y^4}}$

In Exercises 53–58, simplify the expression.

53. $\sqrt{48} - \sqrt{27}$ **54.** $3\sqrt{32} + 4\sqrt{98}$

55. $8\sqrt{3x} - 5\sqrt{3x}$ **56.** $-11\sqrt{36y} - 6\sqrt{y}$

57. $\sqrt{8x^3} + \sqrt{2x}$ **58.** $3\sqrt{14x^2} - \sqrt{56x^2}$

Strength of a Wooden Beam In Exercises 59 and 60, use the figure, which shows the rectangular cross section of a wooden beam cut from a log of diameter 24 inches.

59. Find the area of the cross section when $w = 12\sqrt{2}$ inches and $h = \sqrt{24^2 - (12\sqrt{2})^2}$ inches. What is the shape of the cross section? Explain.

60. The rectangular cross section will have a maximum strength when $w = 8\sqrt{3}$ inches and $h = \sqrt{24^2 - (8\sqrt{3})^2}$ inches. Find the area of the cross section.

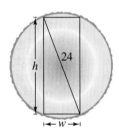

In Exercises 61 and 62, rationalize the denominator of the expression. Then simplify your answer.

61. $\dfrac{1}{3 - \sqrt{5}}$ **62.** $\dfrac{1}{\sqrt{x} - 1}$

∫ In Exercises 63 and 64, rationalize the numerator of the expression. Then simplify your answer.

63. $\dfrac{\sqrt{20}}{4}$ **64.** $\dfrac{\sqrt{2} - \sqrt{11}}{3}$

In Exercises 65–68, simplify the expression.

65. $64^{5/2}$ **66.** $64^{-2/3}$

67. $(-3x^{2/5})(-2x^{1/2})$ **68.** $(x - 1)^{1/3}(x - 1)^{-1/4}$

P.3 In Exercises 69 and 70, write the polynomial in standard form. Then identify the degree and leading coefficient of the polynomial.

69. $15x^2 - 2x^5 + 3x^3 + 5 - x^4$

70. $-2x^4 + x^2 - 10 - x + x^3$

In Exercises 71–78, perform the operations and write the result in standard form.

71. $-(3x^2 + 2x) + (1 - 5x)$ **72.** $8y - [2y^2 - (3y - 8)]$

73. $(2x^3 - 5x^2 + 10x - 7) + (4x^2 - 7x - 2)$

74. $(6x^4 - 4x^3 - x + 3 - 20x^2) - (16 + 9x^4 - 11x^2)$

75. $(a^2 + a - 3)(a^3 + 2)$

76. $(x^3 - 3x)(2x^2 + 3x + 5)$

77. $(y^2 - y)(y^2 + 1)(y^2 + y + 1)$

78. $\left(x - \dfrac{1}{x}\right)(x + 2)$

In Exercises 79–84, find the special product.

79. $(x + 8)(x - 8)$ **80.** $(7x + 4)(7x - 4)$

81. $(x - 4)^3$ **82.** $(2x - 1)^3$

83. $(m - 4 + n)(m - 4 - n)$

84. $(x - y - 6)(x - y + 6)$

85. *Geometry* Use the area model to write two different expressions for the area. Then equate the two expressions and name the algebraic property that is illustrated.

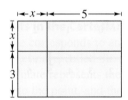

86. *Compound Interest* After 2 years, an investment of $2500 compounded annually at an interest rate r will yield an amount of $2500(1 + r)^2$. Write this polynomial in standard form.

In Exercises 87–92, factor out the common factor.

87. $7x + 35$ **88.** $4b - 12$

89. $x^3 - x$ **90.** $x(x - 3) + 4(x - 3)$

91. $2x^3 + 18x^2 - 4x$ **92.** $-6x^4 - 3x^3 + 12x$

93. *Geometry* The surface area of a right circular cylinder is $S = 2\pi r^2 + 2\pi rh$.

  (a) Draw a right circular cylinder of radius r and height h. Use the figure to explain how the surface area formula is obtained.

  (b) Factor the expression for surface area.

94. *Business* The revenue for selling x units of a product at a price of p dollars per unit is $R = xp$. For a flat panel television the revenue is $R = 1600x - 0.50x^2$. Factor the expression and determine an expression that gives the price in terms of x.

In Exercises 95–102, factor the expression.

95. $x^2 - 169$

96. $9x^2 - \frac{1}{25}$

97. $x^3 + 216$

98. $64x^3 - 27$

99. $x^2 - 6x - 27$

100. $x^2 - 9x + 14$

101. $2x^2 + 21x + 10$

102. $3x^2 + 14x + 8$

In Exercises 103–106, factor by grouping.

103. $x^3 - 4x^2 - 3x + 12$

104. $x^3 - 6x^2 - x + 6$

105. $2x^2 - x - 15$

106. $6x^2 + x - 12$

P.4 In Exercises 107–110, find the domain of the expression.

107. $-5x^2 - x - 1$

108. $9x^4 + 7, \quad x > 0$

109. $\dfrac{4}{2x - 3}$

110. $\sqrt{x + 12}$

In Exercises 111–114, write the rational expression in simplest form.

111. $\dfrac{4x^2}{4x^3 + 28x}$

112. $\dfrac{6xy}{xy + 2x}$

113. $\dfrac{x^2 - x - 30}{x^2 - 25}$

114. $\dfrac{x^2 - 9x + 18}{8x - 48}$

In Exercises 115–122, perform the operations and simplify your answer.

115. $\dfrac{x^2 - 4}{x^4 - 2x^2 - 8} \cdot \dfrac{x^2 + 2}{x^2}$

116. $\dfrac{2x - 1}{x + 1} \cdot \dfrac{x^2 - 1}{2x^2 - 7x + 3}$

117. $\dfrac{x^2(5x - 6)}{2x + 3} \div \dfrac{5x}{2x + 3}$

118. $\dfrac{4x - 6}{(x - 1)^2} \div \dfrac{2x^2 - 3x}{x^2 + 2x - 3}$

119. $x - 1 + \dfrac{1}{x + 2} + \dfrac{1}{x - 1}$

120. $2x + \dfrac{3}{2(x - 4)} - \dfrac{1}{2(x + 2)}$

121. $\dfrac{1}{x} - \dfrac{x - 1}{x^2 + 1}$

122. $\dfrac{1}{x - 1} + \dfrac{1 - x}{x^2 + x + 1}$

In Exercises 123 and 124, simplify the complex fraction.

123. $\dfrac{\left(\dfrac{1}{x} - \dfrac{1}{y}\right)}{(x^2 - y^2)}$

124. $\dfrac{\left(\dfrac{1}{2x - 3} - \dfrac{1}{2x + 3}\right)}{\left(\dfrac{1}{2x} - \dfrac{1}{2x + 3}\right)}$

P.5 In Exercises 125–128, plot the point in the Cartesian plane and determine the quadrant in which it is located.

125. $(8, -3)$

126. $(-4, -9)$

127. $\left(-\frac{5}{2}, 10\right)$

128. $(-6.5, -0.5)$

In Exercises 129 and 130, determine the quadrant(s) in which (x, y) is located so that the conditions are satisfied.

129. $x > 0$ and $y = -2$

130. $xy = 4$

Revenue In Exercises 131 and 132, use the table, which shows the operating revenues (in millions of dollars) for the motion picture industry for the years 1998 to 2003. (Source: U.S. Census Bureau)

Year	Operating revenue (in millions of dollars)
1998	48,002
1999	51,448
2000	54,040
2001	55,937
2002	60,486
2003	64,096

131. Sketch a scatter plot of the data.

132. What statement can be made about the operating revenue for the motion picture industry?

In Exercises 133 and 134, plot the points and find the distance between the points.

133. $(-3, 8), (1, 5)$

134. $(5.6, 0), (0, 8.2)$

In Exercises 135 and 136, plot the points and find the midpoint of the line segment joining the points.

135. $(-12, 5), (4, -7)$

136. $(1.8, 7.4), (-0.6, -14.5)$

In Exercises 137 and 138, write the standard form of the equation of the specified circle.

137. Center: $(3, -1)$; solution point: $(-5, 1)$

138. Endpoints of a diameter: $(-4, 6), (10, -2)$

In Exercises 139 and 140, the polygon is shifted to a new position in the plane. Find the coordinates of the vertices of the polygon in the new position.

139. Original coordinates of vertices:

$(4, 8), (6, 8), (4, 3), (6, 3)$

Shift: three units downward, two units to the left

140. Original coordinates of vertices:

$(0, 1), (3, 3), (0, 5), (-3, 3)$

Shift: five units upward, four units to the right

P.6

141. Consumer Awareness Use a line plot to organize the following sample of prices (in dollars) of running shoes. Which price occurred with the greatest frequency?

100, 65, 67, 88, 69, 60, 100, 100, 88, 79, 99, 75, 65, 89, 68, 74, 100, 66, 81, 95, 75, 69, 85, 91, 71

142. Veterans The list shows the numbers of Gulf War veterans (in thousands) in the 50 states and District of Columbia from 1990 to 2004. Use a frequency distribution and a histogram to organize the data. (Source: Department of Veterans Affairs)

AK 18	AL 81	AR 46	AZ 93
CA 361	CO 89	CT 28	DC 6
DE 13	FL 277	GA 179	HI 20
IA 37	ID 28	IL 133	IN 84
KS 43	KY 62	LA 72	MA 54
MD 95	ME 20	MI 116	MN 55
MO 85	MS 49	MT 16	NC 154
ND 10	NE 28	NH 18	NJ 62
NM 32	NV 41	NY 137	OH 155
OK 65	OR 53	PA 134	RI 11
SC 86	SD 13	TN 97	TX 354
UT 29	VA 196	VT 7	WA 122
WI 65	WV 27	WY 11	

143. Meteorology The normal daily maximum and minimum temperatures (in °F) for each month for the city of Chicago are shown in the table. Construct a double bar graph for the data. (Source: National Climatic Data Center)

Month	Max.	Min.
Jan.	29.6	14.3
Feb.	34.7	19.2
Mar.	46.1	28.5
Apr.	58.0	37.6
May	69.9	47.5
Jun.	79.2	57.2
Jul.	83.5	63.2
Aug.	81.2	62.2
Sep.	73.9	53.7
Oct.	62.1	42.1
Nov.	47.1	31.6
Dec.	34.4	20.4

144. Law Enforcement The table shows the numbers of people indicted for public corruption in the United States from 1995 to 2003. Construct a line graph for the data and state what information the graph reveals. (Source: U.S. Department of Justice)

Year	Number of indictments
1995	1051
1996	984
1997	1057
1998	1174
1999	1134
2000	1000
2001	1087
2002	1136
2003	1150

TABLE FOR **144**

145. Basketball The list shows the average numbers of points per game for the top 20 NBA players for the 2004–2005 regular NBA season. Organize the data in an appropriate display. Explain your choice of graph. (Source: National Basketball Association)

30.7, 27.6, 27.2, 26.1, 26.0, 25.7, 25.5, 24.6, 24.5, 24.3, 24.1, 23.9, 23.0, 22.9, 22.2, 22.2, 22.0, 21.7, 21.7

146. Salaries The table shows the average salaries (in thousands of dollars) for professors, associate professors, assistant professors, and instructors at public institutions of higher education from 2003 to 2005. Organize the data in an appropriate display. Explain your choice of graph. (Source: American Association of University Professors)

Rank	2003	2004	2005
Professor	84.1	85.8	88.5
Associate Professor	61.5	62.4	64.4
Assistant Professor	51.5	52.5	54.3
Instructor	37.2	37.9	39.4

Synthesis

True or False? In Exercises 147 and 148, determine whether the statement is true or false. Justify your answer.

147. $\dfrac{x^3 - 1}{x - 1} = x^2 + x + 1$ for all values of x.

148. A binomial sum squared is equal to the sum of the terms squared.

Error Analysis In Exercises 149 and 150, describe the error.

149. $(2x)^4 = 2x^4$

150. $\sqrt{3^2 + 4^2} = 3 + 4$

151. Writing Explain why $\sqrt{5u} + \sqrt{3u} \neq 2\sqrt{2u}$.

P Chapter Test

See www.CalcChat.com for worked-out solutions to odd-numbered exercises.

Take this test as you would take a test in class. After you are finished, check your work against the answers in the back of the book.

1. Use < or > to show the relationship between $-\frac{10}{3}$ and $-|-4|$.

2. Find the distance between the real numbers -17 and 39.

3. Identify the rule of algebra illustrated by $(5 - x) + 0 = 5 - x$.

In Exercises 4 and 5, evaluate each expression without using a calculator.

4. (a) $27\left(-\frac{2}{3}\right)$ (b) $\dfrac{5}{18} \div \dfrac{15}{8}$ (c) $\left(-\frac{2}{7}\right)^3$ (d) $\left(\dfrac{3^2}{2}\right)^{-3}$

5. (a) $\sqrt{5} \cdot \sqrt{125}$ (b) $\dfrac{\sqrt{72}}{\sqrt{2}}$ (c) $\dfrac{5.4 \times 10^8}{3 \times 10^3}$ (d) $(3 \times 10^4)^3$

In Exercises 6 and 7, simplify each expression.

6. (a) $3z^2(2z^3)^2$ (b) $(u - 2)^{-4}(u - 2)^{-3}$ (c) $\left(\dfrac{x^{-2}y^2}{3}\right)^{-1}$

7. (a) $9z\sqrt{8z} - 3\sqrt{2z^3}$ (b) $-5\sqrt{16y} + 10\sqrt{y}$ (c) $\sqrt[3]{\dfrac{16}{v^5}}$

8. Write the polynomial $3 - 2x^5 + 3x^3 - x^4$ in standard form. Identify the degree and leading coefficient.

In Exercises 9–12, perform the operations and simplify.

9. $(x^2 + 3) - [3x + (8 - x^2)]$

10. $(2x - 5)(4x^2 + 3)$

11. $\dfrac{8x}{x - 3} + \dfrac{24}{3 - x}$

12. $\dfrac{\left(\dfrac{2}{x} - \dfrac{2}{x + 1}\right)}{\left(\dfrac{4}{x^2 - 1}\right)}$

In Exercises 13–15, find the special product.

13. $\left(x + \sqrt{5}\right)\left(x - \sqrt{5}\right)$

14. $(x - 2)^3$

15. $[(x + y) - z][(x + y) + z]$

In Exercises 16–18, factor the expression completely.

16. $2x^4 - 3x^3 - 2x^2$ 17. $x^3 + 2x^2 - 4x - 8$ 18. $8x^3 - 27$

19. Rationalize each denominator: (a) $\dfrac{16}{\sqrt[3]{16}}$, (b) $\dfrac{6}{1 - \sqrt{3}}$, and (c) $\dfrac{1}{\sqrt{x + 2} - \sqrt{2}}$.

20. Write an expression for the area of the shaded region in the figure at the right and simplify the result.

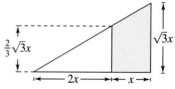

Figure for 20

21. Plot the points $(-2, 5)$ and $(6, 0)$. Find the coordinates of the midpoint of the line segment joining the points and the distance between the points.

22. The numbers (in millions) of votes cast for the Democratic candidates for president in 1980, 1984, 1988, 1992, 1996, 2000, and 2004 were 35.5, 37.5, 41.7, 44.9, 47.4, 51.0, and 58.9, respectively. Construct a bar graph for the data. (Source: Office of the Clerk, U.S. House of Representatives)

Proofs in Mathematics

What does the word *proof* mean to you? In mathematics, the word *proof* is used to mean simply a valid argument. When you are proving a statement or theorem, you must use facts, definitions, and accepted properties in a logical order. You can also use previously proved theorems in your proof. For instance, the Distance Formula is used in the proof of the Midpoint Formula below. There are several different proof methods, which you will see in later chapters.

The Midpoint Formula   (p. 52)

The midpoint of the line segment joining the points (x_1, y_1) and (x_2, y_2) is given by the Midpoint Formula

$$\text{Midpoint} = \left(\frac{x_1 + x_2}{2}, \frac{y_1 + y_2}{2} \right).$$

Proof

Using the figure, you must show that $d_1 = d_2$ and $d_1 + d_2 = d_3$.

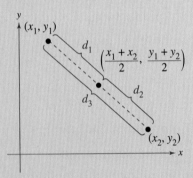

By the Distance Formula, you obtain

$$d_1 = \sqrt{\left(\frac{x_1 + x_2}{2} - x_1 \right)^2 + \left(\frac{y_1 + y_2}{2} - y_1 \right)^2}$$

$$= \frac{1}{2}\sqrt{(x_2 - x_1)^2 + (y_2 - y_1)^2}$$

$$d_2 = \sqrt{\left(x_2 - \frac{x_1 + x_2}{2} \right)^2 + \left(y_2 - \frac{y_1 + y_2}{2} \right)^2}$$

$$= \frac{1}{2}\sqrt{(x_2 - x_1)^2 + (y_2 - y_1)^2}$$

$$d_3 = \sqrt{(x_2 - x_1)^2 + (y_2 - y_1)^2}.$$

So, it follows that $d_1 = d_2$ and $d_1 + d_2 = d_3$.

The Cartesian Plane

The Cartesian plane was named after the French mathematician René Descartes (1596–1650). While Descartes was lying in bed, he noticed a fly buzzing around on the square ceiling tiles. He discovered that the position of the fly could be described by which ceiling tile the fly landed on. This led to the development of the Cartesian plane. Descartes felt that a coordinate plane could be used to facilitate description of the positions of objects.

Chapter 1

Functions and Their Graphs

1.1 Graphs of Equations

1.2 Lines in the Plane

1.3 Functions

1.4 Graphs of Functions

1.5 Shifting, Reflecting, and Stretching Graphs

1.6 Combinations of Functions

1.7 Inverse Functions

Selected Applications

Functions have many real-life applications. The applications listed below represent a small sample of the applications in this chapter.

- Data Analysis,
  Exercise 73, page 86
- Rental Demand,
  Exercise 86, page 99
- Postal Regulations,
  Exercise 81, page 112
- Motor Vehicles,
  Exercise 87, page 113
- Fluid Flow,
  Exercise 92, page 125
- Finance,
  Exercise 58, page 135
- Bacteria,
  Exercise 81, page 146
- Consumer Awareness,
  Exercises 84, page 146
- Shoe Sizes,
  Exercises 103 and 104,
  page 156

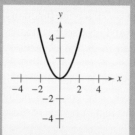

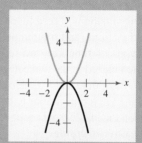

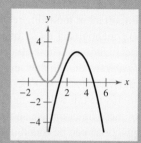

An equation in x and y defines a relationship between the two variables. The equation may be represented as a graph, providing another perspective on the relationship between x and y. In Chapter 1, you will learn how to write and graph linear equations, how to evaluate and find the domains and ranges of functions, and how to graph functions and their transformations.

© Index Stock Imagery

Refrigeration slows down the activity of bacteria in food so that it takes longer for the bacteria to spoil the food. The number of bacteria in a refrigerated food is a function of the amount of time the food has been out of refrigeration.

Introduction to Library of Parent Functions

In Chapter 1, you will be introduced to the concept of a *function*. As you proceed through the text, you will see that functions play a primary role in modeling real-life situations.

There are three basic types of functions that have proven to be the most important in modeling real-life situations. These functions are algebraic functions, exponential and logarithmic functions, and trigonometric and inverse trigonometric functions. These three types of functions are referred to as the *elementary functions*, though they are often placed in the two categories of *algebraic functions* and *transcendental functions*. Each time a new type of function is studied in detail in this text, it will be highlighted in a box similar to this one. The graphs of many of these functions are shown on the inside front cover of this text. A review of these functions can be found in the *Study Capsules*.

Algebraic Functions

These functions are formed by applying algebraic operations to the identity function $f(x) = x$.

Name	Function	Location
Linear	$f(x) = ax + b$	Section 1.2
Quadratic	$f(x) = ax^2 + bx + c$	Section 3.1
Cubic	$f(x) = ax^3 + bx^2 + cx + d$	Section 3.2
Polynomial	$P(x) = a_n x^n + a_{n-1} x^{n-1} + \cdots + a_2 x^2 + a_1 x + a_0$	Section 3.2
Rational	$f(x) = \dfrac{N(x)}{D(x)}$, $N(x)$ and $D(x)$ are polynomial functions	Section 3.5
Radical	$f(x) = \sqrt[n]{P(x)}$	Section 1.3

Transcendental Functions

These functions cannot be formed from the identity function by using algebraic operations.

Name	Function	Location
Exponential	$f(x) = a^x, a > 0, a \neq 1$	Section 4.1
Logarithmic	$f(x) = \log_a x, x > 0, a > 0, a \neq 1$	Section 4.2
Trigonometric	$f(x) = \sin x, f(x) = \cos x, f(x) = \tan x,$	
	$f(x) = \csc x, f(x) = \sec x, f(x) = \cot x$	Not covered in this text.
Inverse Trigonometric	$f(x) = \arcsin x, f(x) = \arccos x, f(x) = \arctan x$	Not covered in this text.

Nonelementary Functions

Some useful nonelementary functions include the following.

Name	Function	Location
Absolute value	$f(x) = |g(x)|$, $g(x)$ is an elementary function	Section 1.3
Piecewise-defined	$f(x) = \begin{cases} 3x + 2, & x \geq 1 \\ -2x + 4, & x < 1 \end{cases}$	Section 1.3
Greatest integer	$f(x) = [\![g(x)]\!]$, $g(x)$ is an elementary function	Section 1.4
Data defined	Formula for temperature: $F = \dfrac{9}{5}C + 32$	Section 1.3

1.1 Graphs of Equations

The Graph of an Equation

News magazines often show graphs comparing the rate of inflation, the federal deficit, or the unemployment rate to the time of year. Businesses use graphs to report monthly sales statistics. Such graphs provide geometric pictures of the way one quantity changes with respect to another. Frequently, the relationship between two quantities is expressed as an **equation**. This section introduces the basic procedure for determining the geometric picture associated with an equation.

For an equation in the variables x and y, a point (a, b) is a **solution point** if substitution of a for x and b for y satisfies the equation. Most equations have *infinitely many* solution points. For example, the equation $3x + y = 5$ has solution points $(0, 5)$, $(1, 2)$, $(2, -1)$, $(3, -4)$, and so on. The set of all solution points of an equation is the **graph of the equation.**

Example 1   Determining Solution Points

Determine whether (a) $(2, 13)$ and (b) $(-1, -3)$ lie on the graph of $y = 10x - 7$.

Solution

a. $y = 10x - 7$ Write original equation.

$13 \overset{?}{=} 10(2) - 7$ Substitute 2 for x and 13 for y.

$13 = 13$ $(2, 13)$ is a solution. ✓

The point $(2, 13)$ *does* lie on the graph of $y = 10x - 7$ because it is a solution point of the equation.

b. $y = 10x - 7$ Write original equation.

$-3 \overset{?}{=} 10(-1) - 7$ Substitute -1 for x and -3 for y.

$-3 \neq -17$ $(-1, -3)$ is not a solution.

The point $(-1, -3)$ *does not* lie on the graph of $y = 10x - 7$ because it is not a solution point of the equation.

✓**CHECKPOINT**   Now try Exercise 3.

The basic technique used for sketching the graph of an equation is the point-plotting method.

> ### Sketching the Graph of an Equation by Point Plotting
>
> 1. If possible, rewrite the equation so that one of the variables is isolated on one side of the equation.
> 2. Make a table of values showing several solution points.
> 3. Plot these points on a rectangular coordinate system.
> 4. Connect the points with a smooth curve or line.

Example 2   Sketching a Graph by Point Plotting

Use point plotting and graph paper to sketch the graph of $3x + y = 6$.

Solution

In this case you can isolate the variable y.

$$y = 6 - 3x \qquad \text{Solve equation for } y.$$

Using negative, zero, and positive values for x, you can obtain the following table of values (solution points).

x	-1	0	1	2	3
$y = 6 - 3x$	9	6	3	0	-3
Solution point	$(-1, 9)$	$(0, 6)$	$(1, 3)$	$(2, 0)$	$(3, -3)$

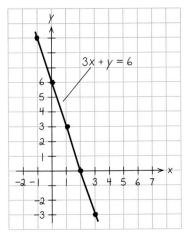

Figure 1.1

Next, plot these points and connect them, as shown in Figure 1.1. It appears that the graph is a straight line. You will study lines extensively in Section 1.2.

CHECKPOINT   Now try Exercise 7.

The points at which a graph touches or crosses an axis are called the **intercepts** of the graph. For instance, in Example 2 the point $(0, 6)$ is the y-intercept of the graph because the graph crosses the y-axis at that point. The point $(2, 0)$ is the x-intercept of the graph because the graph crosses the x-axis at that point.

Example 3   Sketching a Graph by Point Plotting

Use point plotting and graph paper to sketch the graph of $y = x^2 - 2$.

Solution

Because the equation is already solved for y, make a table of values by choosing several convenient values of x and calculating the corresponding values of y.

x	-2	-1	0	1	2	3
$y = x^2 - 2$	2	-1	-2	-1	2	7
Solution point	$(-2, 2)$	$(-1, -1)$	$(0, -2)$	$(1, -1)$	$(2, 2)$	$(3, 7)$

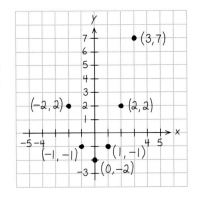

(a)

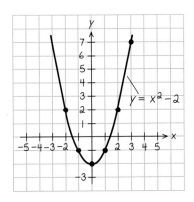

(b)

Figure 1.2

Next, plot the corresponding solution points, as shown in Figure 1.2(a). Finally, connect the points with a smooth curve, as shown in Figure 1.2(b). This graph is called a *parabola*. You will study parabolas in Section 3.1.

CHECKPOINT   Now try Exercise 8.

In this text, you will study two basic ways to create graphs: *by hand* and *using a graphing utility*. For instance, the graphs in Figures 1.1 and 1.2 were sketched by hand and the graph in Figure 1.6 (on page 80) was created using a graphing utility.

Using a Graphing Utility

One of the disadvantages of the point-plotting method is that to get a good idea about the shape of a graph, you need to plot *many* points. With only a few points, you could misrepresent the graph of an equation. For instance, consider the equation

$$y = \frac{1}{30}x(x^4 - 10x^2 + 39).$$

Suppose you plotted only five points: $(-3, -3)$, $(-1, -1)$, $(0, 0)$, $(1, 1)$, and $(3, 3)$, as shown in Figure 1.3(a). From these five points, you might assume that the graph of the equation is a line. That, however, is not correct. By plotting several more points and connecting the points with a smooth curve, you can see that the actual graph is not a line at all, as shown in Figure 1.3(b).

TECHNOLOGY SUPPORT

This section presents a brief overview of how to use a graphing utility to graph an equation. For more extensive coverage of this topic, see Appendix A and the *Graphing Technology Guide* at this textbook's *Online Study Center*.

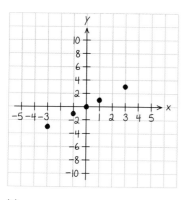

(a)

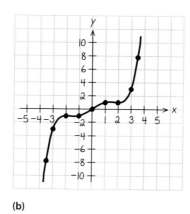

(b)

Figure 1.3

From this, you can see that the point-plotting method leaves you with a dilemma. This method can be very inaccurate if only a few points are plotted, and it is very time-consuming to plot a dozen (or more) points. Technology can help solve this dilemma. Plotting several (even several hundred) points on a rectangular coordinate system is something that a computer or calculator can do easily.

TECHNOLOGY TIP   The point-plotting method is the method used by *all* graphing utilities. Each computer or calculator screen is made up of a grid of hundreds or thousands of small areas called *pixels*. Screens that have many pixels per square inch are said to have a higher *resolution* than screens with fewer pixels.

Using a Graphing Utility to Graph an Equation

To graph an equation involving x and y on a graphing utility, use the following procedure.

1. Rewrite the equation so that y is isolated on the left side.
2. Enter the equation in the graphing utility.
3. Determine a *viewing window* that shows all important features of the graph.
4. Graph the equation.

1.1   Exercises

See www.CalcChat.com for worked-out solutions to odd-numbered exercises.

Vocabulary Check

Fill in the blanks.

1. For an equation in x and y, if substitution of a for x and b for y satisfies the equation, then the point (a, b) is a _____ .

2. The set of all solution points of an equation is the _____ of the equation.

3. The points at which a graph touches or crosses an axis are called the _____ of the graph.

In Exercises 1–6, determine whether each point lies on the graph of the equation.

Equation	Points	
1. $y = \sqrt{x + 4}$	(a) $(0, 2)$	(b) $(5, 3)$
2. $y = x^2 - 3x + 2$	(a) $(2, 0)$	(b) $(-2, 8)$
3. $y = 4 - |x - 2|$	(a) $(1, 5)$	(b) $(1.2, 3.2)$
4. $2x - y - 3 = 0$	(a) $(1, 2)$	(b) $(1, -1)$
5. $x^2 + y^2 = 20$	(a) $(3, -2)$	(b) $(-4, 2)$
6. $y = \frac{1}{3}x^3 - 2x^2$	(a) $\left(2, -\frac{16}{3}\right)$	(b) $(-3, 9)$

In Exercises 7 and 8, complete the table. Use the resulting solution points to sketch the graph of the equation. Use a graphing utility to verify the graph.

7. $3x - 2y = 2$

x	-2	0	$\frac{2}{3}$	1	2
y					
Solution point					

8. $2x + y = x^2$

x	-1	0	1	2	3
y					
Solution point					

9. *Exploration*

(a) Complete the table for the equation $y = \frac{1}{4}x - 3$.

x	-2	-1	0	1	2
y					

(b) Use the solution points to sketch the graph. Then use a graphing utility to verify the graph.

(c) Repeat parts (a) and (b) for the equation $y = -\frac{1}{4}x - 3$. Describe any differences between the graphs.

10. *Exploration*

(a) Complete the table for the equation

$$y = \frac{6x}{x^2 + 1}.$$

x	-2	-1	0	1	2
y					

(b) Use the solution points to sketch the graph. Then use a graphing utility to verify the graph.

(c) Continue the table in part (a) for x-values of 5, 10, 20, and 40. What is the value of y approaching? Can y be negative for positive values of x? Explain.

In Exercises 11–16, match the equation with its graph. [The graphs are labeled (a), (b), (c), (d), (e), and (f).]

(a)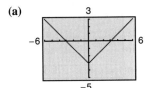

(b)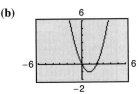

(c)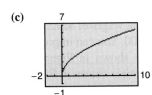

(d)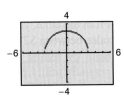

(e)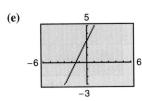

(f)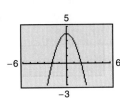

11. $y = 2x + 3$

12. $y = 4 - x^2$

13. $y = x^2 - 2x$

14. $y = \sqrt{9 - x^2}$

15. $y = 2\sqrt{x}$

16. $y = |x| - 3$

In Exercises 17–30, sketch the graph of the equation.

17. $y = -4x + 1$

18. $y = 2x - 3$

19. $y = 2 - x^2$

20. $y = x^2 - 1$

21. $y = x^2 - 3x$

22. $y = -x^2 - 4x$

23. $y = x^3 + 2$

24. $y = x^3 - 3$

25. $y = \sqrt{x - 3}$

26. $y = \sqrt{1 - x}$

27. $y = |x - 2|$

28. $y = 5 - |x|$

29. $x = y^2 - 1$

30. $x = y^2 + 4$

In Exercises 31–44, use a graphing utility to graph the equation. Use a standard viewing window. Approximate any x- or y-intercepts of the graph.

31. $y = x - 7$

32. $y = x + 1$

33. $y = 3 - \frac{1}{2}x$

34. $y = \frac{2}{3}x - 1$

35. $y = \dfrac{2x}{x - 1}$

36. $y = \dfrac{4}{x}$

37. $y = x\sqrt{x + 3}$

38. $y = (6 - x)\sqrt{x}$

39. $y = \sqrt[3]{x - 8}$

40. $y = \sqrt[3]{x + 1}$

41. $x^2 - y = 4x - 3$

42. $2y - x^2 + 8 = 2x$

43. $y - 4x = x^2(x - 4)$

44. $x^3 + y = 1$

In Exercises 45–48, use a graphing utility to graph the equation. Begin by using a standard viewing window. Then graph the equation a second time using the specified viewing window. Which viewing window is better? Explain.

45. $y = \frac{5}{2}x + 5$

46. $y = -3x + 50$

Xmin = 0
Xmax = 6
Xscl = 1
Ymin = 0
Ymax = 10
Yscl = 1

Xmin = -1
Xmax = 4
Xscl = 1
Ymin = -5
Ymax = 60
Yscl = 5

47. $y = -x^2 + 10x - 5$

48. $y = 4(x + 5)\sqrt{4 - x}$

Xmin = -1
Xmax = 11
Xscl = 1
Ymin = -5
Ymax = 25
Yscl = 5

Xmin = -6
Xmax = 6
Xscl = 1
Ymin = -5
Ymax = 50
Yscl = 5

In Exercises 49–54, describe the viewing window of the graph shown.

49. $y = -10x + 50$

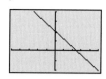

50. $y = 4x^2 - 25$

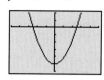

51. $y = \sqrt{x + 2} - 1$

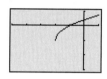

52. $y = x^3 - 3x^2 + 4$

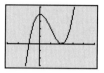

53. $y = |x| + |x - 10|$

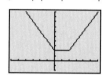

54. $y = 8\sqrt[3]{x - 6}$

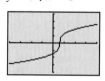

In Exercises 55–58, explain how to use a graphing utility to verify that $y_1 = y_2$. Identify the rule of algebra that is illustrated.

55. $y_1 = \frac{1}{4}(x^2 - 8)$

$y_2 = \frac{1}{4}x^2 - 2$

56. $y_1 = \frac{1}{2}x + (x + 1)$

$y_2 = \frac{3}{2}x + 1$

57. $y_1 = \dfrac{1}{5}[10(x^2 - 1)]$

$y_2 = 2(x^2 - 1)$

58. $y_1 = (x - 3) \cdot \dfrac{1}{x - 3}$

$y_2 = 1$

In Exercises 59–62, use a graphing utility to graph the equation. Use the *trace* feature of the graphing utility to approximate the unknown coordinate of each solution point accurate to two decimal places. (*Hint:* You may need to use the *zoom* feature of the graphing utility to obtain the required accuracy.)

59. $y = \sqrt{5 - x}$

(a) $(2, y)$

(b) $(x, 3)$

60. $y = x^3(x - 3)$

(a) $(2.25, y)$

(b) $(x, 20)$

61. $y = x^5 - 5x$

(a) $(-0.5, y)$

(b) $(x, -4)$

62. $y = |x^2 - 6x + 5|$

(a) $(2, y)$

(b) $(x, 1.5)$

In Exercises 63–66, solve for y and use a graphing utility to graph each of the resulting equations in the same viewing window. (Adjust the viewing window so that the circle appears circular.)

63. $x^2 + y^2 = 16$

64. $x^2 + y^2 = 36$

65. $(x - 1)^2 + (y - 2)^2 = 4$

66. $(x - 3)^2 + (y - 1)^2 = 25$

In Exercises 67 and 68, determine which equation is the best choice for the graph of the circle shown.

67.

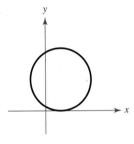

(a) $(x - 1)^2 + (y - 2)^2 = 4$

(b) $(x + 1)^2 + (y - 2)^2 = 4$

(c) $(x - 1)^2 + (y - 2)^2 = 16$

(d) $(x + 1)^2 + (y + 2)^2 = 4$

68.

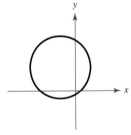

(a) $(x - 2)^2 + (y - 3)^2 = 4$

(b) $(x - 2)^2 + (y - 3)^2 = 16$

(c) $(x + 2)^2 + (y - 3)^2 = 16$

(d) $(x + 2)^2 + (y - 3)^2 = 4$

In Exercises 69 and 70, determine whether each point lies on the graph of the circle. (There may be more than one correct answer.)

69. $(x - 1)^2 + (y - 2)^2 = 25$

(a) $(1, 2)$ (b) $(-2, 6)$

(c) $(5, -1)$ (d) $\left(0, 2 + 2\sqrt{6}\right)$

70. $(x + 2)^2 + (y - 3)^2 = 25$

(a) $(-2, 3)$ (b) $(0, 0)$

(c) $(1, -1)$ (d) $\left(-1, 3 - 2\sqrt{6}\right)$

71. *Depreciation* A manufacturing plant purchases a new molding machine for $225,000. The depreciated value (decreased value) y after t years is $y = 225{,}000 - 20{,}000t$, for $0 \le t \le 8$.

(a) Use the constraints of the model to graph the equation using an appropriate viewing window.

(b) Use the *value* feature or the *zoom* and *trace* features of a graphing utility to determine the value of y when $t = 5.8$. Verify your answer algebraically.

(c) Use the *value* feature or the *zoom* and *trace* features of a graphing utility to determine the value of y when $t = 2.35$. Verify your answer algebraically.

72. *Consumerism* You buy a personal watercraft for $8100. The depreciated value y after t years is $y = 8100 - 929t$, for $0 \le t \le 6$.

(a) Use the constraints of the model to graph the equation using an appropriate viewing window.

(b) Use the *zoom* and *trace* features of a graphing utility to determine the value of t when $y = 5545.25$. Verify your answer algebraically.

(c) Use the *value* feature or the *zoom* and *trace* features of a graphing utility to determine the value of y when $t = 5.5$. Verify your answer algebraically.

73. *Data Analysis* The table shows the median (middle) sales prices (in thousands of dollars) of new one-family homes in the southern United States from 1995 to 2004. (Sources: U.S. Census Bureau and U.S. Department of Housing and Urban Development)

Year	Median sales price, y
1995	124.5
1996	126.2
1997	129.6
1998	135.8
1999	145.9
2000	148.0
2001	155.4
2002	163.4
2003	168.1
2004	181.1

A model for the median sales price during this period is given by

$$y = -0.0049t^3 + 0.443t^2 - 0.75t + 116.7, \quad 5 \le t \le 14$$

where y represents the sales price and t represents the year, with $t = 5$ corresponding to 1995.

(a) Use the model and the *table* feature of a graphing utility to find the median sales prices from 1995 to 2004. How well does the model fit the data? Explain.

(b) Use a graphing utility to graph the data from the table and the model in the same viewing window. How well does the model fit the data? Explain.

(c) Use the model to estimate the median sales prices in 2008 and 2010. Do the values seem reasonable? Explain.

(d) Use the *zoom* and *trace* features of a graphing utility to determine during which year(s) the median sales price was approximately $150,000.

74. **Population Statistics** The table shows the life expectancies of a child (at birth) in the United States for selected years from 1930 to 2000. (Source: U.S. National Center for Health Statistics)

Year	Life expectancy, y
1930	59.7
1940	62.9
1950	68.2
1960	69.7
1970	70.8
1980	73.7
1990	75.4
2000	77.0

A model for the life expectancy during this period is given by

$$y = \frac{59.617 + 1.18t}{1 + 0.012t}, \quad 0 \le t \le 70$$

where y represents the life expectancy and t is the time in years, with $t = 0$ corresponding to 1930.

(a) Use a graphing utility to graph the data from the table above and the model in the same viewing window. How well does the model fit the data? Explain.

(b) What does the y-intercept of the graph of the model represent?

(c) Use the *zoom* and *trace* features of a graphing utility to determine the year when the life expectancy was 73.2. Verify your answer algebraically.

(d) Determine the life expectancy in 1948 both graphically and algebraically.

(e) Use the model to estimate the life expectancy of a child born in 2010.

75. **Geometry** A rectangle of length x and width w has a perimeter of 12 meters.

(a) Draw a diagram that represents the rectangle. Use the specified variables to label its sides.

(b) Show that the width of the rectangle is $w = 6 - x$ and that its area is $A = x(6 - x)$.

(c) Use a graphing utility to graph the area equation.

(d) Use the *zoom* and *trace* features of a graphing utility to determine the value of A when $w = 4.9$ meters. Verify your answer algebraically.

(e) From the graph in part (c), estimate the dimensions of the rectangle that yield a maximum area.

76. Find the standard form of the equation of the circle for which the endpoints of a diameter are $(0, 0)$ and $(4, -6)$.

Synthesis

True or False? In Exercises 77 and 78, determine whether the statement is true or false. Justify your answer.

77. A parabola can have only one x-intercept.

78. The graph of a linear equation can have either no x-intercepts or only one x-intercept.

79. **Writing** Explain how to find an appropriate viewing window for the graph of an equation.

80. **Writing** Your employer offers you a choice of wage scales: a monthly salary of $3000 plus commission of 7% of sales or a salary of $3400 plus a 5% commission. Write a short paragraph discussing how you would choose your option. At what sales level would the options yield the same salary?

81. **Writing** Given the equation $y = 250x + 1000$, write a possible explanation of what the equation could represent in real life.

82. **Writing** Given the equation $y = -0.1x + 10$, write a possible explanation of what the equation could represent in real life.

Skills Review

In Exercises 83–86, perform the operation and simplify.

83. $7\sqrt{72} - 5\sqrt{18}$

84. $-10\sqrt{25y} - \sqrt{y}$

85. $7^{3/2} \cdot 7^{11/2}$

86. $\dfrac{10^{17/4}}{10^{5/4}}$

In Exercises 87 and 88, perform the operation and write the result in standard form.

87. $(9x - 4) + (2x^2 - x + 15)$

88. $(3x^2 - 5)(-x^2 + 1)$

1.2   Lines in the Plane

The Slope of a Line

In this section, you will study lines and their equations. The **slope** of a nonvertical line represents the number of units the line rises or falls vertically for each unit of horizontal change from left to right. For instance, consider the two points (x_1, y_1) and (x_2, y_2) on the line shown in Figure 1.16. As you move from left to right along this line, a change of $(y_2 - y_1)$ units in the vertical direction corresponds to a change of $(x_2 - x_1)$ units in the horizontal direction. That is,

$$y_2 - y_1 = \text{the change in } y$$

and

$$x_2 - x_1 = \text{the change in } x.$$

The slope of the line is given by the ratio of these two changes.

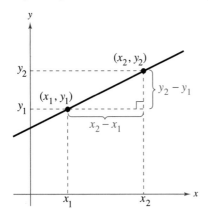

Figure 1.16

Definition of the Slope of a Line

The **slope** m of the nonvertical line through (x_1, y_1) and (x_2, y_2) is

$$m = \frac{y_2 - y_1}{x_2 - x_1} = \frac{\text{change in } y}{\text{change in } x}$$

where $x_1 \neq x_2$.

When this formula for slope is used, the *order of subtraction* is important. Given two points on a line, you are free to label either one of them as (x_1, y_1) and the other as (x_2, y_2). However, once you have done this, you must form the numerator and denominator using the same order of subtraction.

$$m = \frac{y_2 - y_1}{x_2 - x_1} \qquad m = \frac{y_1 - y_2}{x_1 - x_2} \qquad m = \frac{y_2 - y_1}{x_1 - x_2}$$

     Correct   Correct   Incorrect

Throughout this text, the term *line* always means a *straight* line.

Example 1 Finding the Slope of a Line

Find the slope of the line passing through each pair of points.

a. $(-2, 0)$ and $(3, 1)$ **b.** $(-1, 2)$ and $(2, 2)$ **c.** $(0, 4)$ and $(1, -1)$

Solution

Difference in y-values

a. $m = \dfrac{y_2 - y_1}{x_2 - x_1} = \dfrac{1 - 0}{3 - (-2)} = \dfrac{1}{3 + 2} = \dfrac{1}{5}$

Difference in x-values

b. $m = \dfrac{2 - 2}{2 - (-1)} = \dfrac{0}{3} = 0$

c. $m = \dfrac{-1 - 4}{1 - 0} = \dfrac{-5}{1} = -5$

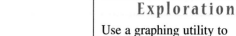

> **Exploration**
>
> Use a graphing utility to compare the slopes of the lines $y = 0.5x$, $y = x$, $y = 2x$, and $y = 4x$. What do you observe about these lines? Compare the slopes of the lines $y = -0.5x$, $y = -x$, $y = -2x$, and $y = -4x$. What do you observe about these lines? (*Hint:* Use a *square setting* to guarantee a true geometric perspective.)

The graphs of the three lines are shown in Figure 1.17. Note that the *square setting* gives the correct "steepness" of the lines.

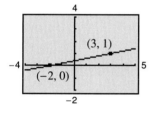

(a)

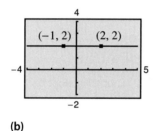

(b)

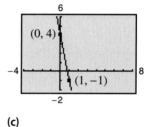

(c)

Figure 1.17

✔CHECKPOINT   Now try Exercise 9.

The definition of slope does not apply to vertical lines. For instance, consider the points $(3, 4)$ and $(3, 1)$ on the vertical line shown in Figure 1.18. Applying the formula for slope, you obtain

$$m = \frac{4 - 1}{3 - 3} = \frac{3}{0}. \qquad \text{Undefined}$$

Because division by zero is undefined, the slope of a vertical line is undefined.

From the slopes of the lines shown in Figures 1.17 and 1.18, you can make the following generalizations about the slope of a line.

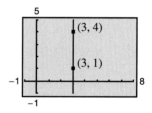

Figure 1.18

> **The Slope of a Line**
>
> 1. A line with positive slope $(m > 0)$ *rises* from left to right.
> 2. A line with negative slope $(m < 0)$ *falls* from left to right.
> 3. A line with zero slope $(m = 0)$ is *horizontal*.
> 4. A line with undefined slope is *vertical*.

The Point-Slope Form of the Equation of a Line

If you know the slope of a line *and* you also know the coordinates of one point on the line, you can find an equation for the line. For instance, in Figure 1.19, let (x_1, y_1) be a point on the line whose slope is m. If (x, y) is any *other* point on the line, it follows that

$$\frac{y - y_1}{x - x_1} = m.$$

This equation in the variables x and y can be rewritten in the **point-slope form** of the equation of a line.

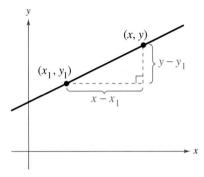

Figure 1.19

Point-Slope Form of the Equation of a Line

The **point-slope form** of the equation of the line that passes through the point (x_1, y_1) and has a slope of m is

$$y - y_1 = m(x - x_1).$$

The point-slope form is most useful for finding the equation of a line if you know at least one point that the line passes through and the slope of the line. You should remember this form of the equation of a line.

Example 2   The Point-Slope Form of the Equation of a Line

Find an equation of the line that passes through the point $(1, -2)$ and has a slope of 3.

Solution

$y - y_1 = m(x - x_1)$	Point-slope form
$y - (-2) = 3(x - 1)$	Substitute for y_1, m, and x_1.
$y + 2 = 3x - 3$	Simplify.
$y = 3x - 5$	Solve for y.

The line is shown in Figure 1.20.

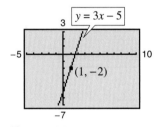

Figure 1.20

✔CHECKPOINT   Now try Exercise 25.

The point-slope form can be used to find an equation of a nonvertical line passing through two points (x_1, y_1) and (x_2, y_2). First, find the slope of the line.

$$m = \frac{y_2 - y_1}{x_2 - x_1}, \quad x_1 \neq x_2$$

Then use the point-slope form to obtain the equation

$$y - y_1 = \frac{y_2 - y_1}{x_2 - x_1}(x - x_1).$$

This is sometimes called the **two-point form** of the equation of a line.

STUDY TIP

When you find an equation of the line that passes through two given points, you need to substitute the coordinates of only one of the points into the point-slope form. It does not matter which point you choose because both points will yield the same result.

Example 3   A Linear Model for Sales Prediction

During 2004, Nike's net sales were $12.25 billion, and in 2005 net sales were $13.74 billion. Write a linear equation giving the net sales y in terms of the year x. Then use the equation to predict the net sales for 2006.   (Source: Nike, Inc.)

Solution

Let $x = 0$ represent 2000. In Figure 1.21, let $(4, 12.25)$ and $(5, 13.74)$ be two points on the line representing the net sales. The slope of this line is

$$m = \frac{13.74 - 12.25}{5 - 4} = 1.49. \qquad m = \frac{y_2 - y_1}{x_2 - x_1}$$

By the point-slope form, the equation of the line is as follows.

$$y - 12.25 = 1.49(x - 4) \qquad \text{Write in point-slope form.}$$

$$y = 1.49x + 6.29 \qquad \text{Simplify.}$$

Now, using this equation, you can predict the 2006 net sales ($x = 6$) to be

$$y = 1.49(6) + 6.29 = 8.94 + 6.29 = \$15.23 \text{ billion.}$$

 CHECKPOINT   Now try Exercise 45.

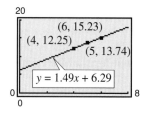

Figure 1.21

Library of Parent Functions: Linear Function

In the next section, you will be introduced to the precise meaning of the term *function*. The simplest type of function is a *linear function* of the form

$$f(x) = mx + b.$$

As its name implies, the graph of a linear function is a line that has a slope of m and a y-intercept at $(0, b)$. The basic characteristics of a linear function are summarized below. (Note that some of the terms below will be defined later in the text.) A review of linear functions can be found in the *Study Capsules*.

Graph of $f(x) = mx + b, m > 0$
Domain: $(-\infty, \infty)$
Range: $(-\infty, \infty)$
x-intercept: $(-b/m, 0)$
y-intercept: $(0, b)$
Increasing

Graph of $f(x) = mx + b, m < 0$
Domain: $(-\infty, \infty)$
Range: $(-\infty, \infty)$
x-intercept: $(-b/m, 0)$
y-intercept: $(0, b)$
Decreasing

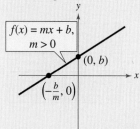

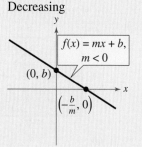

When $m = 0$, the function $f(x) = b$ is called a *constant function* and its graph is a horizontal line.

STUDY TIP

The prediction method illustrated in Example 3 is called **linear extrapolation.** Note in the top figure below that an extrapolated point does not lie between the given points. When the estimated point lies between two given points, as shown in the bottom figure, the procedure used to predict the point is called **linear interpolation.**

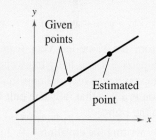

Linear Extrapolation

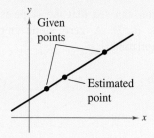

Linear Interpolation

Sketching Graphs of Lines

Many problems in coordinate geometry can be classified as follows.

1. Given a graph (or parts of it), find its equation.
2. Given an equation, sketch its graph.

For lines, the first problem is solved easily by using the point-slope form. This formula, however, is not particularly useful for solving the second type of problem. The form that is better suited to graphing linear equations is the **slope-intercept form** of the equation of a line, $y = mx + b$.

Slope-Intercept Form of the Equation of a Line

The graph of the equation

$$y = mx + b$$

is a line whose slope is m and whose y-intercept is $(0, b)$.

Example 4   Using the Slope-Intercept Form

Determine the slope and y-intercept of each linear equation. Then describe its graph.

a. $x + y = 2$ **b.** $y = 2$

Algebraic Solution

a. Begin by writing the equation in slope-intercept form.

$x + y = 2$	Write original equation.
$y = 2 - x$	Subtract x from each side.
$y = -x + 2$	Write in slope-intercept form.

From the slope-intercept form of the equation, the slope is -1 and the y-intercept is $(0, 2)$. Because the slope is negative, you know that the graph of the equation is a line that falls one unit for every unit it moves to the right.

b. By writing the equation $y = 2$ in slope-intercept form

$$y = (0)x + 2$$

you can see that the slope is 0 and the y-intercept is $(0, 2)$. A zero slope implies that the line is horizontal.

Graphical Solution

a. Solve the equation for y to obtain $y = 2 - x$. Enter this equation in your graphing utility. Use a decimal viewing window to graph the equation. To find the y-intercept, use the *value* or *trace* feature. When $x = 0$, $y = 2$, as shown in Figure 1.22(a). So, the y-intercept is $(0, 2)$. To find the slope, continue to use the *trace* feature. Move the cursor along the line until $x = 1$. At this point, $y = 1$. So the graph falls 1 unit for every unit it moves to the right, and the slope is -1.   •

b. Enter the equation $y = 2$ in your graphing utility and graph the equation. Use the *trace* feature to verify the y-intercept $(0, 2)$, as shown in Figure 1.22(b), and to see that the value of y is the same for all values of x. So, the slope of the horizontal line is 0.

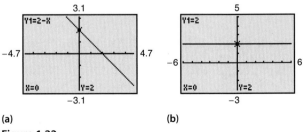

(a)

(b)

Figure 1.22

✔CHECKPOINT   Now try Exercise 47.

From the slope-intercept form of the equation of a line, you can see that a horizontal line ($m = 0$) has an equation of the form $y = b$. This is consistent with the fact that each point on a horizontal line through $(0, b)$ has a y-coordinate of b. Similarly, each point on a vertical line through $(a, 0)$ has an x-coordinate of a. So, a vertical line has an equation of the form $x = a$. This equation cannot be written in slope-intercept form because the slope of a vertical line is undefined. However, *every* line has an equation that can be written in the **general form**

$Ax + By + C = 0$ General form of the equation of a line

where A and B are not *both* zero.

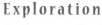

Exploration

Graph the lines $y_1 = 2x + 1$, $y_2 = \frac{1}{2}x + 1$, and $y_3 = -2x + 1$ in the same viewing window. What do you observe?

Graph the lines $y_1 = 2x + 1$, $y_2 = 2x$, and $y_3 = 2x - 1$ in the same viewing window. What do you observe?

Summary of Equations of Lines

1. General form: $Ax + By + C = 0$

2. Vertical line: $x = a$

3. Horizontal line: $y = b$

4. Slope-intercept form: $y = mx + b$

5. Point-slope form: $y - y_1 = m(x - x_1)$

Example 5   Different Viewing Windows

The graphs of the two lines

$y = -x - 1$ and $y = -10x - 1$

are shown in Figure 1.23. Even though the slopes of these lines are quite different (-1 and -10, respectively), the graphs seem misleadingly similar because the viewing windows are different.

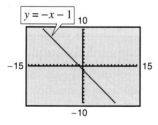

Figure 1.23

✓CHECKPOINT   Now try Exercise 51.

TECHNOLOGY TIP   When a graphing utility is used to graph a line, it is important to realize that the graph of the line may not visually appear to have the slope indicated by its equation. This occurs because of the viewing window used for the graph. For instance, Figure 1.24 shows graphs of $y = 2x + 1$ produced on a graphing utility using three different viewing windows. Notice that the slopes in Figures 1.24(a) and (b) do not visually appear to be equal to 2. However, if you use a *square setting*, as in Figure 1.24(c), the slope visually appears to be 2.

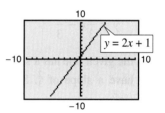

(a)

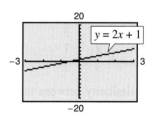

(b)

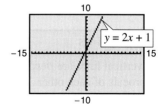

(c)

Figure 1.24

88. *Writing*   Using the results of Exercise 87, write a short paragraph discussing the concepts of *slope* and *average rate of change*.

Synthesis

True or False?   **In Exercises 89 and 90, determine whether the statement is true or false. Justify your answer.**

89. The line through $(-8, 2)$ and $(-1, 4)$ and the line through $(0, -4)$ and $(-7, 7)$ are parallel.

90. If the points $(10, -3)$ and $(2, -9)$ lie on the same line, then the point $\left(-12, -\frac{37}{2}\right)$ also lies on that line.

Exploration   **In Exercises 91–94, use a graphing utility to graph the equation of the line in the form**

$$\frac{x}{a} + \frac{y}{b} = 1, \quad a \neq 0, b \neq 0.$$

Use the graphs to make a conjecture about what a and b represent. Verify your conjecture.

91. $\dfrac{x}{5} + \dfrac{y}{-3} = 1$ **92.** $\dfrac{x}{-6} + \dfrac{y}{2} = 1$

93. $\dfrac{x}{4} + \dfrac{y}{-\frac{2}{3}} = 1$ **94.** $\dfrac{x}{\frac{1}{2}} + \dfrac{y}{5} = 1$

In Exercises 95–98, use the results of Exercises 91–94 to write an equation of the line that passes through the points.

95. *x*-intercept: $(2, 0)$ **96.** *x*-intercept: $(-5, 0)$
     y-intercept: $(0, 3)$ *y*-intercept: $(0, -4)$

97. *x*-intercept: $\left(-\frac{1}{6}, 0\right)$ **98.** *x*-intercept: $\left(\frac{3}{4}, 0\right)$
     y-intercept: $\left(0, -\frac{2}{3}\right)$ *y*-intercept: $\left(0, \frac{4}{5}\right)$

Library of Parent Functions   **In Exercises 99 and 100, determine which equation(s) may be represented by the graph shown. (There may be more than one correct answer.)**

99.   **100.**

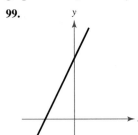   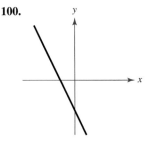

(a) $2x - y = -10$ (a) $2x + y = 5$
(b) $2x + y = 10$ (b) $2x + y = -5$
(c) $x - 2y = 10$ (c) $x - 2y = 5$
(d) $x + 2y = 10$ (d) $x - 2y = -5$

Library of Parent Functions   **In Exercises 101 and 102, determine which pair of equations may be represented by the graphs shown.**

101.   **102.**

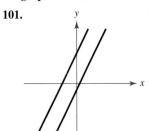   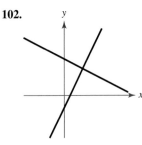

(a) $2x - y = 5$ (a) $2x - y = 2$
   $2x - y = 1$ $x + 2y = 12$
(b) $2x + y = -5$ (b) $x - y = 1$
   $2x + y = 1$ $x + y = 6$
(c) $2x - y = -5$ (c) $2x + y = 2$
   $2x - y = 1$ $x - 2y = 12$
(d) $x - 2y = -5$ (d) $x - 2y = 2$
   $x - 2y = -1$ $x + 2y = 12$

103. *Think About It*   Does every line have both an *x*-intercept and a *y*-intercept? Explain.

104. *Think About It*   Can every line be written in slope-intercept form? Explain.

105. *Think About It*   Does every line have an infinite number of lines that are parallel to the given line? Explain.

106. *Think About It*   Does every line have an infinite number of lines that are perpendicular to the given line? Explain.

Skills Review

In Exercises 107–112, determine whether the expression is a polynomial. If it is, write the polynomial in standard form.

107. $x + 20$ **108.** $3x - 10x^2 + 1$

109. $4x^2 + x^{-1} - 3$ **110.** $2x^2 - 2x^4 - x^3 + 2$

111. $\dfrac{x^2 + 3x + 4}{x^2 - 9}$ **112.** $\sqrt{x^2 + 7x + 6}$

In Exercises 113–116, factor the trinomial.

113. $x^2 - 6x - 27$ **114.** $x^2 - 11x + 28$

115. $2x^2 + 11x - 40$ **116.** $3x^2 - 16x + 5$

117. *Make a Decision*   To work an extended application analyzing the numbers of bachelor's degrees earned by women in the United States from 1985 to 2005, visit this textbook's *Online Study Center*. (Data Source: U.S. Census Bureau)

The *Make a Decision* exercise indicates a multipart exercise using large data sets. Go to this textbook's *Online Study Center* to view these exercises.

1.3   Functions

Introduction to Functions

Many everyday phenomena involve pairs of quantities that are related to each other by some rule of correspondence. The mathematical term for such a rule of correspondence is a **relation.** Here are two examples.

1. The simple interest I earned on an investment of $1000 for 1 year is related to the annual interest rate r by the formula $I = 1000r$.

2. The area A of a circle is related to its radius r by the formula $A = \pi r^2$.

   Not all relations have simple mathematical formulas. For instance, people commonly match up NFL starting quarterbacks with touchdown passes, and hours of the day with temperature. In each of these cases, there is some relation that matches each item from one set with exactly one item from a different set. Such a relation is called a **function.**

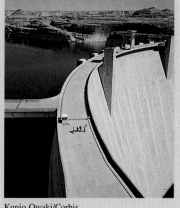

Definition of a Function

A **function** f from a set A to a set B is a relation that assigns to each element x in the set A exactly one element y in the set B. The set A is the **domain** (or set of inputs) of the function f, and the set B contains the **range** (or set of outputs).

To help understand this definition, look at the function that relates the time of day to the temperature in Figure 1.29.

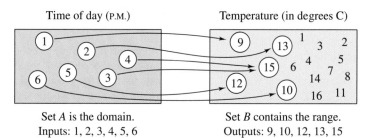

Time of day (P.M.)   Temperature (in degrees C)

Set A is the domain.   Set B contains the range.
Inputs: 1, 2, 3, 4, 5, 6   Outputs: 9, 10, 12, 13, 15

Figure 1.29

This function can be represented by the ordered pairs $\{(1, 9°), (2, 13°), (3, 15°), (4, 15°), (5, 12°), (6, 10°)\}$. In each ordered pair, the first coordinate (x-value) is the **input** and the second coordinate (y-value) is the **output.**

Characteristics of a Function from Set A to Set B

1. Each element of A must be matched with an element of B.

2. Some elements of B may not be matched with any element of A.

3. Two or more elements of A may be matched with the same element of B.

4. An element of A (the domain) cannot be matched with two different elements of B.

Library of Functions: Data Defined Function

Many functions do not have simple mathematical formulas, but are defined by real-life data. Such functions arise when you are using collections of data to model real-life applications. Functions can be represented in four ways.

1. *Verbally* by a sentence that describes how the input variables are related to the output variables

   Example: The input value x is the election year from 1952 to 2004 and the output value y is the elected president of the United States.

2. *Numerically* by a table or a list of ordered pairs that matches input values with output values

   Example: In the set of ordered pairs {(2, 34), (4, 40), (6, 45), (8, 50), (10, 54)}, the input value is the age of a male child in years and the output value is the height of the child in inches.

3. *Graphically* by points on a graph in a coordinate plane in which the input values are represented by the horizontal axis and the output values are represented by the vertical axis

   Example: See Figure 1.30.

4. *Algebraically* by an equation in two variables

   Example: The formula for temperature, $F = \frac{9}{5}C + 32$, where F is the temperature in degrees Fahrenheit and C is the temperature in degrees Celsius, is an equation that represents a function. You will see that it is often convenient to approximate data using a mathematical model or formula.

STUDY TIP

To determine whether or not a relation is a function, you must decide whether each input value is matched with exactly one output value. If any input value is matched with two or more output values, the relation is not a function.

Example 1 Testing for Functions

Decide whether the relation represents y as a function of x.

a.

Input, x	2	2	3	4	5
Output, y	11	10	8	5	1

b.
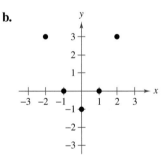

Figure 1.30

Prerequisite Skills

When plotting points in a coordinate plane, the x-coordinate is the directed distance from the y-axis to the point, and the y-coordinate is the directed distance from the x-axis to the point. To review point plotting, see Section P.5.

Solution

a. This table *does not* describe y as a function of x. The input value 2 is matched with two different y-values.

b. The graph in Figure 1.30 *does* describe y as a function of x. Each input value is matched with exactly one output value.

✓CHECKPOINT   Now try Exercise 5.

STUDY TIP

Be sure you see that the *range* of a function is not the same as the use of *range* relating to the viewing window of a graphing utility.

In algebra, it is common to represent functions by equations or formulas involving two variables. For instance, the equation $y = x^2$ represents the variable y as a function of the variable x. In this equation, x is the **independent variable** and y is the **dependent variable.** The domain of the function is the set of all values taken on by the independent variable x, and the range of the function is the set of all values taken on by the dependent variable y.

Example 2   Testing for Functions Represented Algebraically

Which of the equations represent(s) y as a function of x?

a. $x^2 + y = 1$ **b.** $-x + y^2 = 1$

Solution

To determine whether y is a function of x, try to solve for y in terms of x.

a. Solving for y yields

$$x^2 + y = 1 \qquad \text{Write original equation.}$$

$$y = 1 - x^2. \qquad \text{Solve for } y.$$

Each value of x corresponds to exactly one value of y. So, y is a function of x.

b. Solving for y yields

$$-x + y^2 = 1 \qquad \text{Write original equation.}$$

$$y^2 = 1 + x \qquad \text{Add } x \text{ to each side.}$$

$$y = \pm\sqrt{1 + x}. \qquad \text{Solve for } y.$$

The $\pm$ indicates that for a given value of x there correspond two values of y. For instance, when $x = 3$, $y = 2$ or $y = -2$. So, y is not a function of x.

✓CHECKPOINT   Now try Exercise 19.

Function Notation

When an equation is used to represent a function, it is convenient to name the function so that it can be referenced easily. For example, you know that the equation $y = 1 - x^2$ describes y as a function of x. Suppose you give this function the name "f." Then you can use the following **function notation.**

Input	Output	Equation
x	$f(x)$	$f(x) = 1 - x^2$

The symbol $f(x)$ is read as the *value of f at x* or simply *f of x*. The symbol $f(x)$ corresponds to the y-value for a given x. So, you can write $y = f(x)$. Keep in mind that f is the *name* of the function, whereas $f(x)$ is the *output value* of the function at the *input value x*. In function notation, the *input* is the independent variable and the *output* is the dependent variable. For instance, the function $f(x) = 3 - 2x$ has *function values* denoted by $f(-1), f(0)$, and so on. To find these values, substitute the specified input values into the given equation.

For $x = -1$, $f(-1) = 3 - 2(-1) = 3 + 2 = 5.$

For $x = 0$, $f(0) = 3 - 2(0) = 3 - 0 = 3.$

Exploration

Use a graphing utility to graph $x^2 + y = 1$. Then use the graph to write a convincing argument that each x-value has at most one y-value.

Use a graphing utility to graph $-x + y^2 = 1$. (*Hint:* You will need to use two equations.) Does the graph represent y as a function of x? Explain.

TECHNOLOGY TIP

You can use a graphing utility to evaluate a function. Go to this textbook's *Online Study Center* and use the Evaluating an Algebraic Expression program. The program will prompt you for a value of x, and then evaluate the expression in the equation editor for that value of x. Try using the program to evaluate several different functions of x.

Although f is often used as a convenient function name and x is often used as the independent variable, you can use other letters. For instance,

$$f(x) = x^2 - 4x + 7, \quad f(t) = t^2 - 4t + 7, \quad \text{and} \quad g(s) = s^2 - 4s + 7$$

all define the same function. In fact, the role of the independent variable is that of a "placeholder." Consequently, the function could be written as

$$f(\quad) = (\quad)^2 - 4(\quad) + 7.$$

Example 3   Evaluating a Function

Let $g(x) = -x^2 + 4x + 1$. Find (a) $g(2)$, (b) $g(t)$, and (c) $g(x + 2)$.

Solution

a. Replacing x with 2 in $g(x) = -x^2 + 4x + 1$ yields the following.

$$g(2) = -(2)^2 + 4(2) + 1 = -4 + 8 + 1 = 5$$

b. Replacing x with t yields the following.

$$g(t) = -(t)^2 + 4(t) + 1 = -t^2 + 4t + 1$$

c. Replacing x with $x + 2$ yields the following.

$$
\begin{aligned}
g(x + 2) &= -(x + 2)^2 + 4(x + 2) + 1 && \text{Substitute } x + 2 \text{ for } x. \\
&= -(x^2 + 4x + 4) + 4x + 8 + 1 && \text{Multiply.} \\
&= -x^2 - 4x - 4 + 4x + 8 + 1 && \text{Distributive Property} \\
&= -x^2 + 5 && \text{Simplify.}
\end{aligned}
$$

✓*CHECKPOINT*   Now try Exercise 29.

In Example 3, note that $g(x + 2)$ is not equal to $g(x) + g(2)$. In general, $g(u + v) \neq g(u) + g(v)$.

Library of Parent Functions: Piecewise–Defined Function

A *piecewise-defined function* is a function that is defined by two or more equations over a specified domain. The *absolute value function* given by $f(x) = |x|$ can be written as a piecewise-defined function. The basic characteristics of the absolute value function are summarized below. A review of piecewise-defined functions can be found in the *Study Capsules*.

Graph of $f(x) = |x| = \begin{cases} x, & x \geq 0 \\ -x, & x < 0 \end{cases}$

Domain: $(-\infty, \infty)$
Range: $[0, \infty)$
Intercept: $(0, 0)$
Decreasing on $(-\infty, 0)$
Increasing on $(0, \infty)$

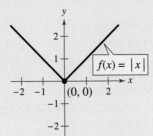

Example 4   A Piecewise-Defined Function

Evaluate the function when $x = -1$ and $x = 0$.

$$f(x) = \begin{cases} x^2 + 1, & x < 0 \\ x - 1, & x \geq 0 \end{cases}$$

Solution

Because $x = -1$ is less than 0, use $f(x) = x^2 + 1$ to obtain

$$f(-1) = (-1)^2 + 1 = 2.$$

For $x = 0$, use $f(x) = x - 1$ to obtain

$$f(0) = 0 - 1 = -1.$$

✓CHECKPOINT   Now try Exercise 37.

TECHNOLOGY TIP

Most graphing utilities can graph piecewise-defined functions. For instructions on how to enter a piecewise-defined function into your graphing utility, consult your user's manual. You may find it helpful to set your graphing utility to *dot mode* before graphing such functions.

The Domain of a Function

The domain of a function can be described explicitly or it can be *implied* by the expression used to define the function. The **implied domain** is the set of all real numbers for which the expression is defined. For instance, the function

$$f(x) = \frac{1}{x^2 - 4}$$ Domain excludes x-values that result in division by zero.

has an implied domain that consists of all real x other than $x = \pm 2$. These two values are excluded from the domain because division by zero is undefined. Another common type of implied domain is that used to avoid even roots of negative numbers. For example, the function

$$f(x) = \sqrt{x}$$ Domain excludes x-values that result in even roots of negative numbers.

is defined only for $x \geq 0$. So, its implied domain is the interval $[0, \infty)$. In general, the domain of a function *excludes* values that would cause division by zero *or* result in the even root of a negative number.

Exploration

Use a graphing utility to graph $y = \sqrt{4 - x^2}$. What is the domain of this function? Then graph $y = \sqrt{x^2 - 4}$. What is the domain of this function? Do the domains of these two functions overlap? If so, for what values?

Library of Parent Functions: Radical Function

Radical functions arise from the use of rational exponents. The most common radical function is the *square root function* given by $f(x) = \sqrt{x}$. The basic characteristics of the square root function are summarized below. A review of radical functions can be found in the *Study Capsules*.

Graph of $f(x) = \sqrt{x}$
Domain: $[0, \infty)$
Range: $[0, \infty)$
Intercept: $(0, 0)$
Increasing on $(0, \infty)$

STUDY TIP

Because the square root function is not defined for $x < 0$, you must be careful when analyzing the domains of complicated functions involving the square root symbol.

Example 5   Finding the Domain of a Function

Find the domain of each function.

a. $f: \{(-3, 0), (-1, 4), (0, 2), (2, 2), (4, -1)\}$

b. $g(x) = -3x^2 + 4x + 5$

c. $h(x) = \dfrac{1}{x + 5}$

d. Volume of a sphere: $V = \frac{4}{3}\pi r^3$

e. $k(x) = \sqrt{4 - 3x}$

Prerequisite Skills

In Example 5(e), $4 - 3x \geq 0$ is a linear inequality. To review solving of linear inequalities, see Appendix D. You will study more about inequalities in Section 2.5.

Solution

a. The domain of f consists of all first coordinates in the set of ordered pairs.

$$\text{Domain} = \{-3, -1, 0, 2, 4\}$$

b. The domain of g is the set of all *real* numbers.

c. Excluding x-values that yield zero in the denominator, the domain of h is the set of all real numbers x except $x = -5$.

d. Because this function represents the volume of a sphere, the values of the radius r must be positive. So, the domain is the set of all real numbers r such that $r > 0$.

e. This function is defined only for x-values for which $4 - 3x \geq 0$. By solving this inequality, you will find that the domain of k is all real numbers that are less than or equal to $\frac{4}{3}$.

✔CHECKPOINT   Now try Exercise 59.

In Example 5(d), note that the *domain of a function may be implied by the physical context*. For instance, from the equation $V = \frac{4}{3}\pi r^3$, you would have no reason to restrict r to positive values, but the physical context implies that a sphere cannot have a negative or zero radius.

For some functions, it may be easier to find the domain and range of the function by examining its graph.

Example 6   Finding the Domain and Range of a Function

Use a graphing utility to find the domain and range of the function

$$f(x) = \sqrt{9 - x^2}.$$

Solution

Graph the function as $y = \sqrt{9 - x^2}$, as shown in Figure 1.31. Using the *trace* feature of a graphing utility, you can determine that the x-values extend from -3 to 3 and the y-values extend from 0 to 3. So, the domain of the function f is all real numbers such that $-3 \leq x \leq 3$ and the range of f is all real numbers such that $0 \leq y \leq 3$.

✔CHECKPOINT   Now try Exercise 67.

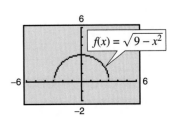

Figure 1.31

Applications

Example 7   Cellular Communications Employees

The number N (in thousands) of employees in the cellular communications industry in the United States increased in a linear pattern from 1998 to 2001 (see Figure 1.32). In 2002, the number dropped, then continued to increase through 2004 in a *different* linear pattern. These two patterns can be approximated by the function

$$N(t) = \begin{cases} 23.5t - 53.6, & 8 \le t \le 11 \\ 16.8t - 10.4, & 12 \le t \le 14 \end{cases}$$

where t represents the year, with $t = 8$ corresponding to 1998. Use this function to approximate the number of employees for each year from 1998 to 2004. (Source: Cellular Telecommunications & Internet Association)

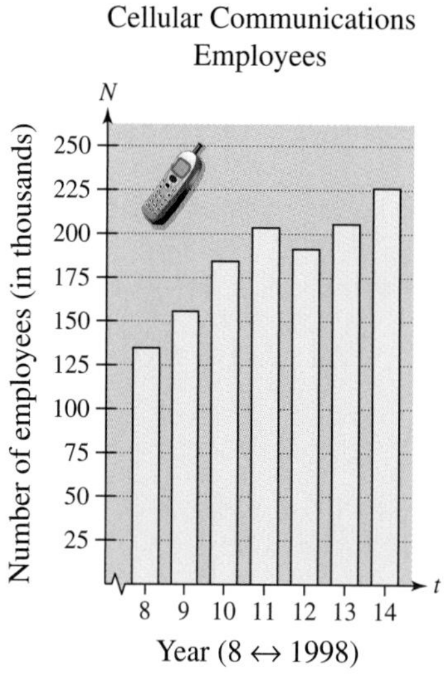

Cellular Communications Employees

Solution

From 1998 to 2001, use $N(t) = 23.5t - 53.6$.

$$\underbrace{134.4,}_{1998} \ \underbrace{157.9,}_{1999} \ \underbrace{181.4,}_{2000} \ \underbrace{204.9}_{2001}$$

From 2002 to 2004, use $N(t) = 16.8t - 10.4$.

$$\underbrace{191.2,}_{2002} \ \underbrace{208.0,}_{2003} \ \underbrace{224.8}_{2004}$$

Figure 1.32

✓CHECKPOINT   Now try Exercise 87.

Example 8   The Path of a Baseball

A baseball is hit at a point 3 feet above the ground at a velocity of 100 feet per second and an angle of 45°. The path of the baseball is given by the function

$$f(x) = -0.0032x^2 + x + 3$$

where x and $f(x)$ are measured in feet. Will the baseball clear a 10-foot fence located 300 feet from home plate?

Algebraic Solution

The height of the baseball is a function of the horizontal distance from home plate. When $x = 300$, you can find the height of the baseball as follows.

$$f(x) = -0.0032x^2 + x + 3 \qquad \text{Write original function.}$$

$$f(300) = -0.0032(300)^2 + 300 + 3 \qquad \text{Substitute 300 for } x.$$

$$= 15 \qquad \text{Simplify.}$$

When $x = 300$, the height of the baseball is 15 feet, so the baseball will clear a 10-foot fence.

Graphical Solution

Use a graphing utility to graph the function $y = -0.0032x^2 + x + 3$. Use the *value* feature or the *zoom* and *trace* features of the graphing utility to estimate that $y = 15$ when $x = 300$, as shown in Figure 1.33. So, the ball will clear a 10-foot fence.

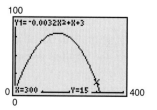

Figure 1.33

✓CHECKPOINT   Now try Exercise 89.

Difference Quotients

One of the basic definitions in calculus employs the ratio

$$\frac{f(x + h) - f(x)}{h}, \qquad h \neq 0.$$

This ratio is called a **difference quotient,** as illustrated in Example 9.

Example 9   Evaluating a Difference Quotient

For $f(x) = x^2 - 4x + 7$, find $\dfrac{f(x + h) - f(x)}{h}$.

Solution

$$\frac{f(x + h) - f(x)}{h} = \frac{[(x + h)^2 - 4(x + h) + 7] - (x^2 - 4x + 7)}{h}$$

$$= \frac{x^2 + 2xh + h^2 - 4x - 4h + 7 - x^2 + 4x - 7}{h}$$

$$= \frac{2xh + h^2 - 4h}{h}$$

$$= \frac{h(2x + h - 4)}{h} = 2x + h - 4, \ h \neq 0$$

✓CHECKPOINT   Now try Exercise 93.

Summary of Function Terminology

Function: A **function** is a relationship between two variables such that to each value of the independent variable there corresponds exactly one value of the dependent variable.

Function Notation: $y = f(x)$

    f is the *name* of the function.
    y is the **dependent variable,** or output value.
    x is the **independent variable,** or input value.
    $f(x)$ is the *value of the function at x.*

Domain: The **domain** of a function is the set of all values (inputs) of the independent variable for which the function is defined. If *x* is in the domain of *f, f* is said to be *defined* at *x.* If *x* is not in the domain of *f, f* is said to be *undefined* at *x.*

Range: The **range** of a function is the set of all values (outputs) assumed by the dependent variable (that is, the set of all function values).

Implied Domain: If *f* is defined by an algebraic expression and the domain is not specified, the **implied domain** consists of all real numbers for which the expression is defined.

STUDY TIP

Notice in Example 9 that *h* cannot be zero in the original expression. Therefore, you must restrict the domain of the simplified expression by adding $h \neq 0$ so that the simplified expression is equivalent to the original expression.

The symbol $\int$ indicates an example or exercise that highlights algebraic techniques specifically used in calculus.

1.3 Exercises

See www.CalcChat.com for worked-out solutions to odd-numbered exercises.

Vocabulary Check

Fill in the blanks.

1. A relation that assigns to each element x from a set of inputs, or _____ , exactly one element y in a set of outputs, or _____ , is called a _____ .

2. For an equation that represents y as a function of x, the _____ variable is the set of all x in the domain, and the _____ variable is the set of all y in the range.

3. The function $f(x) = \begin{cases} x^2 - 4, & x \le 0 \\ 2x + 1, & x > 0 \end{cases}$ is an example of a _____ function.

4. If the domain of the function f is not given, then the set of values of the independent variable for which the expression is defined is called the _____ .

5. In calculus, one of the basic definitions is that of a _____ , given by $\dfrac{f(x + h) - f(x)}{h}, h \ne 0$.

In Exercises 1–4, does the relation describe a function? Explain your reasoning.

1. *Domain   Range* 2. *Domain   Range*

3. *Domain   Range* 4. *Domain   Range*

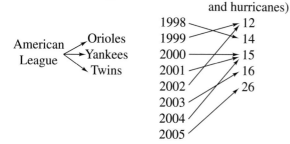

In Exercises 5–8, decide whether the relation represents y as a function of x. Explain your reasoning.

5.

Input, x	-3	-1	0	1	3
Output, y	-9	-1	0	1	9

6.

Input, x	0	1	2	1	0
Output, y	-4	-2	0	2	4

7.

Input, x	10	7	4	7	10
Output, y	3	6	9	12	15

8.

Input, x	0	3	9	12	15
Output, y	3	3	3	3	3

In Exercises 9 and 10, which sets of ordered pairs represent functions from A to B? Explain.

9. $A = \{0, 1, 2, 3\}$ and $B = \{-2, -1, 0, 1, 2\}$
   (a) $\{(0, 1), (1, -2), (2, 0), (3, 2)\}$
   (b) $\{(0, -1), (2, 2), (1, -2), (3, 0), (1, 1)\}$
   (c) $\{(0, 0), (1, 0), (2, 0), (3, 0)\}$
   (d) $\{(0, 2), (3, 0), (1, 1)\}$

10. $A = \{a, b, c\}$ and $B = \{0, 1, 2, 3\}$
    (a) $\{(a, 1), (c, 2), (c, 3), (b, 3)\}$
    (b) $\{(a, 1), (b, 2), (c, 3)\}$
    (c) $\{(1, a), (0, a), (2, c), (3, b)\}$
    (d) $\{(c, 0), (b, 0), (a, 3)\}$

Circulation of Newspapers   **In Exercises 11 and 12, use the graph, which shows the circulation (in millions) of daily newspapers in the United States.** (Source: Editor & Publisher Company)

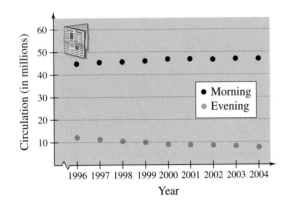

Year

11. Is the circulation of morning newspapers a function of the year? Is the circulation of evening newspapers a function of the year? Explain.

12. Let $f(x)$ represent the circulation of evening newspapers in year x. Find $f(2004)$.

In Exercises 13–24, determine whether the equation represents y as a function of x.

13. $x^2 + y^2 = 4$ 14. $x = y^2 + 1$

15. $y = \sqrt{x^2 - 1}$ 16. $y = \sqrt{x + 5}$

17. $2x + 3y = 4$ 18. $x = -y + 5$

19. $y^2 = x^2 - 1$ 20. $x + y^2 = 3$

21. $y = |4 - x|$ 22. $|y| = 4 - x$

23. $x = -7$ 24. $y = 8$

In Exercises 25 and 26, fill in the blanks using the specified function and the given values of the independent variable. Simplify the result.

25. $f(x) = \dfrac{1}{x + 1}$

  (a) $f(4) = \dfrac{1}{(\ \ ) + 1}$ (b) $f(0) = \dfrac{1}{(\ \ ) + 1}$

  (c) $f(4t) = \dfrac{1}{(\ \ ) + 1}$ (d) $f(x + c) = \dfrac{1}{(\ \ ) + 1}$

26. $g(x) = x^2 - 2x$

  (a) $g(2) = (\ \ )^2 - 2(\ \ )$

  (b) $g(-3) = (\ \ )^2 - 2(\ \ )$

  (c) $g(t + 1) = (\ \ )^2 - 2(\ \ )$

  (d) $g(x + c) = (\ \ )^2 - 2(\ \ )$

In Exercises 27–42, evaluate the function at each specified value of the independent variable and simplify.

27. $f(t) = 3t + 1$

  (a) $f(2)$ (b) $f(-4)$ (c) $f(t + 2)$

28. $g(y) = 7 - 3y$

  (a) $g(0)$ (b) $g\left(\frac{7}{3}\right)$ (c) $g(s + 2)$

29. $h(t) = t^2 - 2t$

  (a) $h(2)$ (b) $h(1.5)$ (c) $h(x + 2)$

30. $V(r) = \frac{4}{3}\pi r^3$

  (a) $V(3)$ (b) $V\left(\frac{3}{2}\right)$ (c) $V(2r)$

31. $f(y) = 3 - \sqrt{y}$

  (a) $f(4)$ (b) $f(0.25)$ (c) $f(4x^2)$

32. $f(x) = \sqrt{x + 8} + 2$

  (a) $f(-8)$ (b) $f(1)$ (c) $f(x - 8)$

33. $q(x) = \dfrac{1}{x^2 - 9}$

  (a) $q(0)$ (b) $q(3)$ (c) $q(y + 3)$

34. $q(t) = \dfrac{2t^2 + 3}{t^2}$

  (a) $q(2)$ (b) $q(0)$ (c) $q(-x)$

35. $f(x) = \dfrac{|x|}{x}$

  (a) $f(3)$ (b) $f(-3)$ (c) $f(t)$

36. $f(x) = |x| + 4$

  (a) $f(4)$ (b) $f(-4)$ (c) $f(t)$

37. $f(x) = \begin{cases} 2x + 1, & x < 0 \\ 2x + 2, & x \geq 0 \end{cases}$

  (a) $f(-1)$ (b) $f(0)$ (c) $f(2)$

38. $f(x) = \begin{cases} 2x + 5, & x \leq 0 \\ 2 - x^2, & x > 0 \end{cases}$

  (a) $f(-2)$ (b) $f(0)$ (c) $f(1)$

39. $f(x) = \begin{cases} x^2 + 2, & x \leq 1 \\ 2x^2 + 2, & x > 1 \end{cases}$

  (a) $f(-2)$ (b) $f(1)$ (c) $f(2)$

40. $f(x) = \begin{cases} x^2 - 4, & x \leq 0 \\ 1 - 2x^2, & x > 0 \end{cases}$

  (a) $f(-2)$ (b) $f(0)$ (c) $f(1)$

41. $f(x) = \begin{cases} x + 2, & x < 0 \\ 4, & 0 \leq x < 2 \\ x^2 + 1, & x \geq 2 \end{cases}$

  (a) $f(-2)$ (b) $f(1)$ (c) $f(4)$

42. $f(x) = \begin{cases} 5 - 2x, & x < 0 \\ 5, & 0 \le x < 1 \\ 4x + 1, & x \ge 1 \end{cases}$

  (a) $f(-2)$ (b) $f\left(\frac{1}{2}\right)$ (c) $f(1)$

In Exercises 43–46, complete the table.

43. $h(t) = \frac{1}{2}|t + 3|$

t	-5	-4	-3	-2	-1
$h(t)$					

44. $f(s) = \dfrac{|s - 2|}{s - 2}$

s	0	1	$\frac{3}{2}$	$\frac{5}{2}$	4
$f(s)$					

45. $f(x) = \begin{cases} -\frac{1}{2}x + 4, & x \le 0 \\ (x - 2)^2, & x > 0 \end{cases}$

x	-2	-1	0	1	2
$f(x)$					

46. $h(x) = \begin{cases} 9 - x^2, & x < 3 \\ x - 3, & x \ge 3 \end{cases}$

x	1	2	3	4	5
$h(x)$					

In Exercises 47–50, find all real values of x such that $f(x) = 0$.

47. $f(x) = 15 - 3x$ **48.** $f(x) = 5x + 1$

49. $f(x) = \dfrac{3x - 4}{5}$ **50.** $f(x) = \dfrac{2x - 3}{7}$

In Exercises 51 and 52, find the value(s) of x for which $f(x) = g(x)$.

51. $f(x) = x^2, \quad g(x) = x + 2$

52. $f(x) = x^2 + 2x + 1, \quad g(x) = 7x - 5$

In Exercises 53–62, find the domain of the function.

53. $f(x) = 5x^2 + 2x - 1$ **54.** $g(x) = 1 - 2x^2$

55. $h(t) = \dfrac{4}{t}$ **56.** $s(y) = \dfrac{3y}{y + 5}$

57. $f(x) = \sqrt[3]{x - 4}$ **58.** $f(x) = \sqrt[4]{x^2 + 3x}$

59. $g(x) = \dfrac{1}{x} - \dfrac{3}{x + 2}$ **60.** $h(x) = \dfrac{10}{x^2 - 2x}$

61. $g(y) = \dfrac{y + 2}{\sqrt{y - 10}}$ **62.** $f(x) = \dfrac{\sqrt{x + 6}}{6 + x}$

In Exercises 63–66, use a graphing utility to graph the function. Find the domain and range of the function.

63. $f(x) = \sqrt{4 - x^2}$ **64.** $f(x) = \sqrt{x^2 + 1}$

65. $g(x) = |2x + 3|$ **66.** $g(x) = |x - 5|$

In Exercises 67–70, assume that the domain of f is the set $A = \{-2, -1, 0, 1, 2\}$. Determine the set of ordered pairs representing the function f.

67. $f(x) = x^2$ **68.** $f(x) = x^2 - 3$

69. $f(x) = |x| + 2$ **70.** $f(x) = |x + 1|$

71. Geometry Write the area A of a circle as a function of its circumference C.

72. Geometry Write the area A of an equilateral triangle as a function of the length s of its sides.

73. Exploration The cost per unit to produce a radio model is $60. The manufacturer charges $90 per unit for orders of 100 or less. To encourage large orders, the manufacturer reduces the charge by $0.15 per radio for each unit ordered in excess of 100 (for example, there would be a charge of $87 per radio for an order size of 120).

(a) The table shows the profit P (in dollars) for various numbers of units ordered, x. Use the table to estimate the maximum profit.

Units, x	Profit, P
110	3135
120	3240
130	3315
140	3360
150	3375
160	3360
170	3315

(b) Plot the points (x, P) from the table in part (a). Does the relation defined by the ordered pairs represent P as a function of x?

(c) If P is a function of x, write the function and determine its domain.

74. *Exploration* An open box of maximum volume is to be made from a square piece of material, 24 centimeters on a side, by cutting equal squares from the corners and turning up the sides (see figure).

(a) The table shows the volume V (in cubic centimeters) of the box for various heights x (in centimeters). Use the table to estimate the maximum volume.

Height, x	Volume, V
1	484
2	800
3	972
4	1024
5	980
6	864

(b) Plot the points (x, V) from the table in part (a). Does the relation defined by the ordered pairs represent V as a function of x?

(c) If V is a function of x, write the function and determine its domain.

(d) Use a graphing utility to plot the point from the table in part (a) with the function from part (c). How closely does the function represent the data? Explain.

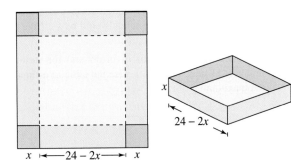

75. *Geometry* A right triangle is formed in the first quadrant by the x- and y-axes and a line through the point $(2, 1)$ (see figure). Write the area A of the triangle as a function of x, and determine the domain of the function.

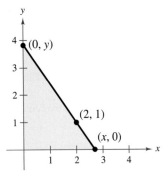

76. *Geometry* A rectangle is bounded by the x-axis and the semicircle $y = \sqrt{36 - x^2}$ (see figure). Write the area A of the rectangle as a function of x, and determine the domain of the function.

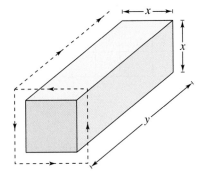

77. *Postal Regulations* A rectangular package to be sent by the U.S. Postal Service can have a maximum combined length and girth (perimeter of a cross section) of 108 inches (see figure).

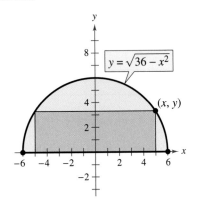

(a) Write the volume V of the package as a function of x. What is the domain of the function?

(b) Use a graphing utility to graph the function. Be sure to use an appropriate viewing window.

(c) What dimensions will maximize the volume of the package? Explain.

78. *Cost, Revenue, and Profit* A company produces a toy for which the variable cost is \$12.30 per unit and the fixed costs are \$98,000. The toy sells for \$17.98. Let x be the number of units produced and sold.

(a) The total cost for a business is the sum of the variable cost and the fixed costs. Write the total cost C as a function of the number of units produced.

(b) Write the revenue R as a function of the number of units sold.

(c) Write the profit P as a function of the number of units sold. (*Note: $P = R - C$.*)

Revenue In Exercises 79–82, use the table, which shows the monthly revenue y (in thousands of dollars) of a landscaping business for each month of 2006, with x = 1 representing January.

Month, x	Revenue, y
1	5.2
2	5.6
3	6.6
4	8.3
5	11.5
6	15.8
7	12.8
8	10.1
9	8.6
10	6.9
11	4.5
12	2.7

A mathematical model that represents the data is

$$f(x) = \begin{cases} -1.97x + 26.3 \\ 0.505x^2 - 1.47x + 6.3 \end{cases}.$$

79. What is the domain of each part of the piecewise-defined function? Explain your reasoning.

80. Use the mathematical model to find $f(5)$. Interpret your result in the context of the problem.

81. Use the mathematical model to find $f(11)$. Interpret your result in the context of the problem.

82. How do the values obtained from the model in Exercises 80 and 81 compare with the actual data values?

83. *Motor Vehicles* The numbers n (in billions) of miles traveled by vans, pickup trucks, and sport utility vehicles in the United States from 1990 to 2003 can be approximated by the model

$$n(t) = \begin{cases} -6.13t^2 + 75.8t + 577, & 0 \le t \le 6 \\ 24.9t + 672, & 6 < t \le 13 \end{cases}$$

where t represents the year, with t = 0 corresponding to 1990. Use the *table* feature of a graphing utility to approximate the number of miles traveled by vans, pickup trucks, and sport utility vehicles for each year from 1990 to 2003. (Source: U.S. Federal Highway Administration)

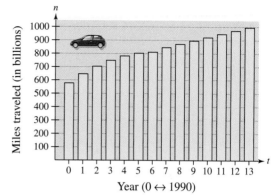

Figure for 83

84. *Transportation* For groups of 80 or more people, a charter bus company determines the rate per person according to the formula

Rate $= 8 - 0.05(n - 80)$, $n \ge 80$

where the rate is given in dollars and n is the number of people.

(a) Write the revenue R of the bus company as a function of n.

(b) Use the function from part (a) to complete the table. What can you conclude?

n	90	100	110	120	130	140	150
R(n)							

(c) Use a graphing utility to graph R and determine the number of people that will produce a maximum revenue. Compare the result with your conclusion from part (b).

85. *Physics* The force F (in tons) of water against the face of a dam is estimated by the function

$$F(y) = 149.76\sqrt{10}\,y^{5/2}$$

where y is the depth of the water (in feet).

(a) Complete the table. What can you conclude from it?

y	5	10	20	30	40
F(y)					

(b) Use a graphing utility to graph the function. Describe your viewing window.

(c) Use the table to approximate the depth at which the force against the dam is 1,000,000 tons. How could you find a better estimate?

(d) Verify your answer in part (c) graphically.

86. *Data Analysis* The graph shows the retail sales (in billions of dollars) of prescription drugs in the United States from 1995 through 2004. Let $f(x)$ represent the retail sales in year x. (Source: National Association of Chain Drug Stores)

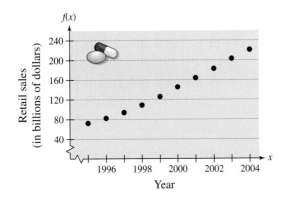

(a) Find $f(2000)$.

(b) Find $\dfrac{f(2004) - f(1995)}{2004 - 1995}$

and interpret the result in the context of the problem.

(c) An approximate model for the function is

$$P(t) = -0.0982t^3 + 3.365t^2 - 18.85t + 94.8,$$
$$5 \le t \le 14$$

where P is the retail sales (in billions of dollars) and t represents the year, with $t = 5$ corresponding to 1995. Complete the table and compare the results with the data in the graph.

t	5	6	7	8	9	10	11	12	13	14
$P(t)$										

(d) Use a graphing utility to graph the model and the data in the same viewing window. Comment on the validity of the model.

∫ In Exercises 87–92, find the difference quotient and simplify your answer.

87. $f(x) = 2x,$ $\dfrac{f(x + c) - f(x)}{c},$ $c \ne 0$

88. $g(x) = 3x - 1,$ $\dfrac{g(x + h) - g(x)}{h},$ $h \ne 0$

89. $f(x) = x^2 - x + 1,$ $\dfrac{f(2 + h) - f(2)}{h},$ $h \ne 0$

90. $f(x) = x^3 + x,$ $\dfrac{f(x + h) - f(x)}{h},$ $h \ne 0$

91. $f(t) = \dfrac{1}{t},$ $\dfrac{f(t) - f(1)}{t - 1},$ $t \ne 1$

92. $f(x) = \dfrac{4}{x + 1},$ $\dfrac{f(x) - f(7)}{x - 7},$ $x \ne 7$

Synthesis

True or False? In Exercises 93 and 94, determine whether the statement is true or false. Justify your answer.

93. The domain of the function $f(x) = x^4 - 1$ is $(-\infty, \infty)$, and the range of $f(x)$ is $(0, \infty)$.

94. The set of ordered pairs $\{(-8, -2), (-6, 0), (-4, 0), (-2, 2), (0, 4), (2, -2)\}$ represents a function.

Library of Parent Functions In Exercises 95–98, write a piecewise-defined function for the graph shown.

95.

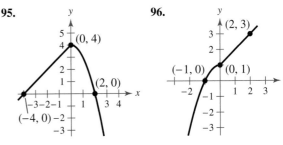

96.

97.

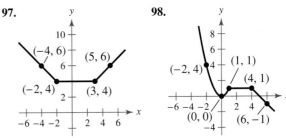

98.

99. *Writing* In your own words, explain the meanings of *domain* and *range*.

100. *Think About It* Describe an advantage of function notation.

Skills Review

In Exercises 101–104, perform the operation and simplify.

101. $12 - \dfrac{4}{x + 2}$

102. $\dfrac{3}{x^2 + x - 20} + \dfrac{x}{x^2 + 4x - 5}$

103. $\dfrac{2x^3 + 11x^2 - 6x}{5x} \cdot \dfrac{x + 10}{2x^2 + 5x - 3}$

104. $\dfrac{x + 7}{2(x - 9)} \div \dfrac{x - 7}{2(x - 9)}$

The symbol ∫ indicates an example or exercise that highlights algebraic techniques specifically used in calculus.

1.4   Graphs of Functions

The Graph of a Function

In Section 1.3, functions were represented graphically by points on a graph in a coordinate plane in which the input values are represented by the horizontal axis and the output values are represented by the vertical axis. The **graph of a function** f is the collection of ordered pairs $(x, f(x))$ such that x is in the domain of f. As you study this section, remember the geometric interpretations of x and $f(x)$.

x = the directed distance from the y-axis

$f(x)$ = the directed distance from the x-axis

Example 1 shows how to use the graph of a function to find the domain and range of the function.

Example 1   Finding the Domain and Range of a Function

Use the graph of the function f shown in Figure 1.34 to find (a) the domain of f, (b) the function values $f(-1)$ and $f(2)$, and (c) the range of f.

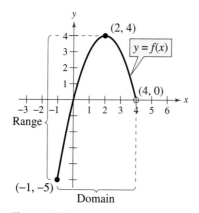

Figure 1.34

What you should learn

- Find the domains and ranges of functions and use the Vertical Line Test for functions.
- Determine intervals on which functions are increasing, decreasing, or constant.
- Determine relative maximum and relative minimum values of functions.
- Identify and graph step functions and other piecewise-defined functions.
- Identify even and odd functions.

Why you should learn it

Graphs of functions provide a visual relationship between two variables. For example, in Exercise 88 on page 125, you will use the graph of a step function to model the cost of sending a package.

Stephen Chernin/Getty Images

Solution

a. The closed dot at $(-1, -5)$ indicates that $x = -1$ is in the domain of f, whereas the open dot at $(4, 0)$ indicates that $x = 4$ is not in the domain. So, the domain of f is all x in the interval $[-1, 4)$.

b. Because $(-1, -5)$ is a point on the graph of f, it follows that

$$f(-1) = -5.$$

Similarly, because $(2, 4)$ is a point on the graph of f, it follows that

$$f(2) = 4.$$

c. Because the graph does not extend below $f(-1) = -5$ or above $f(2) = 4$, the range of f is the interval $[-5, 4]$.

✓CHECKPOINT   Now try Exercise 3.

STUDY TIP

The use of dots (open or closed) at the extreme left and right points of a graph indicates that the graph does not extend beyond these points. If no such dots are shown, assume that the graph extends beyond these points.

Example 2   Finding the Domain and Range of a Function

Find the domain and range of

$$f(x) = \sqrt{x - 4}.$$

Algebraic Solution

Because the expression under a radical cannot be negative, the domain of $f(x) = \sqrt{x - 4}$ is the set of all real numbers such that $x - 4 \geq 0$. Solve this linear inequality for x as follows. (For help with solving linear inequalities, see Appendix D.)

$$x - 4 \geq 0 \qquad \text{Write original inequality.}$$

$$x \geq 4 \qquad \text{Add 4 to each side.}$$

So, the domain is the set of all real numbers greater than or equal to 4. Because the value of a radical expression is never negative, the range of $f(x) = \sqrt{x - 4}$ is the set of all nonnegative real numbers.

Graphical Solution

Use a graphing utility to graph the equation $y = \sqrt{x - 4}$, as shown in Figure 1.35. Use the *trace* feature to determine that the x-coordinates of points on the graph extend from 4 to the right. When x is greater than or equal to 4, the expression under the radical is nonnegative. So, you can conclude that the domain is the set of all real numbers greater than or equal to 4. From the graph, you can see that the y-coordinates of points on the graph extend from 0 upwards. So you can estimate the range to be the set of all nonnegative real numbers.

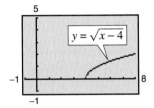

Figure 1.35

✓CHECKPOINT   Now try Exercise 7.

By the definition of a function, at most one y-value corresponds to a given x-value. It follows, then, that a vertical line can intersect the graph of a function at most once. This leads to the **Vertical Line Test** for functions.

> **Vertical Line Test for Functions**
>
> A set of points in a coordinate plane is the graph of y as a function of x if and only if no vertical line intersects the graph at more than one point.

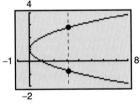

(a)

Example 3   Vertical Line Test for Functions

Use the Vertical Line Test to decide whether the graphs in Figure 1.36 represent y as a function of x.

Solution

a. This is *not* a graph of y as a function of x because you can find a vertical line that intersects the graph twice.

b. This *is* a graph of y as a function of x because every vertical line intersects the graph at most once.

✓CHECKPOINT   Now try Exercise 17.

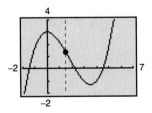

(b)

Figure 1.36

Increasing and Decreasing Functions

The more you know about the graph of a function, the more you know about the function itself. Consider the graph shown in Figure 1.37. Moving from *left to right*, this graph falls from $x = -2$ to $x = 0$, is constant from $x = 0$ to $x = 2$, and rises from $x = 2$ to $x = 4$.

Increasing, Decreasing, and Constant Functions

A function f is **increasing** on an interval if, for any x_1 and x_2 in the interval,

$$x_1 < x_2 \text{ implies } f(x_1) < f(x_2).$$

A function f is **decreasing** on an interval if, for any x_1 and x_2 in the interval,

$$x_1 < x_2 \text{ implies } f(x_1) > f(x_2).$$

A function f is **constant** on an interval if, for any x_1 and x_2 in the interval,

$$f(x_1) = f(x_2).$$

Example 4   Increasing and Decreasing Functions

In Figure 1.38, determine the open intervals on which each function is increasing, decreasing, or constant.

Solution

a. Although it might appear that there is an interval in which this function is constant, you can see that if $x_1 < x_2$, then $(x_1)^3 < (x_2)^3$, which implies that $f(x_1) < f(x_2)$. So, the function is increasing over the entire real line.

b. This function is increasing on the interval $(-\infty, -1)$, decreasing on the interval $(-1, 1)$, and increasing on the interval $(1, \infty)$.

c. This function is increasing on the interval $(-\infty, 0)$, constant on the interval $(0, 2)$, and decreasing on the interval $(2, \infty)$.

✔CHECKPOINT   Now try Exercise 21.

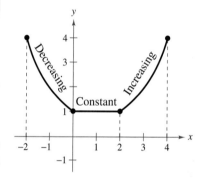

Figure 1.37

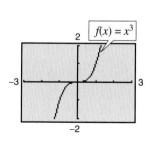

(a)

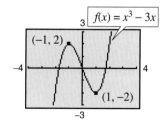

(b)

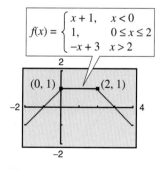

(c)

Figure 1.38

TECHNOLOGY TIP

Most graphing utilities are designed to graph functions of x more easily than other types of equations. For instance, the graph shown in Figure 1.36(a) represents the equation $x - (y - 1)^2 = 0$. To use a graphing utility to duplicate this graph you must first solve the equation for y to obtain $y = 1 \pm \sqrt{x}$, and then graph the two equations $y_1 = 1 + \sqrt{x}$ and $y_2 = 1 - \sqrt{x}$ in the same viewing window.

Relative Minimum and Maximum Values

The points at which a function changes its increasing, decreasing, or constant behavior are helpful in determining the relative maximum or relative minimum values of the function.

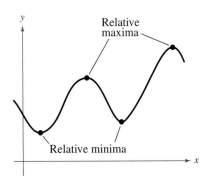

Figure 1.39

Definitions of Relative Minimum and Relative Maximum

A function value $f(a)$ is called a **relative minimum** of f if there exists an interval (x_1, x_2) that contains a such that

$\quad x_1 < x < x_2 \quad$ implies $\quad f(a) \le f(x)$.

A function value $f(a)$ is called a **relative maximum** of f if there exists an interval (x_1, x_2) that contains a such that

$\quad x_1 < x < x_2 \quad$ implies $\quad f(a) \ge f(x)$.

Figure 1.39 shows several different examples of relative minima and relative maxima. In Section 3.1, you will study a technique for finding the *exact points* at which a second-degree polynomial function has a relative minimum or relative maximum. For the time being, however, you can use a graphing utility to find reasonable approximations of these points.

Example 5   Approximating a Relative Minimum

Use a graphing utility to approximate the relative minimum of the function given by $f(x) = 3x^2 - 4x - 2$.

Solution

The graph of f is shown in Figure 1.40. By using the *zoom* and *trace* features of a graphing utility, you can estimate that the function has a relative minimum at the point

$\quad (0.67, -3.33)$.   See Figure 1.41.

Later, in Section 3.1, you will be able to determine that the exact point at which the relative minimum occurs is $\left(\frac{2}{3}, -\frac{10}{3}\right)$.

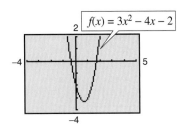

Figure 1.40

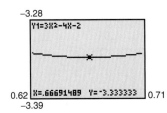

Figure 1.41

✔CHECKPOINT   Now try Exercise 31.

TECHNOLOGY TIP

When you use a graphing utility to estimate the x- and y-values of a relative minimum or relative maximum, the *zoom* feature will often produce graphs that are nearly flat, as shown in Figure 1.41. To overcome this problem, you can manually change the vertical setting of the viewing window. The graph will stretch vertically if the values of Ymin and Ymax are closer together.

TECHNOLOGY TIP   Some graphing utilities have built-in programs that will find minimum or maximum values. These features are demonstrated in Example 6.

Example 6   Approximating Relative Minima and Maxima

Use a graphing utility to approximate the relative minimum and relative maximum of the function given by $f(x) = -x^3 + x$.

Solution

The graph of f is shown in Figure 1.42. By using the *zoom* and *trace* features or the *minimum* and *maximum* features of the graphing utility, you can estimate that the function has a relative minimum at the point

$(-0.58, -0.38)$ See Figure 1.43.

and a relative maximum at the point

$(0.58, 0.38)$.   See Figure 1.44.

If you take a course in calculus, you will learn a technique for finding the exact points at which this function has a relative minimum and a relative maximum.

 CHECKPOINT   Now try Exercise 33.

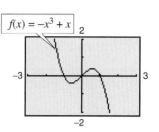

Figure 1.42

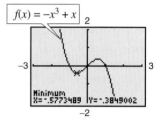

Figure 1.43

Example 7   Temperature

During a 24-hour period, the temperature y (in degrees Fahrenheit) of a certain city can be approximated by the model

$$y = 0.026x^3 - 1.03x^2 + 10.2x + 34, \qquad 0 \le x \le 24$$

where x represents the time of day, with $x = 0$ corresponding to 6 A.M. Approximate the maximum and minimum temperatures during this 24-hour period.

Solution

To solve this problem, graph the function as shown in Figure 1.45. Using the *zoom* and *trace* features or the *maximum* feature of a graphing utility, you can determine that the maximum temperature during the 24-hour period was approximately 64°F. This temperature occurred at about 12:36 P.M. ($x \approx 6.6$), as shown in Figure 1.46. Using the *zoom* and *trace* features or the *minimum* feature, you can determine that the minimum temperature during the 24-hour period was approximately 34°F, which occurred at about 1:48 A.M. ($x \approx 19.8$), as shown in Figure 1.47.

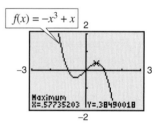

Figure 1.44

TECHNOLOGY SUPPORT

For instructions on how to use the *minimum* and *maximum* features, see Appendix A; for specific keystrokes, go to this textbook's *Online Study Center.*

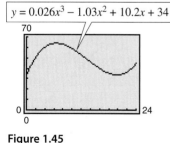

Figure 1.45

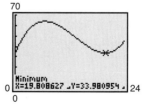

Figure 1.46   **Figure 1.47**

 CHECKPOINT   Now try Exercise 91.

Graphing Step Functions and Piecewise-Defined Functions

Library of Parent Functions: Greatest Integer Function

The *greatest integer function*, denoted by $[\![x]\!]$ and defined as the greatest integer less than or equal to x, has an infinite number of breaks or steps—one at each integer value in its domain. The basic characteristics of the greatest integer function are summarized below. A review of the greatest integer function can be found in the *Study Capsules*.

Graph of $f(x) = [\![x]\!]$

Domain: $(-\infty, \infty)$

Range: the set of integers

x-intercepts: in the interval $[0, 1)$

y-intercept: $(0, 0)$

Constant between each pair of consecutive integers

Jumps vertically one unit at each integer value

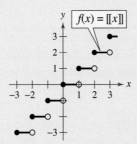

Could you describe the greatest integer function using a piecewise-defined function? How does the graph of the greatest integer function differ from the graph of a line with a slope of zero?

TECHNOLOGY TIP

Most graphing utilities display graphs in *connected mode*, which means that the graph has no breaks. When you are sketching graphs that do have breaks, it is better to use *dot mode*. Graph the greatest integer function [often called Int (x) in *connected* and *dot modes*, and compare the two results.

Because of the vertical jumps described above, the greatest integer function is an example of a **step function** whose graph resembles a set of stairsteps. Some values of the greatest integer function are as follows.

$$[\![-1]\!] = (\text{greatest integer} \leq -1) = -1$$

$$\left[\!\!\left[\tfrac{1}{10}\right]\!\!\right] = \left(\text{greatest integer} \leq \tfrac{1}{10}\right) = 0$$

$$[\![1.5]\!] = (\text{greatest integer} \leq 1.5) = 1$$

In Section 1.3, you learned that a piecewise-defined function is a function that is defined by two or more equations over a specified domain. To sketch the graph of a piecewise-defined function, you need to sketch the graph of each equation on the appropriate portion of the domain.

Example 8 Graphing a Piecewise-Defined Function

Sketch the graph of $f(x) = \begin{cases} 2x + 3, & x \leq 1 \\ -x + 4, & x > 1 \end{cases}$ by hand.

Solution

This piecewise-defined function is composed of two linear functions. At and to the left of $x = 1$, the graph is the line given by $y = 2x + 3$. To the right of $x = 1$, the graph is the line given by $y = -x + 4$ (see Figure 1.48). Notice that the point $(1, 5)$ is a solid dot and the point $(1, 3)$ is an open dot. This is because $f(1) = 5$.

✓CHECKPOINT   Now try Exercise 43.

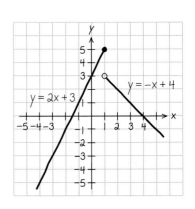

Figure 1.48

Even and Odd Functions

A graph has *symmetry with respect to the y-axis* if whenever (x, y) is on the graph, so is the point $(-x, y)$. A graph has *symmetry with respect to the origin* if whenever (x, y) is on the graph, so is the point $(-x, -y)$. A graph has *symmetry with respect to the x-axis* if whenever (x, y) is on the graph, so is the point $(x, -y)$. A function whose graph is symmetric with respect to the y-axis is an **even function.** A function whose graph is symmetric with respect to the origin is an **odd function.** A graph that is symmetric with respect to the x-axis is not the graph of a function (except for the graph of $y = 0$). These three types of symmetry are illustrated in Figure 1.49.

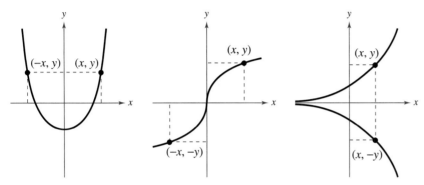

Symmetric to y-axis
Even function

Symmetric to origin
Odd function

Symmetric to x-axis
Not a function

Figure 1.49

Test for Even and Odd Functions

A function f is **even** if, for each x in the domain of f, $f(-x) = f(x)$.
A function f is **odd** if, for each x in the domain of f, $f(-x) = -f(x)$.

Example 9   Testing for Evenness and Oddness

Is the function given by $f(x) = |x|$ even, odd, or neither?

Algebraic Solution

This function is even because

$$f(-x) = |-x|$$
$$= |x|$$
$$= f(x).$$

Graphical Solution

Use a graphing utility to enter $y = |x|$ in the *equation editor*, as shown in Figure 1.50. Then graph the function using a standard viewing window, as shown in Figure 1.51. You can see that the graph appears to be symmetric about the y-axis. So, the function is even.

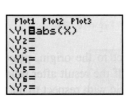

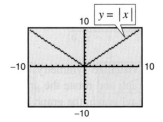

✓CHECKPOINT   Now try Exercise 59.

Figure 1.50

Figure 1.51

126   Chapter 1   Functions and Their Graphs

Synthesis

True or False?   **In Exercises 93 and 94, determine whether the statement is true or false. Justify your answer.**

93. A function with a square root cannot have a domain that is the set of all real numbers.

94. It is possible for an odd function to have the interval $[0, \infty)$ as its domain.

Think About It   **In Exercises 95–100, match the graph of the function with the best choice that describes the situation.**

(a) The air temperature at a beach on a sunny day

(b) The height of a football kicked in a field goal attempt

(c) The number of children in a family over time

(d) The population of California as a function of time

(e) The depth of the tide at a beach over a 24-hour period

(f) The number of cupcakes on a tray at a party

95.

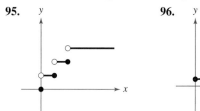

96.

97.

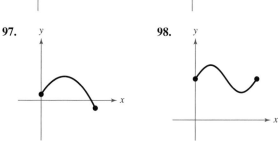

98.

99.

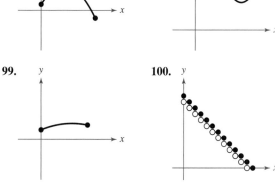

100.

101. *Proof*   Prove that a function of the following form is odd.

$$y = a_{2n+1}x^{2n+1} + a_{2n-1}x^{2n-1} + \cdots + a_3x^3 + a_1x$$

102. *Proof*   Prove that a function of the following form is even.

$$y = a_{2n}x^{2n} + a_{2n-2}x^{2n-2} + \cdots + a_2x^2 + a_0$$

103. If f is an even function, determine if g is even, odd, or neither. Explain.

(a) $g(x) = -f(x)$ 　　(b) $g(x) = f(-x)$

(c) $g(x) = f(x) - 2$ 　(d) $g(x) = -f(x - 2)$

104. *Think About It*   Does the graph in Exercise 16 represent x as a function of y? Explain.

105. *Think About It*   Does the graph in Exercise 17 represent x as a function of y? Explain.

106. *Writing*   Write a short paragraph describing three different functions that represent the behaviors of quantities between 1995 and 2006. Describe one quantity that decreased during this time, one that increased, and one that was constant. Present your results graphically.

Skills Review

In Exercises 107–110, identify the terms. Then identify the coefficients of the variable terms of the expression.

107. $-2x^2 + 8x$ 　　　　**108.** $10 + 3x$

109. $\dfrac{x}{3} - 5x^2 + x^3$ 　　**110.** $7x^4 + \sqrt{2}x^2$

In Exercises 111–114, find (a) the distance between the two points and (b) the midpoint of the line segment joining the points.

111. $(-2, 7), (6, 3)$

112. $(-5, 0), (3, 6)$

113. $\left(\frac{5}{2}, -1\right), \left(-\frac{3}{2}, 4\right)$

114. $\left(-6, \frac{2}{3}\right), \left(\frac{3}{4}, \frac{1}{6}\right)$

In Exercises 115–118, evaluate the function at each specified value of the independent variable and simplify.

115. $f(x) = 5x - 1$

(a) $f(6)$ 　(b) $f(-1)$ 　(c) $f(x - 3)$

116. $f(x) = -x^2 - x + 3$

(a) $f(4)$ 　(b) $f(-2)$ 　(c) $f(x - 2)$

117. $f(x) = x\sqrt{x - 3}$

(a) $f(3)$ 　(b) $f(12)$ 　(c) $f(6)$

118. $f(x) = -\frac{1}{2}x|x + 1|$

(a) $f(-4)$ 　(b) $f(10)$ 　(c) $f\left(-\frac{2}{3}\right)$

∫ **In Exercises 119 and 120, find the difference quotient and simplify your answer.**

119. $f(x) = x^2 - 2x + 9, \dfrac{f(3 + h) - f(3)}{h}, h \neq 0$

120. $f(x) = 5 + 6x - x^2, \dfrac{f(6 + h) - f(6)}{h}, h \neq 0$

Exa

Co

a.

Alg

a.

b.

c.

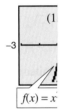

(1

−3

$f(x) = x$

(a) Vertical

Figure 1.5

✔**CHECKPOINT**

Example 1

Compare the

a. $g(x) = x^3$

Solution

a. Graph $f(x$
   graph of g

b. Graph $f(x$
   graph of h

c. Graph $f(x$
   the graph
   upward.

Example 2

The graph of
is a transforr

−6

Figure 1.59

m

he

Solution

a. The grapl
   So, the ec

b. The grapl
   of one ur
   $h(x) = (x$

✔**CHECKPOIN**

1.5 Shifting, Reflecting, and Stretching Graphs

Summary of Graphs of Parent Functions

One of the goals of this text is to enable you to build your intuition for the basic shapes of the graphs of different types of functions. For instance, from your study of lines in Section 1.2, you can determine the basic shape of the graph of the linear function $f(x) = mx + b$. Specifically, you know that the graph of this function is a line whose slope is m and whose y-intercept is $(0, b)$.

The six graphs shown in Figure 1.55 represent the most commonly used functions in algebra. Familiarity with the basic characteristics of these simple graphs will help you analyze the shapes of more complicated graphs.

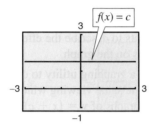

(a) Constant Function

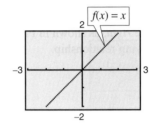

(b) Identity Function

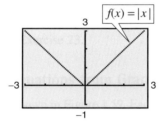

(c) Absolute Value Function

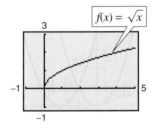

(d) Square Root Function

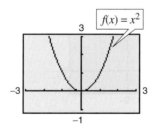

(e) Quadratic Function

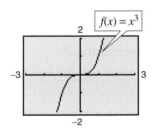

(f) Cubic Function

Figure 1.55

Throughout this section, you will discover how many complicated graphs are derived by shifting, stretching, shrinking, or reflecting the parent graphs shown above. Shifts, stretches, shrinks, and reflections are called *transformations*. Many graphs of functions can be created from combinations of these transformations.

Vertical ª   Rᵉ

Many functi   An
parent functi   yoᵤ
graph of   imₐ

$$h(x) = x$$

by shifting th
function nota

$$h(x) = ᵡ$$

$$= f$$

Similarly, yo

$$g(x) = ($$

by shifting th
In this case,

$$g(x) = ($$

$$= f$$

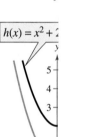

$h(x) = x^2 + ?$

Figure 1.56
two units

The foll

Vertical aᵣ

Let c be a
of $y = f(x$

1. Vert

2. Vert

3. Hor

4. Hor

In items 3 aᵣ
and $h(x) = ₗ$

Eₓ

Th
is

-3

Fiᵍ

Sᵒ

a.

b.

1.7 Exercises

See www.CalcChat.com for worked-out solutions to odd-numbered exercises.

Vocabulary Check

Fill in the blanks.

1. If the composite functions $f(g(x)) = x$ and $g(f(x)) = x$, then the function g is the _____ function of f, and is denoted by _____ .

2. The domain of f is the _____ of f^{-1}, and the _____ of f^{-1} is the range of f.

3. The graphs of f and f^{-1} are reflections of each other in the line _____ .

4. To have an inverse function, a function f must be _____ ; that is, $f(a) = f(b)$ implies $a = b$.

5. A graphical test for the existence of an inverse function is called the _____ Line Test.

In Exercises 1–8, find the inverse function of f informally. Verify that $f(f^{-1}(x)) = x$ and $f^{-1}(f(x)) = x$.

1. $f(x) = 6x$

2. $f(x) = \frac{1}{3}x$

3. $f(x) = x + 7$

4. $f(x) = x - 3$

5. $f(x) = 2x + 1$

6. $f(x) = \frac{x - 1}{4}$

7. $f(x) = \sqrt[3]{x}$

8. $f(x) = x^5$

In Exercises 9–14, (a) show that f and g are inverse functions algebraically and (b) use a graphing utility to create a table of values for each function to numerically show that f and g are inverse functions.

9. $f(x) = -\frac{7}{2}x - 3, \quad g(x) = -\frac{2x + 6}{7}$

10. $f(x) = \frac{x - 9}{4}, \quad g(x) = 4x + 9$

11. $f(x) = x^3 + 5, \quad g(x) = \sqrt[3]{x - 5}$

12. $f(x) = \frac{x^3}{2}, \quad g(x) = \sqrt[3]{2x}$

13. $f(x) = -\sqrt{x - 8}, \quad g(x) = 8 + x^2, \quad x \le 0$

14. $f(x) = \sqrt[3]{3x - 10}, \quad g(x) = \frac{x^3 + 10}{3}$

In Exercises 15–20, show that f and g are inverse functions algebraically. Use a graphing utility to graph f and g in the same viewing window. Describe the relationship between the graphs.

15. $f(x) = x^3, \quad g(x) = \sqrt[3]{x}$

16. $f(x) = \frac{1}{x}, \quad g(x) = \frac{1}{x}$

17. $f(x) = \sqrt{x - 4}; \quad g(x) = x^2 + 4, \quad x \ge 0$

18. $f(x) = 9 - x^2, \quad x \ge 0; \quad g(x) = \sqrt{9 - x}$

19. $f(x) = 1 - x^3, \quad g(x) = \sqrt[3]{1 - x}$

20. $f(x) = \frac{1}{1 + x}, \quad x \ge 0; \quad g(x) = \frac{1 - x}{x}, \quad 0 < x \le 1$

In Exercises 21–24, match the graph of the function with the graph of its inverse function. [The graphs of the inverse functions are labeled (a), (b), (c), and (d).]

(a)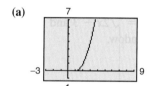

(b)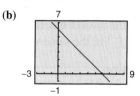

(c)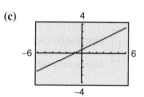

(d)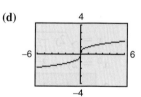

21.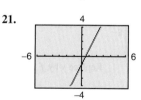

22.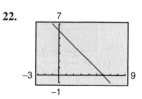

23.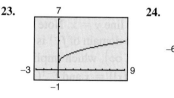

24.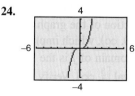

In Exercises 25–28, show that f and g are inverse functions (a) graphically and (b) numerically.

25. $f(x) = 2x, \quad g(x) = \dfrac{x}{2}$

26. $f(x) = x - 5, \quad g(x) = x + 5$

27. $f(x) = \dfrac{x - 1}{x + 5}, \quad g(x) = -\dfrac{5x + 1}{x - 1}$

28. $f(x) = \dfrac{x + 3}{x - 2}, \quad g(x) = \dfrac{2x + 3}{x - 1}$

In Exercises 29–34, determine if the graph is that of a function. If so, determine if the function is one-to-one.

29.
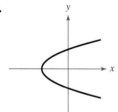

30.
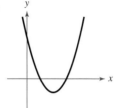

31.
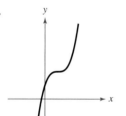

32.
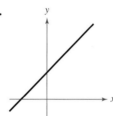

33.
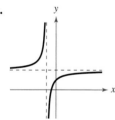

34.
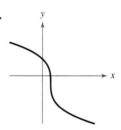

In Exercises 35–46, use a graphing utility to graph the function and use the Horizontal Line Test to determine whether the function is one-to-one and so has an inverse function exists.

35. $f(x) = 3 - \frac{1}{2}x$

36. $f(x) = \frac{1}{4}(x + 2)^2 - 1$

37. $h(x) = \dfrac{x^2}{x^2 + 1}$

38. $g(x) = \dfrac{4 - x}{6x^2}$

39. $h(x) = \sqrt{16 - x^2}$

40. $f(x) = -2x\sqrt{16 - x^2}$

41. $f(x) = 10$

42. $f(x) = -0.65$

43. $g(x) = (x + 5)^3$

44. $f(x) = x^5 - 7$

45. $h(x) = |x + 4| - |x - 4|$

46. $f(x) = -\dfrac{|x - 6|}{|x + 6|}$

In Exercises 47–58, determine algebraically whether the function is one-to-one. Verify your answer graphically.

47. $f(x) = x^4$

48. $g(x) = x^2 - x^4$

49. $f(x) = \dfrac{3x + 4}{5}$

50. $f(x) = 3x + 5$

51. $f(x) = \dfrac{1}{x^2}$

52. $h(x) = \dfrac{4}{x^2}$

53. $f(x) = (x + 3)^2, \quad x \geq -3$

54. $q(x) = (x - 5)^2, \quad x \leq 5$

55. $f(x) = \sqrt{2x + 3}$

56. $f(x) = \sqrt{x - 2}$

57. $f(x) = |x - 2|, \quad x \leq 2$

58. $f(x) = \dfrac{x^2}{x^2 + 1}$

In Exercises 59–68, find the inverse function of f algebraically. Use a graphing utility to graph both f and f^{-1} in the same viewing window. Describe the relationship between the graphs.

59. $f(x) = 2x - 3$

60. $f(x) = 3x$

61. $f(x) = x^5$

62. $f(x) = x^3 + 1$

63. $f(x) = x^{3/5}$

64. $f(x) = x^2, \quad x \geq 0$

65. $f(x) = \sqrt{4 - x^2}, \quad 0 \leq x \leq 2$

66. $f(x) = \sqrt{16 - x^2}, \quad -4 \leq x \leq 0$

67. $f(x) = \dfrac{4}{x}$

68. $f(x) = \dfrac{6}{\sqrt{x}}$

Think About It   In Exercises 69–78, restrict the domain of the function f so that the function is one-to-one and has an inverse function. Then find the inverse function f^{-1}. State the domains and ranges of f and f^{-1}. Explain your results. (There are many correct answers.)

69. $f(x) = (x - 2)^2$

70. $f(x) = 1 - x^4$

71. $f(x) = |x + 2|$

72. $f(x) = |x - 2|$

73. $f(x) = (x + 3)^2$

74. $f(x) = (x - 4)^2$

75. $f(x) = -2x^2 + 5$

76. $f(x) = \frac{1}{2}x^2 - 1$

77. $f(x) = |x - 4| + 1$

78. $f(x) = -|x - 1| - 2$

1.2 **In Exercises 17–22, plot the two points and find the slope of the line passing through the points.**

17. $(-3, 2), (8, 2)$

18. $(7, -1), (7, 12)$

19. $\left(\frac{3}{2}, 1\right), \left(5, \frac{5}{2}\right)$

20. $\left(-\frac{3}{4}, \frac{5}{6}\right), \left(\frac{1}{2}, -\frac{5}{2}\right)$

21. $(-4.5, 6), (2.1, 3)$

22. $(-2.7, -6.3), (-1, -1.2)$

In Exercises 23–32, use the point on the line and the slope of the line to find the general form of the equation of the line, and find three additional points through which the line passes. (There are many correct answers.)

	Point	Slope
23.	$(2, -1)$	$m = \frac{1}{4}$
24.	$(-3, 5)$	$m = -\frac{3}{2}$
25.	$(0, -5)$	$m = \frac{3}{2}$
26.	$(3, 0)$	$m = -\frac{2}{3}$
27.	$\left(\frac{1}{5}, -5\right)$	$m = -1$
28.	$\left(0, \frac{7}{8}\right)$	$m = -\frac{4}{5}$
29.	$(-2, 6)$	$m = 0$
30.	$(-8, 8)$	$m = 0$
31.	$(10, -6)$	m is undefined.
32.	$(5, 4)$	m is undefined.

In Exercises 33–36, find the slope-intercept form of the equation of the line that passes through the points. Use a graphing utility to graph the line.

33. $(2, -1), (4, -1)$ **34.** $(0, 0), (0, 10)$

35. $(-1, 0), (6, 2)$ **36.** $(1, 6), (4, 2)$

Rate of Change **In Exercises 37 and 38, you are given the dollar value of a product in 2008 *and* the rate at which the value of the item is expected to change during the next 5 years. Use this information to write a linear equation that gives the dollar value V of the product in terms of the year t. (Let $t = 8$ represent 2008.)**

	2008 Value	Rate
37.	$12,500	$850 increase per year
38.	$72.95	$5.15 decrease per year

39. *Sales* During the second and third quarters of the year, an e-commerce business had sales of $160,000 and $185,000, respectively. The growth of sales follows a linear pattern. Estimate sales during the fourth quarter.

40. *Depreciation* The dollar value of a DVD player in 2006 is $225. The product will decrease in value at an expected rate of $12.75 per year.

(a) Write a linear equation that gives the dollar value V of the DVD player in terms of the year t. (Let $t = 6$ represent 2006.)

(b) Use a graphing utility to graph the equation found in part (a). Be sure to choose an appropriate viewing window. State the dimensions of your viewing window, and explain why you chose the values that you did.

(c) Use the *value* or *trace* feature of your graphing utility to estimate the dollar value of the DVD player in 2010. Confirm your answer algebraically.

(d) According to the model, when will the DVD player have no value?

In Exercises 41–44, write the slope-intercept forms of the equations of the lines through the given point (a) parallel to the given line and (b) perpendicular to the given line. Verify your result with a graphing utility (use a *square setting*).

	Point	Line
41.	$(3, -2)$	$5x - 4y = 8$
42.	$(-8, 3)$	$2x + 3y = 5$
43.	$(-6, 2)$	$x = 4$
44.	$(3, -4)$	$y = 2$

1.3 **In Exercises 45 and 46, which sets of ordered pairs represent functions from A to B? Explain.**

45. $A = \{10, 20, 30, 40\}$ and $B = \{0, 2, 4, 6\}$

(a) $\{(20, 4), (40, 0), (20, 6), (30, 2)\}$

(b) $\{(10, 4), (20, 4), (30, 4), (40, 4)\}$

(c) $\{(40, 0), (30, 2), (20, 4), (10, 6)\}$

(d) $\{(20, 2), (10, 0), (40, 4)\}$

46. $A = \{u, v, w\}$ and $B = \{-2, -1, 0, 1, 2\}$

(a) $\{(v, -1), (u, 2), (w, 0), (u, -2)\}$

(b) $\{(u, -2), (v, 2), (w, 1)\}$

(c) $\{(u, 2), (v, 2), (w, 1), (w, 1)\}$

(d) $\{(w, -2), (v, 0), (w, 2)\}$

In Exercises 47–50, determine whether the equation represents y as a function of x.

47. $16x^2 - y^2 = 0$ **48.** $2x - y - 3 = 0$

49. $y = \sqrt{1 - x}$ **50.** $|y| = x + 2$

In Exercises 51–54, evaluate the function at each specified value of the independent variable, and simplify.

51. $f(x) = x^2 + 1$
  (a) $f(1)$ (b) $f(-3)$
  (c) $f(b^3)$ (d) $f(x - 1)$

52. $g(x) = x^{4/3}$
  (a) $g(8)$ (b) $g(t + 1)$
  (c) $g(-27)$ (d) $g(-x)$

53. $h(x) = \begin{cases} 2x + 1, & x \le -1 \\ x^2 + 2, & x > -1 \end{cases}$
  (a) $h(-2)$ (b) $h(-1)$
  (c) $h(0)$ (d) $h(2)$

54. $f(x) = \dfrac{3}{2x - 5}$
  (a) $f(1)$ (b) $f(-2)$
  (c) $f(t)$ (d) $f(10)$

In Exercises 55–60, find the domain of the function.

55. $f(x) = \dfrac{x - 1}{x + 2}$ **56.** $f(x) = \dfrac{x^2}{x^2 + 1}$

57. $f(x) = \sqrt{25 - x^2}$ **58.** $f(x) = \sqrt{x^2 - 16}$

59. $g(s) = \dfrac{5s + 5}{3s - 9}$ **60.** $f(x) = \dfrac{2x + 1}{3x + 4}$

61. *Cost* A hand tool manufacturer produces a product for which the variable cost is $5.35 per unit and the fixed costs are $16,000. The company sells the product for $8.20 and can sell all that it produces.
  (a) Write the total cost C as a function of x, the number of units produced.
  (b) Write the profit P as a function of x.

62. *Consumerism* The retail sales R (in billions of dollars) of lawn care products and services in the United States from 1997 to 2004 can be approximated by the model

$$R(t) = \begin{cases} 0.126t^2 - 0.89t + 6.8, & 7 \le t < 11 \\ 0.1442t^3 - 5.611t^2 + 71.10t - 282.4, & 11 \le t \le 14 \end{cases}$$

where t represents the year, with $t = 7$ corresponding to 1997. Use the *table* feature of a graphing utility to approximate the retail sales of lawn care products and services for each year from 1997 to 2004. (Source: The National Gardening Association)

In Exercises 63 and 64, find the difference quotient and simplify your answer.

63. $f(x) = 2x^2 + 3x - 1$, $\dfrac{f(x + h) - f(x)}{h}$, $h \ne 0$

64. $f(x) = x^3 - 5x^2 + x$, $\dfrac{f(x + h) - f(x)}{h}$, $h \ne 0$

1.4 In Exercises 65–68, use a graphing utility to graph the function and estimate its domain and range. Then find the domain and range algebraically.

65. $f(x) = 3 - 2x^2$ **66.** $f(x) = \sqrt{2x^2 - 1}$

67. $h(x) = \sqrt{36 - x^2}$ **68.** $g(x) = |x + 5|$

In Exercises 69–72, (a) use a graphing utility to graph the equation and (b) use the Vertical Line Test to determine whether y is a function of x.

69. $y = \dfrac{x^2 + 3x}{6}$ **70.** $y = -\dfrac{2}{3}|x + 5|$

71. $3x + y^2 = 2$ **72.** $x^2 + y^2 = 49$

In Exercises 73–76, (a) use a graphing utility to graph the function and (b) determine the open intervals on which the function is increasing, decreasing, or constant.

73. $f(x) = x^3 - 3x$ **74.** $f(x) = \sqrt{x^2 - 9}$

75. $f(x) = x\sqrt{x - 6}$ **76.** $f(x) = \dfrac{|x + 8|}{2}$

In Exercises 77–80, use a graphing utility to approximate (to two decimal places) any relative minimum or relative maximum values of the function.

77. $f(x) = (x^2 - 4)^2$ **78.** $f(x) = x^2 - x - 1$

79. $h(x) = 4x^3 - x^4$ **80.** $f(x) = x^3 - 4x^2 - 1$

In Exercises 81–84, sketch the graph of the function by hand.

81. $f(x) = \begin{cases} 3x + 5, & x < 0 \\ x - 4, & x \ge 0 \end{cases}$

82. $f(x) = \begin{cases} x^2 + 7, & x < 1 \\ x^2 - 5x + 6, & x \ge 1 \end{cases}$

83. $f(x) = [\![x]\!] + 3$ **84.** $f(x) = [\![x + 2]\!]$

In Exercises 85 and 86, determine algebraically whether the function is even, odd, or neither. Verify your answer using a graphing utility.

85. $f(x) = (x^2 - 8)^2$ **86.** $f(x) = 2x^3 - x^2$

1.5 In Exercises 87–90, identify the parent function and describe the transformation shown in the graph. Write an equation for the graphed function.

87.

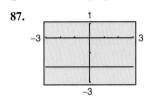

88.

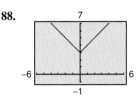

89.

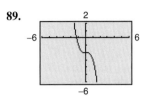

90.

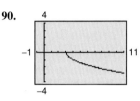

In Exercises 91–94, use the graph of $y = f(x)$ to graph the function.

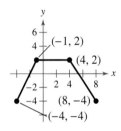

91. $y = f(-x)$

92. $y = -f(x)$

93. $y = f(x) - 2$

94. $y = f(x - 1)$

In Exercises 95–100, h is related to one of the six parent functions on page 127. (a) Identify the parent function f. (b) Describe the sequence of transformations from f to h. (c) Sketch the graph of h by hand. (d) Use function notation to write h in terms of the parent function f.

95. $h(x) = |x| + 9$

96. $h(x) = (x - 2)^3 + 5$

97. $h(x) = -\sqrt{x} + 5$

98. $h(x) = -(x + 2)^2 - 8$

99. $h(x) = \frac{1}{2}(x - 3)^2 - 6$

100. $h(x) = 2\sqrt{x} + 5$

1.6 In Exercises 101–106, find two functions f and g such that $(f \circ g)(x) = h(x)$. (There are many correct answers.)

101. $h(x) = (x + 3)^2$

102. $h(x) = (1 - 2x)^3$

103. $h(x) = \sqrt{4x + 2}$

104. $h(x) = \sqrt[3]{(x + 2)^2}$

105. $h(x) = \dfrac{4}{x + 2}$

106. $h(x) = \dfrac{6}{(3x + 1)^3}$

Data Analysis In Exercises 107 and 108, the numbers (in millions) of students taking the SAT (y_1) and ACT (y_2) for the years 1990 through 2004 can be modeled by $y_1 = 0.00204t^2 + 0.0015t + 1.021$ and $y_2 = 0.0274t + 0.785$, where t represents the year, with $t = 0$ corresponding to 1990. (Source: College Entrance Examination Board and ACT, Inc.)

107. Use a graphing utility to graph y_1, y_2, and $y_1 + y_2$ in the same viewing window.

108. Use the model $y_1 + y_2$ to estimate the total number of students taking the SAT and ACT in 2008.

1.7 In Exercises 109 and 110, find the inverse function of f informally. Verify that $f(f^{-1}(x)) = x$ and $f^{-1}(f(x)) = x$.

109. $f(x) = \frac{1}{2}x + 3$

110. $f(x) = \dfrac{x - 4}{5}$

In Exercises 111 and 112, show that f and g are inverse functions (a) graphically and (b) numerically.

111. $f(x) = 3 - 4x$, $g(x) = \dfrac{3 - x}{4}$

112. $f(x) = \sqrt{x + 1}$, $g(x) = x^2 - 1, x \geq 0$

In Exercises 113–116, use a graphing utility to graph the function and use the Horizontal Line Test to determine whether the function is one-to-one and an inverse function exists.

113. $f(x) = \frac{1}{2}x - 3$

114. $f(x) = (x - 1)^2$

115. $h(t) = \dfrac{2}{t - 3}$

116. $g(x) = \sqrt{x + 6}$

In Exercises 117–122, find the inverse function of f algebraically.

117. $f(x) = \frac{1}{2}x - 5$

118. $f(x) = \dfrac{7x + 3}{8}$

119. $f(x) = 4x^3 - 3$

120. $f(x) = 5x^3 + 2$

121. $f(x) = \sqrt{x + 10}$

122. $f(x) = 4\sqrt{6 - x}$

Synthesis

True or False? In Exercises 123–125, determine whether the statement is true or false. Justify your answer.

123. If the graph of the common function $f(x) = x^2$ is moved six units to the right, moved three units upward, and reflected in the x-axis, then the point $(-1, 28)$ will lie on the graph of the transformation.

124. If $f(x) = x^n$ where n is odd, f^{-1} exists.

125. There exists no function f such that $f = f^{-1}$.

1 Chapter Test

See www.CalcChat.com for worked-out solutions to odd-numbered exercises.

Take this test as you would take a test in class. After you are finished, check your work against the answers in the back of the book.

In Exercises 1–6, use the point-plotting method to graph the equation by hand and identify any x- and y-intercepts. Verify your results using a graphing utility.

1. $y = 2|x| - 1$ **2.** $y = 2x - \frac{8}{5}$

3. $y = 2x^2 - 4x$ **4.** $y = x^3 - x$

5. $y = -x^2 + 4$ **6.** $y = \sqrt{x - 2}$

7. Find equations of the lines that pass through the point $(0, 4)$ and are (a) parallel to and (b) perpendicular to the line $5x + 2y = 3$.

8. Find the slope-intercept form of the equation of the line that passes through the points $(2, -1)$ and $(-3, 4)$.

9. Does the graph at the right represent y as a function of x? Explain.

10. Evaluate $f(x) = |x + 2| - 15$ at each value of the independent variable and simplify.

(a) $f(-8)$ (b) $f(14)$ (c) $f(t - 6)$

11. Find the domain of $f(x) = 10 - \sqrt{3 - x}$.

12. An electronics company produces a car stereo for which the variable cost is $5.60 and the fixed costs are $24,000. The product sells for $99.50. Write the total cost C as a function of the number of units produced and sold, x. Write the profit P as a function of the number of units produced and sold, x.

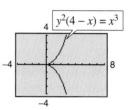

$y^2(4 - x) = x^3$

Figure for 9

In Exercises 13 and 14, determine algebraically whether the function is even, odd, or neither.

13. $f(x) = 2x^3 - 3x$ **14.** $f(x) = 3x^4 + 5x^2$

In Exercises 15 and 16, determine the open intervals on which the function is increasing, decreasing, or constant.

15. $h(x) = \frac{1}{4}x^4 - 2x^2$ **16.** $g(t) = |t + 2| - |t - 2|$

In Exercises 17 and 18, use a graphing utility to approximate (to two decimal places) any relative minimum or relative maximum values of the function.

17. $f(x) = -x^3 - 5x^2 + 12$ **18.** $f(x) = x^5 - x^3 + 2$

In Exercises 19–21, (a) identify the parent function f, (b) describe the sequence of transformations from f to g, and (c) sketch the graph of g.

19. $g(x) = -2(x - 5)^3 + 3$ **20.** $g(x) = \sqrt{-x - 7}$ **21.** $g(x) = 4|-x| - 7$

22. Use the functions $f(x) = x^2$ and $g(x) = \sqrt{2 - x}$ to find the specified function and its domain.

(a) $(f - g)(x)$ (b) $\left(\dfrac{f}{g}\right)(x)$ (c) $(f \circ g)(x)$ (d) $(g \circ f)(x)$

In Exercises 23–25, determine whether the function has an inverse function, and if so, find the inverse function.

23. $f(x) = x^3 + 8$ **24.** $f(x) = x^2 + 6$ **25.** $f(x) = \dfrac{3x\sqrt{x}}{8}$

Proofs in Mathematics

Conditional Statements

Many theorems are written in the **if-then form** "if p, then q," which is denoted by

$p \rightarrow q$ Conditional statement

where p is the **hypothesis** and q is the **conclusion**. Here are some other ways to express the conditional statement $p \rightarrow q$.

p implies q. p, only if q. p is sufficient for q.

Conditional statements can be either true or false. The conditional statement $p \rightarrow q$ is false only when p is true and q is false. To show that a conditional statement is true, you must prove that the conclusion follows for all cases that fulfill the hypothesis. To show that a conditional statement is false, you need only to describe a single **counterexample** that shows that the statement is not always true.

For instance, $x = -4$ is a counterexample that shows that the following statement is false.

If $x^2 = 16$, then $x = 4$.

The hypothesis "$x^2 = 16$" is true because $(-4)^2 = 16$. However, the conclusion "$x = 4$" is false. This implies that the given conditional statement is false.

For the conditional statement $p \rightarrow q$, there are three important associated conditional statements.

1. The **converse** of $p \rightarrow q$: $q \rightarrow p$
2. The **inverse** of $p \rightarrow q$: $\sim p \rightarrow \sim q$
3. The **contrapositive** of $p \rightarrow q$: $\sim q \rightarrow \sim p$

The symbol $\sim$ means the **negation** of a statement. For instance, the negation of "The engine is running" is "The engine is not running."

Example   Writing the Converse, Inverse, and Contrapositive

Write the converse, inverse, and contrapositive of the conditional statement "If I get a B on my test, then I will pass the course."

Solution

a. *Converse:* If I pass the course, then I got a B on my test.

b. *Inverse:* If I do not get a B on my test, then I will not pass the course.

c. *Contrapositive:* If I do not pass the course, then I did not get a B on my test.

In the example above, notice that neither the converse nor the inverse is logically equivalent to the original conditional statement. On the other hand, the contrapositive *is* logically equivalent to the original conditional statement.

Chapter 2

Solving Equations and Inequalities

2.1 Linear Equations and Problem Solving

2.2 Solving Equations Graphically

2.3 Complex Numbers

2.4 Solving Quadratic Equations Algebraically

2.5 Solving Other Types of Equations Algebraically

2.6 Solving Inequalities Algebraically and Graphically

2.7 Linear Models and Scatter Plots

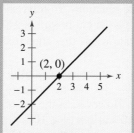
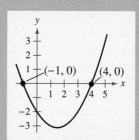
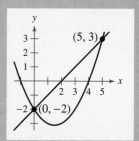

Solving real-life applications requires the ability to solve many types of equations—linear, quadratic, and polynomial as well as equations involving fractions, radicals, and absolute values. In Chapter 2, you will learn algebraic and graphical methods for solving a variety of equations and inequalities. You will also learn how to perform operations on complex numbers and plot complex numbers in a complex plane.

© Jonathan Blair/Corbis

Selected Applications

Equations and inequalities have many real-life applications. The applications listed below represent a small sample of the applications in this chapter.

- Anthropology, Exercises 57 and 58, page 173
- Hospitals, Exercise 80, page 185
- Fractals, Exercises 77 and 78, page 194
- Flying Distance, Exercise 89, page 208
- Transplants, Exercise 77, page 217
- Juvenile Crime, Exercise 78, page 217
- Education, Exercise 83, page 230
- Music, Exercises 89–92, page 231
- Hooke's Law, Exercise 11, page 238

Linear equations can be used to model the relationship between the length of a human's femur and the height of the human. These equations help researchers learn about ancient cultures.

2.1   Linear Equations and Problem Solving

Equations and Solutions of Equations

An **equation** in x is a statement that two algebraic expressions are equal. For example, $3x - 5 = 7$, $x^2 - x - 6 = 0$, and $\sqrt{2x} = 4$ are equations. To **solve** an equation in x means to find all values of x for which the equation is true. Such values are **solutions.** For instance, $x = 4$ is a solution of the equation $3x - 5 = 7$, because $3(4) - 5 = 7$ is a true statement.

The solutions of an equation depend on the kinds of numbers being considered. For instance, in the set of rational numbers, $x^2 = 10$ has no solution because there is no rational number whose square is 10. However, in the set of real numbers the equation has the two solutions $x = \sqrt{10}$ and $x = -\sqrt{10}$.

An equation that is true for *every* real number in the domain of the variable is called an **identity.** For example, $x^2 - 9 = (x + 3)(x - 3)$ is an identity because it is a true statement for any real value of x, and $x/(3x^2) = 1/(3x)$, where $x \neq 0$, is an identity because it is true for any nonzero real value of x.

An equation that is true for just *some* (or even none) of the real numbers in the domain of the variable is called a **conditional equation.** For example, the equation $x^2 - 9 = 0$ is conditional because $x = 3$ and $x = -3$ are the only values in the domain that satisfy the equation. The equation $2x + 1 = 2x - 3$ is also conditional because there are no real values of x for which the equation is true. Learning to solve conditional equations is the primary focus of this chapter.

A **linear equation in one variable** x is an equation that can be written in the standard form $ax + b = 0$, where a and b are real numbers, with $a \neq 0$. For a review of solving one- and two-step linear equations, see Appendix D.

To solve an equation involving fractional expressions, find the least common denominator (LCD) of all terms in the equation and multiply every term by this LCD. This procedure clears the equation of fractions, as demonstrated in Example 1.

What you should learn

- Solve equations involving fractional expressions.
- Write and use mathematical models to solve real-life problems.
- Use common formulas to solve real-life problems.

Why you should learn it

Linear equations are useful for modeling situations in which you need to find missing information. For instance, Exercise 68 on page 174 shows how to use a linear equation to determine the height of a flagpole by measuring its shadow.

Sergio Piumatti

Example 1   Solving an Equation Involving Fractions

Solve $\dfrac{x}{3} + \dfrac{3x}{4} = 2$.

Solution

$$\frac{x}{3} + \frac{3x}{4} = 2 \qquad \text{Write original equation.}$$

$$(12)\frac{x}{3} + (12)\frac{3x}{4} = (12)2 \qquad \text{Multiply each term by the LCD of 12.}$$

$$4x + 9x = 24 \qquad \text{Divide out and multiply.}$$

$$13x = 24 \qquad \text{Combine like terms.}$$

$$x = \frac{24}{13} \qquad \text{Divide each side by 13.}$$

✓**CHECKPOINT**   Now try Exercise 23.

STUDY TIP

After solving an equation, you should check each solution in the original equation. For instance, you can check the solution to Example 1 as follows.

$$\frac{x}{3} + \frac{3x}{4} = 2$$

$$\frac{\frac{24}{13}}{3} + \frac{3\left(\frac{24}{13}\right)}{4} \overset{?}{=} 2$$

$$\frac{8}{13} + \frac{18}{13} \overset{?}{=} 2$$

$$2 = 2 \checkmark$$

When multiplying or dividing an equation by a *variable* expression, it is possible to introduce an **extraneous solution**—one that does not satisfy the original equation. The next example demonstrates the importance of checking your solution when you have multiplied or divided by a variable expression.

Example 2 An Equation with an Extraneous Solution

Solve $\dfrac{1}{x-2} = \dfrac{3}{x+2} - \dfrac{6x}{x^2-4}$.

Algebraic Solution

The LCD is

$$x^2 - 4 = (x+2)(x-2).$$

Multiplying each term by the LCD and simplifying produces the following.

$$\frac{1}{x-2}(x+2)(x-2)$$

$$= \frac{3}{x+2}(x+2)(x-2) - \frac{6x}{x^2-4}(x+2)(x-2)$$

$$x + 2 = 3(x-2) - 6x, \quad x \neq \pm 2$$

$$x + 2 = 3x - 6 - 6x$$

$$4x = -8$$

$$x = -2 \qquad \text{Extraneous solution}$$

A check of $x = -2$ in the original equation shows that it yields a denominator of zero. So, $x = -2$ is an extraneous solution, and the original equation has *no solution*.

✓CHECKPOINT   Now try Exercise 39.

Graphical Solution

Use a graphing utility (in *dot* mode) to graph the left and right sides of the equation

$$y_1 = \frac{1}{x-2} \quad \text{and} \quad y_2 = \frac{3}{x+2} - \frac{6x}{x^2-4}$$

in the same viewing window, as shown in Figure 2.1. The graphs of the equations do not appear to intersect. This means that there is no point for which the left side of the equation y_1 is equal to the right side of the equation y_2. So, the equation appears to have *no solution*.

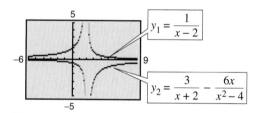

Figure 2.1

Using Mathematical Models to Solve Problems

One of the primary goals of this text is to learn how algebra can be used to solve problems that occur in real-life situations. This procedure, introduced in Chapter 1, is called **mathematical modeling.**

A good approach to mathematical modeling is to use two stages. Begin by using the verbal description of the problem to form a *verbal model.* Then, after assigning labels to the quantities in the verbal model, form a *mathematical model* or an *algebraic equation.*

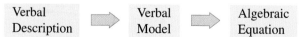

When you are trying to construct a verbal model, it is helpful to look for a *hidden equality*—a statement that two algebraic expressions are equal. These two expressions might be explicitly stated as being equal, or they might be known to be equal (based on prior knowledge or experience).

TECHNOLOGY TIP

Notice in Figure 2.1 that the equations were graphed using the *dot* mode of a graphing utility. In this text, a blue or light red curve is placed behind the graphing utility's display to indicate where the graph should appear. You will learn more about how graphing utilities graph these types of equations in Section 3.6.

Example 3 Finding the Dimensions of a Room

A rectangular family room is twice as long as it is wide, and its perimeter is 84 feet. Find the dimensions of the family room.

Solution

For this problem, it helps to draw a diagram, as shown in Figure 2.2.

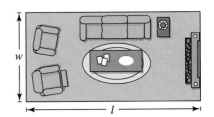

Figure 2.2

Verbal Model: $2 \cdot \boxed{\text{Length}} + 2 \cdot \boxed{\text{Width}} = \boxed{\text{Perimeter}}$

Labels:
Perimeter $= 84$ (feet)
Width $= w$ (feet)
Length $= l = 2w$ (feet)

Equation:
$2(2w) + 2w = 84$ Original equation
$6w = 84$ Combine like terms.
$w = 14$ Divide each side by 6.

Because the length is twice the width, you have

$l = 2w$ Length is twice width.
$ = 2(14)$ Substitute 14 for w.
$ = 28.$ Simplify.

So, the dimensions of the room are 14 feet by 28 feet.

✔CHECKPOINT   Now try Exercise 59.

Example 4 A Distance Problem

A plane is flying nonstop from New York to San Francisco, a distance of about 2600 miles, as shown in Figure 2.3. After $1\frac{1}{2}$ hours in the air, the plane flies over Chicago (a distance of about 800 miles from New York). Estimate the time it will take the plane to fly from New York to San Francisco.

Solution

Verbal Model: $\boxed{\text{Distance}} = \boxed{\text{Rate}} \cdot \boxed{\text{Time}}$

Labels:
Distance $= 2600$ (miles)

Rate $= \dfrac{\text{Distance to Chicago}}{\text{Time to Chicago}} = \dfrac{800}{1.5}$ (miles per hour)

Time $= t$ (hours)

Equation:
$2600 = \dfrac{800}{1.5}t$

$4.875 = t$

The trip will take about 4.875 hours, or about 4 hours and 53 minutes.

✔CHECKPOINT   Now try Exercise 63.

San Francisco   Chicago   New York

Figure 2.3

Example 5   Height of a Building

To determine the height of the Aon Center Building (in Chicago), you measure the shadow cast by the building and find it to be 142 feet long, as shown in Figure 2.4. Then you measure the shadow cast by a 48-inch post and find it to be 6 inches long. Estimate the building's height.

Solution

To solve this problem, you use a result from geometry that states that the ratios of corresponding sides of similar triangles are equal.

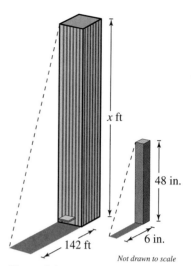

x ft

48 in.

142 ft

6 in.

Not drawn to scale

Figure 2.4

Verbal Model:

$$\frac{\text{Height of building}}{\text{Length of building's shadow}} = \frac{\text{Height of post}}{\text{Length of post's shadow}}$$

Labels: Height of building $= x$ (feet)
Length of building's shadow $= 142$ (feet)
Height of post $= 48$ (inches)
Length of post's shadow $= 6$ (inches)

Equation: $\dfrac{x}{142} = \dfrac{48}{6}$ ➡ $x = 1136$

So, the Aon Center Building is about 1136 feet high.

✓**CHECKPOINT**   Now try Exercise 67.

Example 6   An Inventory Problem

A store has $30,000 of inventory in 13-inch and 19-inch color televisions. The profit on a 13-inch set is 22% and the profit on a 19-inch set is 40%. The profit for the entire stock is 35%. How much was invested in each type of television?

Solution

Verbal Model:

$$\boxed{\text{Profit from 13-inch sets}} + \boxed{\text{Profit from 19-inch sets}} = \boxed{\text{Total profit}}$$

Labels: Inventory of 13-inch sets $= x$ (dollars)
Inventory of 19-inch sets $= 30{,}000 - x$ (dollars)
Profit from 13-inch sets $= 0.22x$ (dollars)
Profit from 19-inch sets $= 0.40(30{,}000 - x)$ (dollars)
Total profit $= 0.35(30{,}000) = 10{,}500$ (dollars)

Equation: $0.22x + 0.40(30{,}000 - x) = 10{,}500$

$$-0.18x = -1500$$

$$x \approx 8333.33$$

So, $8333.33 was invested in 13-inch sets and $30{,}000 - x$, or $21,666.67, was invested in 19-inch sets.

✓**CHECKPOINT**   Now try Exercise 73.

> ### STUDY TIP
>
> Notice in the solution of Example 6 that percents are expressed as decimals. For instance, 22% is written as 0.22.

Common Formulas

Many common types of geometric, scientific, and investment problems use ready-made equations called **formulas.** Knowing these formulas will help you translate and solve a wide variety of real-life applications.

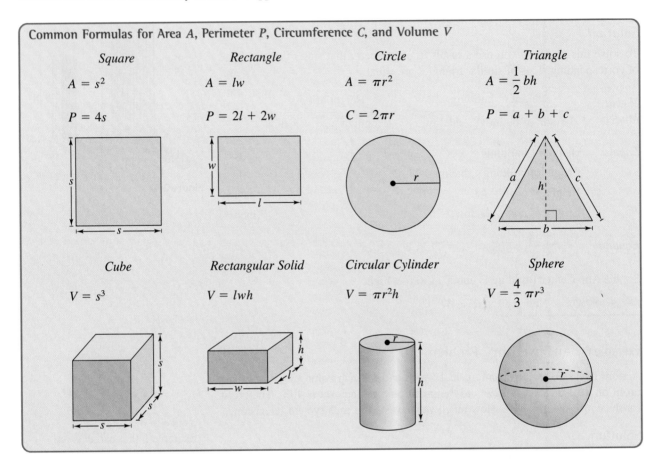

Common Formulas for Area A, Perimeter P, Circumference C, and Volume V

Square

$A = s^2$

$P = 4s$

Rectangle

$A = lw$

$P = 2l + 2w$

Circle

$A = \pi r^2$

$C = 2\pi r$

Triangle

$A = \dfrac{1}{2} bh$

$P = a + b + c$

Cube

$V = s^3$

Rectangular Solid

$V = lwh$

Circular Cylinder

$V = \pi r^2 h$

Sphere

$V = \dfrac{4}{3} \pi r^3$

Miscellaneous Common Formulas

Temperature:	$F = \dfrac{9}{5}C + 32$	F = degrees Fahrenheit, C = degrees Celsius
Simple Interest:	$I = Prt$	I = interest, P = principal (original deposit), r = annual interest rate, t = time in years
Compound Interest:	$A = P\left(1 + \dfrac{r}{n}\right)^{nt}$	A = balance, P = principal (original deposit), r = annual interest rate, n = compoundings (number of times interest is calculated) per year, t = time in years
Distance:	$d = rt$	d = distance traveled, r = rate, t = time

When working with applied problems, you may find it helpful to rewrite a common formula. For instance, the formula for the perimeter of a rectangle, $P = 2l + 2w$, can be solved for w as $w = \frac{1}{2}(P - 2l)$.

Example 7 Using a Formula

A cylindrical can has a volume of 600 cubic centimeters and a radius of 4 centimeters, as shown in Figure 2.5. Find the height of the can.

Solution

The formula for the volume of a cylinder is $V = \pi r^2 h$. To find the height of the can, solve for h.

$$h = \frac{V}{\pi r^2}$$

Then, using $V = 600$ and $r = 4$, find the height.

$$h = \frac{600}{\pi(4)^2} = \frac{600}{16\pi} \approx 11.94$$

You can use unit analysis to check that your answer is reasonable.

$$\frac{600 \text{ cm}^3}{16\pi \text{ cm}^2} \approx 11.94 \text{ cm}$$

 Now try Exercise 77.

Figure 2.5

Example 8 Using a Formula

The average daily temperature in San Diego, California is 64.4°F. What is San Diego's average daily temperature in degrees Celsius? (Source: U.S. National Oceanic and Atmospheric Administration)

Solution

First solve for C in the formula for temperature. Then use $F = 64.4$ to find the temperature in degrees Celsius.

$$F = \frac{9}{5}C + 32 \qquad \text{Formula for temperature}$$

$$F - 32 = \frac{9}{5}C \qquad \text{Subtract 32 from each side.}$$

$$\frac{5}{9}(F - 32) = C \qquad \text{Multiply each side by } \tfrac{5}{9}.$$

$$\frac{5}{9}(64.4 - 32) = C \qquad \text{Substitute 64.4 for } F.$$

$$18 = C \qquad \text{Simplify.}$$

The average daily temperature in San Diego is 18°C.

 Now try Exercise 81.

> ### STUDY TIP
>
> Once you have rewritten the formula for temperature, you can easily find other Celsius values. Simply substitute other Fahrenheit values and evaluate.

61. *Course Grade* To get an A in a course, you must have an average of at least 90 on four tests of 100 points each. The scores on your first three tests were 87, 92, and 84.

(a) Write a verbal model for the test average for the course.

(b) What must you score on the fourth test to get an A for the course?

62. *Course Grade* You are taking a course that has four tests. The first three tests are 100 points each and the fourth test is 200 points. To get an A in the course, you must have an average of at least 90% on the four tests. Your scores on the first three tests were 87, 92, and 84. What must you score on the fourth test to get an A for the course?

63. *Travel Time* You are driving on a Canadian freeway to a town that is 300 kilometers from your home. After 30 minutes you pass a freeway exit that you know is 50 kilometers from your home. Assuming that you continue at the same constant speed, how long will it take for the entire trip?

64. *Travel Time* On the first part of a 317-mile trip, a salesperson averaged 58 miles per hour. The salesperson averaged only 52 miles per hour on the last part of the trip because of an increased volume of traffic. The total time of the trip was 5 hours and 45 minutes. Find the amount of time at each of the two speeds.

65. *Average Speed* A truck driver traveled at an average speed of 55 miles per hour on a 200-mile trip to pick up a load of freight. On the return trip (with the truck fully loaded), the average speed was 40 miles per hour. Find the average speed for the round trip.

66. *Wind Speed* An executive flew in the corporate jet to a meeting in a city 1500 kilometers away. After traveling the same amount of time on the return flight, the pilot mentioned that they still had 300 kilometers to go. The air speed of the plane was 600 kilometers per hour. How fast was the wind blowing? (Assume that the wind direction was parallel to the flight path and constant all day.)

67. *Height* To obtain the height of a barn silo, you measure the silo's shadow and find that it is 80 feet long. You also measure the shadow of a four-foot stake and find that it is $3\frac{1}{2}$ feet long.

(a) Draw a diagram that illustrates the problem. Let h represent the height of the silo.

(b) Find the height of the silo.

68. *Height* A person who is 6 feet tall walks away from a flagpole toward the tip of the shadow of the flagpole. When the person is 30 feet from the flagpole, the tips of the person's shadow and the shadow cast by the flagpole coincide at a point 5 feet in front of the person.

(a) Draw a diagram that illustrates the problem. Let h represent the height of the flagpole.

(b) Find the height of the flagpole.

69. *Simple Interest* Find the interest on a $5000 bond that pays an annual percentage rate of $6\frac{1}{2}\%$ for 6 years.

70. *Simple Interest* A certificate of deposit with an initial deposit of $8000 accumulates $400 interest in 2 years. Find the annual interest rate.

71. *Investment* You plan to invest $12,000 in two funds paying $4\frac{1}{2}\%$ and 5% simple interest. (There is more risk in the 5% fund.) Your goal is to obtain a total annual interest income of $560 from the investments. What is the smallest amount you can invest in the 5% fund in order to meet your objective?

72. *Investment* You plan to invest $25,000 in two funds paying 3% and $4\frac{1}{2}\%$ simple interest. (There is more risk in the $4\frac{1}{2}\%$ fund.) Your goal is to obtain a total annual interest income of $1000 from the investments. What is the smallest amount you can invest in the $4\frac{1}{2}\%$ fund in order to meet your objective?

73. *Inventory* A store has $50,000 of inventory in DVD players and VCRs. The profit on a DVD player is 30% and the profit on a VCR is 25%. The profit on the entire stock is 29%. How much is invested in DVD players and how much is invested in VCRs?

74. *Inventory* A store has $4500 of inventory in 8×10 picture frames and 5×7 picture frames. The profit on an 8×10 frame is 25% and the profit on a 5×7 frame is 22%. The profit on the entire stock is 24%. How much is invested in the 8×10 picture frames and how much is invested in the 5×7 picture frames?

75. *Mixture Problem* A grocer mixes peanuts that cost $2.49 per pound and walnuts that cost $3.89 per pound to make 100 pounds of a mixture that costs $3.19 per pound. How much of each kind of nut is put into the mixture?

76. *Mixture Problem* A forester mixes gasoline and oil to make 2 gallons of mixture for his two-cycle chainsaw engine. This mixture is 32 parts gasoline and 1 part oil. How much gasoline must be added to bring the mixture to 40 parts gasoline and 1 part oil?

77. *Height* A triangular sail has an area of 182.25 square feet. The sail has a base of 13.5 feet. Find the height of the sail.

78. *Area* The figure shows three squares. The perimeter of square I is 20 inches and the perimeter of square II is 32 inches. Find the area of square III.

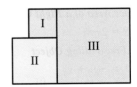

79. Geometry The volume of a rectangular package is 2304 cubic inches. The length of the package is 3 times its width, and the height is $1\frac{1}{2}$ times its width.

(a) Draw a diagram that illustrates the problem. Label the height, width, and length accordingly.

(b) Find the dimensions of the package.

80. Geometry The volume of a globe is about 47,712.94 cubic centimeters. Use a graphing utility to find the radius of the globe. Round your result to two decimal places.

81. Meteorology The line graph shows the temperatures (in degrees Fahrenheit) on a summer day in Buffalo, New York from 10:00 A.M. to 6:00 P.M. Create a new line graph showing the temperatures throughout the day in degrees Celsius.

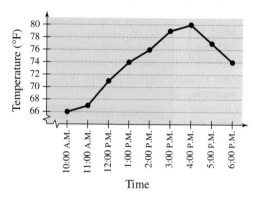

82. Meteorology The average daily temperature in San Francisco, California is 57.3°F. What is San Francisco's average daily temperature in degrees Celsius? (U.S. National Oceanic and Atmospheric Administration)

Statics **In Exercises 83 and 84, you have a uniform beam of length L with a fulcrum x feet from one end (see figure). Objects with weights W_1 and W_2 are placed at opposite ends of the beam. The beam will balance when**

$$W_1 x = W_2(L - x).$$

Find x such that the beam will balance.

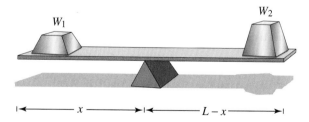

83. Two children weighing 50 pounds and 75 pounds are going to play on a seesaw that is 10 feet long.

84. A person weighing 200 pounds is attempting to move a 550-pound rock with a bar that is 5 feet long.

Synthesis

True or False? **In Exercises 85 and 86, determine whether the statement is true or false. Justify your answer.**

85. The equation

$$x(3 - x) = 10$$

is a linear equation.

86. The volume of a cube with a side length of 9.5 inches is greater than the volume of a sphere with a radius of 5.9 inches.

In Exercises 87 and 88, write a linear equation that has the given solution. (There are many correct answers.)

87. $x = -3$

88. $x = \frac{1}{4}$

89. Think About It What is meant by *equivalent equations*? Give an example of two equivalent equations.

90. Writing In your own words, describe how to clear an equation of fractions.

91. Think About It Find c such that $x = 3$ is a solution to the linear equation $2x - 5c = 10 + 3c - 3x$.

92. Think About It Find c such that $x = 2$ is a solution to the linear equation $5x + 2c = 12 + 4x - 2c$.

Skills Review

In Exercises 93–98, sketch the graph of the equation by hand. Verify using a graphing utility.

93. $y = \frac{5}{8}x - 2$

94. $y = \dfrac{3x - 5}{2} + 2$

95. $y = (x - 3)^2 + 7$

96. $y = \frac{1}{3}x^2 - 4$

97. $y = -\frac{1}{2}|x + 4| - 1$

98. $y = |x - 2| + 10$

In Exercises 99–104, evaluate the combination of functions for $f(x) = -x^2 + 4$ and $g(x) = 6x - 5$.

99. $(f + g)(-3)$

100. $(g - f)(-1)$

101. $(fg)(8)$

102. $\left(\dfrac{f}{g}\right)\left(\dfrac{1}{2}\right)$

103. $(f \circ g)(4)$

104. $(g \circ f)(2)$

The close connection among *x*-intercepts, zeros, and solutions is crucial to your study of algebra. You can take advantage of this connection in two ways. Use your algebraic "equation-solving skills" to find the *x*-intercepts of a graph and your "graphing skills" to approximate the solutions of an equation.

Finding Solutions Graphically

Polynomial equations of degree 1 or 2 can be solved in relatively straightforward ways. Solving polynomial equations of higher degrees can, however, be quite difficult, especially if you rely only on algebraic techniques. For such equations, a graphing utility can be very helpful.

> **Graphical Approximations of Solutions of an Equation**
>
> 1. Write the equation in *general form*, $f(x) = 0$, with the nonzero terms on one side of the equation and zero on the other side.
>
> 2. Use a graphing utility to graph the function $y = f(x)$. Be sure the viewing window shows all the relevant features of the graph.
>
> 3. Use the *zero* or *root* feature or the *zoom* and *trace* features of the graphing utility to approximate the *x*-intercepts of the graph of *f*.

In Chapter 3 you will learn techniques for determining the number of solutions of a polynomial equation. For now, you should know that a polynomial equation of degree *n* cannot have more than *n* different solutions.

Example 3 Finding Solutions of an Equation Graphically

Use a graphing utility to approximate the solutions of $2x^3 - 3x + 2 = 0$.

Solution

Graph the function $y = 2x^3 - 3x + 2$. You can see from the graph that there is one *x*-intercept. It lies between -2 and -1 and is approximately -1.5. By using the *zero* or *root* feature of a graphing utility, you can improve the approximation. Choose a left bound of $x = -2$ (see Figure 2.9) and a right bound of $x = -1$ (see Figure 2.10). To two-decimal-place accuracy, the solution is $x \approx -1.48$, as shown in Figure 2.11. Check this approximation on your calculator. You will find that the value of *y* is $y = 2(-1.48)^3 - 3(-1.48) + 2 \approx -0.04$.

Exploration

In Chapter 3 you will learn that a cubic equation such as

$$24x^3 - 36x + 17 = 0$$

can have up to three real solutions. Use a graphing utility to graph

$$y = 24x^3 - 36x + 17.$$

Describe a viewing window that enables you to determine the number of real solutions of the equation

$$24x^3 - 36x + 17 = 0.$$

Use the same technique to determine the number of real solutions of

$$97x^3 - 102x^2 - 200x - 63 = 0.$$

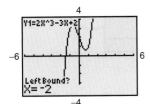

Figure 2.9

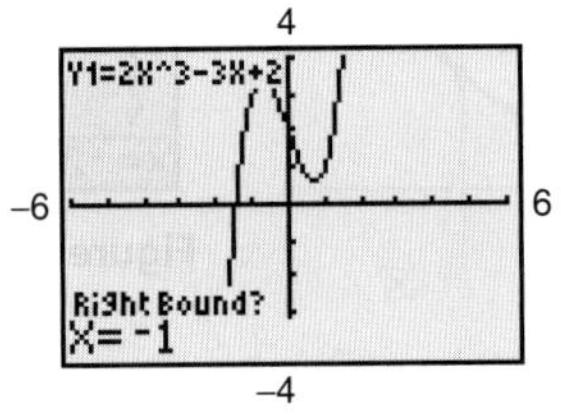

Figure 2.10

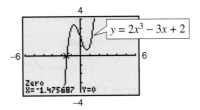

Figure 2.11

✔CHECKPOINT   Now try Exercise 37.

TECHNOLOGY TIP   You can also use a graphing utility's *zoom* and *trace* features to approximate the solution of an equation. Here are some suggestions for using the *zoom-in* feature of a graphing utility.

1. With each successive zoom-in, adjust the *x*-scale (if necessary) so that the resulting viewing window shows at least the two scale marks between which the solution lies.

2. The accuracy of the approximation will always be such that the error is less than the distance between two scale marks.

3. If you have a *trace* feature on your graphing utility, you can generally add one more decimal place of accuracy without changing the viewing window.

Unless stated otherwise, this book will approximate all real solutions with an error of *at most* 0.01.

TECHNOLOGY SUPPORT

For instructions on how to use the *zoom* and *trace* features and the *zero* or *root* feature, see Appendix A; for specific keystrokes, go to this textbook's *Online Study Center.*

Example 4   Approximating Solutions of an Equation Graphically

Use a graphing utility to approximate the solutions of

$$x^2 + 3 = 5x.$$

Solution

In general form, this equation is

$$x^2 - 5x + 3 = 0. \qquad \text{Equation in general form}$$

So, you can begin by graphing

$$y = x^2 - 5x + 3 \qquad \text{Function to be graphed}$$

as shown in Figure 2.12. This graph has two *x*-intercepts, and by using the *zoom* and *trace* features you can approximate the corresponding solutions to be $x \approx 0.70$ and $x \approx 4.30$, as shown in Figures 2.13 and 2.14.

TECHNOLOGY TIP

Remember that the more decimal places in the solution, the more accurate the solution is. You can reach the desired accuracy when zooming in as follows.

• To approximate the zero to the nearest hundredth, set the *x*-scale to 0.01.

• To approximate the zero to the nearest thousandth, set the *x*-scale to 0.001.

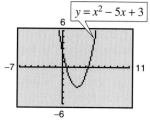

Figure 2.12

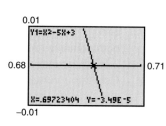

Figure 2.13

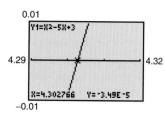

Figure 2.14

✓**CHECKPOINT**   Now try Exercise 41.

TECHNOLOGY TIP   Remember from Example 3 that the built-in *zero* and *root* features of a graphing utility will approximate solutions of equations or *x*-intercepts of graphs. If your graphing utility has such features, try using them to approximate the solutions in Example 4.

Points of Intersection of Two Graphs

An ordered pair that is a solution of two different equations is called a **point of intersection** of the graphs of the two equations. For instance, in Figure 2.15 you can see that the graphs of the following equations have two points of intersection.

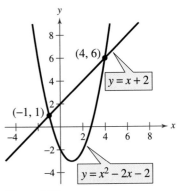

$y = x + 2$	Equation 1
$y = x^2 - 2x - 2$	Equation 2

The point $(-1, 1)$ is a solution of both equations, and the point $(4, 6)$ is a solution of both equations. To check this algebraically, substitute $x = -1$ and $x = 4$ into each equation.

Figure 2.15

Check that $(-1, 1)$ *is a solution.*

Equation 1: $y = -1 + 2 = 1$ Solution checks. ✓

Equation 2: $y = (-1)^2 - 2(-1) - 2 = 1$ Solution checks. ✓

Check that $(4, 6)$ *is a solution.*

Equation 1: $y = 4 + 2 = 6$ Solution checks. ✓

Equation 2: $y = (4)^2 - 2(4) - 2 = 6$ Solution checks. ✓

TECHNOLOGY SUPPORT

For instructions on how to use the *intersect* feature, see Appendix A; for specific keystrokes, go to this textbook's *Online Study Center*.

To find the points of intersection of the graphs of two equations, solve each equation for y (or x) and set the two results equal to each other. The resulting equation will be an equation in one variable, which can be solved using standard procedures, as shown in Example 5.

Example 5 Finding Points of Intersection

Find the points of intersection of the graphs of $2x - 3y = -2$ and $4x - y = 6$.

Algebraic Solution

To begin, solve each equation for y to obtain

$$y = \frac{2}{3}x + \frac{2}{3} \quad \text{and} \quad y = 4x - 6.$$

Next, set the two expressions for y equal to each other and solve the resulting equation for x, as follows.

$\frac{2}{3}x + \frac{2}{3} = 4x - 6$	Equate expressions for y.
$2x + 2 = 12x - 18$	Multiply each side by 3.
$-10x = -20$	Subtract $12x$ and 2 from each side.
$x = 2$	Divide each side by -10.

When $x = 2$, the y-value of each of the original equations is 2. So, the point of intersection is $(2, 2)$.

✓CHECKPOINT   Now try Exercise 65.

Graphical Solution

To begin, solve each equation for y to obtain $y_1 = \frac{2}{3}x + \frac{2}{3}$ and $y_2 = 4x - 6$. Then use a graphing utility to graph both equations in the same viewing window. In Figure 2.16, the graphs appear to have one point of intersection. Use the *intersect* feature of the graphing utility to approximate the point of intersection to be $(2, 2)$.

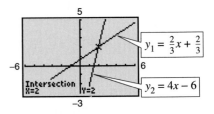

Figure 2.16

TECHNOLOGY TIP Another way to approximate the points of intersection of two graphs is to graph both equations with a graphing utility and use the *zoom* and *trace* features to find the point or points at which the two graphs intersect.

Example 6 Approximating Points of Intersection Graphically

Approximate the point(s) of intersection of the graphs of the following equations.

$$y = x^2 - 3x - 4 \qquad \text{Equation 1 (quadratic function)}$$

$$y = x^3 + 3x^2 - 2x - 1 \qquad \text{Equation 2 (cubic function)}$$

Solution

Begin by using a graphing utility to graph both functions, as shown in Figure 2.17. From this display, you can see that the two graphs have only one point of intersection. Then, using the *zoom* and *trace* features, approximate the point of intersection to be $(-2.17, 7.25)$, as shown in Figure 2.18.

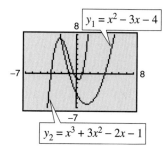

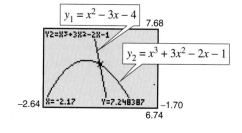

Figure 2.17   **Figure 2.18**

To test the reasonableness of this approximation, you can evaluate both functions at $x = -2.17$.

Quadratic Function:

$$y = (-2.17)^2 - 3(-2.17) - 4$$

$$\approx 7.22$$

Cubic Function:

$$y = (-2.17)^3 + 3(-2.17)^2 - 2(-2.17) - 1$$

$$\approx 7.25$$

Because both functions yield approximately the same y-value, you can conclude that the approximate coordinates of the point of intersection are $x \approx -2.17$ and $y \approx 7.25$.

✓CHECKPOINT   Now try Exercise 69.

TECHNOLOGY TIP

The table shows some points on the graphs of the equations in Example 5. Find the points of intersection of the graphs by finding the value(s) of x for which y_1 and y_2 are equal.

X	Y1	Y2
-1	0	-10
0	.66667	-6
1	1.3333	-2
2		2
3	2.6667	6
4	3.3333	10
5	4	14

X=2

Prerequisite Skills

Review the techniques for evaluating functions in Section 1.3, if you have difficulty with this example.

TECHNOLOGY TIP If you choose to use the *intersect* feature of your graphing utility to find the point of intersection of the graphs in Example 6, you will see that it yields the same result.

The method shown in Example 6 gives a nice graphical picture of the points of intersection of two graphs. However, for actual approximation purposes, it is better to use the algebraic procedure described in Example 5. That is, the point of intersection of $y = x^2 - 3x - 4$ and $y = x^3 + 3x^2 - 2x - 1$ coincides with the solution of the equation

$$x^3 + 3x^2 - 2x - 1 = x^2 - 3x - 4 \qquad \text{Equate } y\text{-values.}$$

$$x^3 + 2x^2 + x + 3 = 0. \qquad \text{Write in general form.}$$

By graphing $y = x^3 + 2x^2 + x + 3$ on a graphing utility and using the *zoom* and *trace* features (or the *zero* or *root* feature), you can approximate the solution of this equation to be $x \approx -2.17$.

Example 7   A Historical Look at Newspapers

Between 1990 and 2004, the number of morning newspapers M in the United States was *increasing* and the number of evening newspapers E was *decreasing*. Two models that approximate the numbers of newspapers are

$$M = 18.5t + 564, \quad 0 \le t \le 14 \qquad \text{Morning newspapers}$$

$$E = -30.9t + 1054, \quad 0 \le t \le 14 \qquad \text{Evening newspapers}$$

where t represents the year, with $t = 0$ corresponding to 1990. According to these two models, when would you expect the number of morning newspapers to have exceeded the number of evening newspapers?   (Source: Editor & Publisher Co.)

Algebraic Solution

Set the two expressions equal to each other and solve the resulting equation for t, as follows.

$$18.5t + 564 = -30.9t + 1054 \qquad \text{Equate expressions.}$$

$$49.4t + 564 = 1054 \qquad \text{Add } 30.9t \text{ to each side.}$$

$$49.4t = 490 \qquad \text{Subtract 564 from each side.}$$

$$t = \frac{490}{49.4} \qquad \text{Divide each side by 49.4.}$$

$$t \approx 9.92 \qquad \text{Use a calculator.}$$

So, from the given models, you would expect that the number of morning newspapers exceeded the number of evening newspapers sometime during 1999.

Graphical Solution

Use a graphing utility to graph both equations in the same viewing window. From Figure 2.19, the graphs appear to have one point of intersection. Use the *intersect* feature of the graphing utility to approximate the point of intersection to be (9.92, 747.50). So, you would expect that the number of morning newspapers exceeded the number of evening newspapers sometime during 1999.

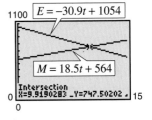

Figure 2.19

✓CHECKPOINT   Now try Exercise 81.

TECHNOLOGY TIP   If you choose to use the *zoom* and *trace* features of your graphing utility to find the point of intersection of the graphs in Example 7, you will see that these features yield the same result.

2.2 Exercises

Vocabulary Check

Fill in the blanks.

1. The points $(a, 0)$ and $(0, b)$ are called the _____ and _____ , respectively, of the graph of an equation.

2. A _____ of a function is a number a such that $f(a) = 0$.

3. An ordered pair that is a solution of two different equations is called a _____ of the graphs of the two equations.

In Exercises 1–10, find the x- and y-intercepts of the graph of the equation.

1. $y = x - 5$

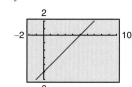

2. $y = -\frac{3}{4}x - 3$

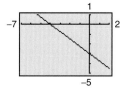

3. $y = x^2 + x - 2$

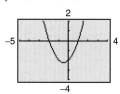

4. $y = 4 - x^2$

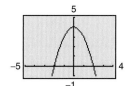

5. $y = x\sqrt{x + 2}$

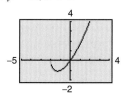

6. $y = -\frac{1}{2}x\sqrt{x + 3} + 1$

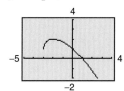

7. $y = \dfrac{4}{x}$

8. $y = \dfrac{3x - 1}{4x}$

9. $xy - 2y - x + 1 = 0$

10. $xy - x + 4y = 0$

Graphical Analysis **In Exercises 11–14, use a graphing utility to graph the equation and approximate any x- and y-intercepts. Verify your results algebraically.**

11. $y = 2(x - 1) - 4$

12. $y = 4(x + 3) - 2$

13. $y = 20 - (3x - 10)$

14. $y = 10 + 2(x - 2)$

In Exercises 15–20, the zero(s) of the function are given. Verify the zero(s) both algebraically and graphically.

Function	Zero(s)
15. $f(x) = 5(4 - x)$	$x = 4$
16. $f(x) = 3(x - 5) + 9$	$x = 2$
17. $f(x) = x^3 - 6x^2 + 5x$	$x = 0, 5, 1$
18. $f(x) = x^3 - 9x^2 + 18x$	$x = 0, 3, 6$
19. $f(x) = \dfrac{x + 2}{3} - \dfrac{x - 1}{5} - 1$	$x = 1$
20. $f(x) = x - 3 - \dfrac{10}{x}$	$x = -2, 5$

In Exercises 21–34, solve the equation algebraically. Then write the equation in the form $f(x) = 0$ and use a graphing utility to verify the algebraic solution.

21. $2.7x - 0.4x = 1.2$ 22. $3.5x - 8 = 0.5x$

23. $25(x - 3) = 12(x + 2) - 10$

24. $1200 = 300 + 2(x - 500)$

25. $\dfrac{3x}{2} + \dfrac{1}{4}(x - 2) = 10$ 26. $\dfrac{2x}{3} + \dfrac{1}{2}(x - 5) = 6$

27. $0.60x + 0.40(100 - x) = 1.2$

28. $0.75x + 0.2(80 - x) = 20$

29. $\dfrac{x - 3}{3} = \dfrac{3x - 5}{2}$ 30. $\dfrac{x - 3}{25} = \dfrac{x - 5}{12}$

31. $\dfrac{x - 5}{4} + \dfrac{x}{2} = 10$ 32. $\dfrac{x - 5}{10} - \dfrac{x - 3}{5} = 1$

33. $(x + 2)^2 = x^2 - 6x + 1$

34. $(x + 1)^2 + 2(x - 2) = (x + 1)(x - 2)$

In Exercises 35–54, use a graphing utility to approximate any solutions of the equation. [Remember to write the equation in the form $f(x) = 0$.]

35. $\frac{1}{4}(x^2 - 10x + 17) = 0$ 36. $-\frac{1}{2}(x^2 - 6x + 6) = 0$

37. $x^3 + x + 4 = 0$ 38. $\frac{1}{9}x^3 + x + 4 = 0$

39. $2x^3 - x^2 - 18x + 9 = 0$

40. $4x^3 + 12x^2 - 26x - 24 = 0$

41. $x^4 = 2x^3 + 1$

42. $x^5 = 3 + 2x^3$

43. $\dfrac{2}{x + 2} = 3$

44. $\dfrac{1}{x - 3} = 2$

45. $\dfrac{5}{x} = 1 + \dfrac{3}{x + 2}$

46. $\dfrac{3}{x} + 1 = \dfrac{3}{x - 1}$

47. $|x - 3| = 4$

48. $|x + 1| = 6$

49. $|3x - 2| - 1 = 4$

50. $|4x + 1| + 2 = 8$

51. $\sqrt{x - 2} = 3$

52. $\sqrt{x - 4} = 8$

53. $2 + \sqrt{x - 5} = 6$

54. $1 + \sqrt{x + 3} = 6$

55. *Exploration*

(a) Use a graphing utility to complete the table. Determine the interval in which the solution to the equation $3.2x - 5.8 = 0$ is located. Explain your reasoning.

x	-1	0	1	2	3	4
$3.2x - 5.8$						

(b) Use a graphing utility to complete the table. Determine the interval in which the solution to the equation $3.2x - 5.8 = 0$ is located. Explain how this process can be used to approximate the solution to any desired degree of accuracy.

x	1.5	1.6	1.7	1.8	1.9	2
$3.2x - 5.8$						

(c) Use a graphing utility to verify graphically the solution to $3.2x - 5.8 = 0$ found in part (b).

56. *Exploration* Use the procedure in Exercise 55 to approximate the solution of the equation $0.3(x - 1.5) - 2 = 0$ accurate to two decimal places.

In Exercises 57–64, determine any point(s) of intersection algebraically. Then verify your result numerically by creating a table of values for each function.

57. $y = 2 - x$
$y = 2x - 1$

58. $y = 7 - x$
$y = \frac{3}{2} - \frac{11}{2}x$

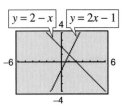

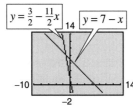

59. $2x + y = 6$
$-x + y = 0$

60. $x - y = -4$
$x + 2y = 5$

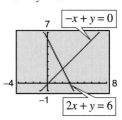

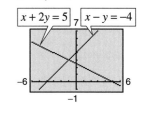

61. $x - y = 10$
$x + 2y = 4$

62. $4x - y = 4$
$x - 4y = 1$

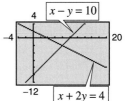

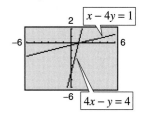

63. $y = x^2 - x + 1$
$y = x^2 + 2x + 4$

64. $y = -x^2 + 3x + 1$
$y = -x^2 - 2x - 4$

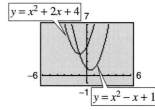

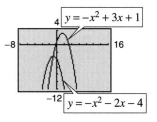

In Exercises 65–70, use a graphing utility to approximate any points of intersection of the graphs of the equations. Check your results algebraically.

65. $y = 9 - 2x$
$y = x - 3$

66. $x - 3y = -2$
$5x - 2y = 11$

67. $y = 4 - x^2$
$y = 2x - 1$

68. $x^3 - y = 3$
$2x + y = 5$

69. $y = 2x^2$
$y = x^4 - 2x^2$

70. $y = -x$
$y = 2x - x^2$

In Exercises 71 and 72, evaluate the expression in two ways. (a) Calculate entirely on your calculator by storing intermediate results and then rounding the final answer to two decimal places. (b) Round both the numerator and denominator to two decimal places before dividing, and then round the final answer to two decimal places. Does the method in part (b) decrease the accuracy? Explain.

71. $\dfrac{1 + 0.73205}{1 - 0.73205}$

72. $\dfrac{1 + 0.86603}{1 - 0.86603}$

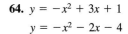

73. *Travel Time* On the first part of a 280-mile trip, a salesperson averaged 63 miles per hour. The salesperson averaged only 54 miles per hour on the last part of the trip because of an increased volume of traffic.

(a) Write the total time t for the trip as a function of the distance x traveled at an average speed of 63 miles per hour.

(b) Use a graphing utility to graph the time function. What is the domain of the function?

(c) Approximate the number of miles traveled at 63 miles per hour when the total time is 4 hours and 45 minutes.

74. *Production* An electronics company has fixed costs of $25,000 per month and a variable cost of $18.65 per 13-inch TV/VCR combination manufactured. (*Fixed costs are those that occur regardless of the level of production.*)

(a) Write the total monthly costs C as a function of the number of units x produced.

(b) Use a graphing utility to graph the cost function.

(c) Use the graph from part (b) to approximate the number of units that can be produced per month if total costs cannot exceed $200,000. Verify algebraically. Is this problem better solved algebraically or graphically? Explain.

75. *Mixture Problem* A 55-gallon barrel contains a mixture with a concentration of 33% sodium chloride. You remove x gallons of this mixture and replace it with 100% sodium chloride.

(a) Write the amount A of sodium chloride in the final mixture as a function of x.

(b) Use a graphing utility to graph the concentration function. What is the domain of the function?

(c) Approximate (accurate to one decimal place) the value of x when the final mixture is 60% sodium chloride.

76. *Geometry* A rectangular horse corral with a perimeter of 230 meters has a length of x.

(a) Draw a diagram that gives a visual representation of the problem.

(b) Write the corral's area A as a function of x.

(c) Use a graphing utility to graph the area function. What is the domain of the function?

(d) Approximate (accurate to one decimal place) the dimensions of the corral when its area is 2000 square meters.

Geometry **In Exercises 77 and 78, (a) write a function for the area of the region, (b) use a graphing utility to graph the function, and (c) approximate the value of x when the area of the region is 200 square units.**

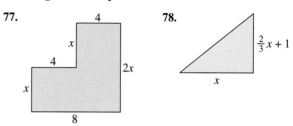

77.   78.

79. *Income Tax* The following information describes a possible negative income tax for a family consisting of two adults and two children. The plan would guarantee the poor a minimum income while encouraging a family to increase its private income $(0 \le x \le 20{,}000)$. (A *subsidy* is a grant of money.)

Family's earned income: $I = x$

Subsidy: $S = 10{,}000 - \frac{1}{2}x$

Total income: $T = I + S$

(a) Write the total income T in terms of x.

(b) Use a graphing utility to find the earned income x when the subsidy is $6600. Verify your answer algebraically.

(c) Use a graphing utility to find the earned income x when the total income is $13,800. Verify your answer algebraically.

(d) Find the subsidy S graphically when the total income is $12,500.

80. *Hospitals* The numbers y of hospitals in the United States from 1990 to 2003 can be modeled by the linear model $y = -77.6t + 6671, 0 \le t \le 13$, where t is the year, with $t = 0$ corresponding to 1990. (Source: Health Forum)

(a) According to the model, when did the number of hospitals drop to 6000?

(b) What is the slope of the model and what does it tell you about the number of hospitals in the United States?

(c) Do you think the model can be used to predict the numbers of hospitals in the Unites States for years beyond 2003? If so, for what time period? Explain.

(d) Explain, both algebraically and graphically, how you could find when the number of hospitals drops to 5000 according to the model.

81. *State Populations* The populations (in thousands) of South Carolina S and Arizona A from 1980 to 2004 can be modeled by

$$S = 45.2t + 3087, \quad 0 \le t \le 24$$

$$A = 128.2t + 2533, \quad 0 \le t \le 24$$

where t represents the year, with $t = 0$ corresponding to 1980. (Source: U.S. Census Bureau)

(a) Use a graphing utility to graph each model in the same viewing window over the appropriate domain. Approximate the point of intersection. Round your result to one decimal place. Explain the meaning of the coordinates of the point.

(b) Find the point of intersection algebraically. Round your result to one decimal place. What does the point of intersection represent?

(c) Explain the meaning of the slopes of both models and what it tells you about the population growth rates.

(d) Use the models to estimate the population of each state in 2010. Do the values seem reasonable? Explain.

82. *Geometry* Consider the swimming pool in the figure. (When finding its volume, use the fact that the volume is the area of the region on the vertical sidewall times the width of the pool.)

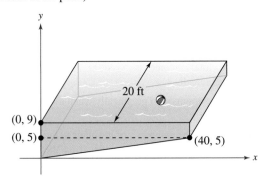

(a) Find the volume of the pool.

(b) Find an equation of the line representing the base of the pool.

(c) The depth of the water at the deep end of the pool is d feet. Show that the volume of water is

$$V(d) = \begin{cases} 80d^2, & 0 \le d \le 5 \\ 800d - 2000, & 5 < d \le 9 \end{cases}.$$

(d) Graph the volume function.

(e) Use a graphing utility to complete the table.

d	3	5	7	8
V				

(f) Approximate the depth of the water at the deep end when the volume is 4800 cubic feet.

(g) How many gallons of water are in the pool? (There are 7.48 gallons of water in 1 cubic foot.)

Synthesis

True or False? **In Exercises 83–85, determine whether the statement is true or false. Justify your answer.**

83. To find the y-intercept of a graph, let $x = 0$ and solve the equation for y.

84. Every linear equation has at least one y-intercept or x-intercept.

85. Two linear equations can have either one point of intersection or no points of intersection.

86. *Writing* You are solving the equation

$$\frac{x}{x-1} - \frac{99}{100} = 0$$

for x, and you obtain $x = -99.1$ as your solution. Substituting this value back into the equation produces

$$\frac{-99.1}{-99.1-1} - \frac{99}{100} = 0.00000999 = 9.99 \times 10^{-6} \approx 0.$$

Is -99.1 a good approximation of the solution? Write a short paragraph explaining why or why not.

Exploration **In Exercises 87–90, use the table to solve each linear equation where $y_1 = f(x)$ and $y_2 = g(x)$.**

X	Y1	Y2
-2	-15	0
-1	-12	2
0	-9	4
1	-6	6
2	-3	8
3	0	10
4	3	12

X= -2

87. $f(x) = 0$ **88.** $g(x) = 0$

89. $g(x) = -f(x)$ **90.** $g(x) = 4f(x)$

Skills Review

In Exercises 91–94, rationalize the denominator.

91. $\dfrac{12}{5\sqrt{3}}$ **92.** $\dfrac{4}{\sqrt{10}-2}$

93. $\dfrac{3}{8+\sqrt{11}}$ **94.** $\dfrac{14}{3\sqrt{10}-1}$

In Exercises 95–98, find the product.

95. $(x+6)(3x-5)$ **96.** $(3x+13)(4x-7)$

97. $(2x-9)(2x+9)$ **98.** $(4x+1)^2$

2.3   Complex Numbers

The Imaginary Unit *i*

Some quadratic equations have no real solutions. For instance, the quadratic equation $x^2 + 1 = 0$ has no real solution because there is no real number x that can be squared to produce -1. To overcome this deficiency, mathematicians created an expanded system of numbers using the **imaginary unit *i*,** defined as

$$i = \sqrt{-1} \qquad \text{Imaginary unit}$$

where $i^2 = -1$. By adding real numbers to real multiples of this imaginary unit, you obtain the set of **complex numbers.** Each complex number can be written in the **standard form** $a + bi$. For instance, the standard form of the complex number $\sqrt{-9} - 5$ is $-5 + 3i$ because

$$\sqrt{-9} - 5 = \sqrt{3^2(-1)} - 5 = 3\sqrt{-1} - 5 = 3i - 5 = -5 + 3i.$$

In the standard form $a + bi$, the real number a is called the **real part** of the **complex number** $a + bi$, and the number bi (where b is a real number) is called the **imaginary part** of the complex number.

Definition of a Complex Number

If a and b are real numbers, the number $a + bi$ is a **complex number,** and it is said to be written in **standard form.** If $b = 0$, the number $a + bi = a$ is a real number. If $b \neq 0$, the number $a + bi$ is called an **imaginary number.** A number of the form bi, where $b \neq 0$, is called a **pure imaginary number.**

The set of real numbers is a subset of the set of complex numbers, as shown in Figure 2.20. This is true because every real number a can be written as a complex number using $b = 0$. That is, for every real number a, you can write $a = a + 0i$.

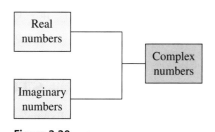

Figure 2.20

Equality of Complex Numbers

Two complex numbers $a + bi$ and $c + di$, written in standard form, are equal to each other

$$a + bi = c + di \qquad \text{Equality of two complex numbers}$$

if and only if $a = c$ and $b = d$.

What you should learn

- Use the imaginary unit *i* to write complex numbers.
- Add, subtract, and multiply complex numbers.
- Use complex conjugates to write the quotient of two complex numbers in standard form.
- Plot complex numbers in the complex plane.

Why you should learn it

Complex numbers are used to model numerous aspects of the natural world, such as the impedance of an electrical circuit, as shown in Exercises 79 and 80 on page 194.

Phil Degginger/Getty Images

55. $\dfrac{i}{3-2i} + \dfrac{2i}{3+8i}$ **56.** $\dfrac{1+i}{i} - \dfrac{3}{4-i}$

In Exercises 57–62, simplify the complex number and write it in standard form.

57. $-6i^3 + i^2$ **58.** $4i^2 - 2i^3$

59. $\left(\sqrt{-75}\right)^3$ **60.** $\left(\sqrt{-2}\right)^6$

61. $\dfrac{1}{i^3}$ **62.** $\dfrac{1}{(2i)^3}$

63. Cube each complex number. What do you notice?

   (a) 2 (b) $-1 + \sqrt{3}i$ (c) $-1 - \sqrt{3}i$

64. Raise each complex number to the fourth power and simplify.

   (a) 2 (b) -2 (c) $2i$ (d) $-2i$

In Exercises 65–70, determine the complex number shown in the complex plane.

65.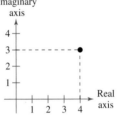

66.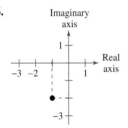

67.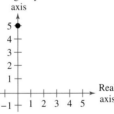

68.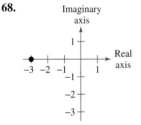

69.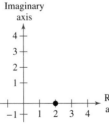

70.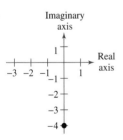

In Exercises 71–76, plot the complex number in the complex plane.

71. $4 - 5i$ **72.** $-7 + 2i$

73. $3i$ **74.** $-5i$

75. 1 **76.** -6

Fractals   In Exercises 77 and 78, find the first six terms of the sequence given on page 191. From the terms, do you think the given complex number is in the Mandelbrot Set? Explain your reasoning.

77. $c = \frac{1}{2}i$ **78.** $c = 2$

Impedance   In Exercises 79 and 80, use the following information. The opposition to current in an electrical circuit is called its impedance. The impedance z in a parallel circuit with two pathways satisfies the equation $1/z = 1/z_1 + 1/z_2$ where z_1 is the impedance (in ohms) of pathway 1 and z_2 is the impedance (in ohms) of pathway 2. Use the table to determine the impedance of the parallel circuit. (*Hint:* You can find the impedance of each pathway in a parallel circuit by adding the impedances of all components in the pathway.)

	Resistor	Inductor	Capacitor
Symbol	—⋀⋀⋀— $a\ \Omega$	—⟋⟋⟋— $b\ \Omega$	—⊣⊢— $c\ \Omega$
Impedance	a	bi	$-ci$

79.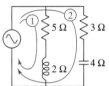

80.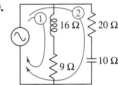

Synthesis

True or False?   In Exercises 81–86, determine whether the statement is true or false. Justify your answer.

81. There is no complex number that is equal to its conjugate.

82. $i^{44} + i^{150} - i^{74} - i^{109} + i^{61} = -1$

83. The sum of two imaginary numbers is always an imaginary number.

84. The product of two imaginary numbers is always an imaginary number.

85. The conjugate of the product of two complex numbers is equal to the product of the conjugates of the two complex numbers.

86. The conjugate of the sum of two complex numbers is equal to the sum of the conjugates of the two complex numbers.

Skills Review

In Exercises 87–90, perform the operation and write the result in standard form.

87. $(4x - 5)(4x + 5)$ **88.** $(x + 2)^3$

89. $\left(3x - \frac{1}{2}\right)(x + 4)$ **90.** $(2x - 5)^2$

2.4   Solving Quadratic Equations Algebraically

Quadratic Equations

A **quadratic equation in x** is an equation that can be written in the general form

$$ax^2 + bx + c = 0$$

where a, b, and c are real numbers with $a \neq 0$. A quadratic equation in x is also known as a **second-degree polynomial equation in x.** You should be familiar with the following four methods for solving quadratic equations.

Solving a Quadratic Equation

Factoring: If $ab = 0$, then $a = 0$ or $b = 0$.   Zero-Factor Property

Example: $x^2 - x - 6 = 0$

$$(x - 3)(x + 2) = 0$$

$$x - 3 = 0 \implies x = 3$$

$$x + 2 = 0 \implies x = -2$$

Extracting Square Roots: If $u^2 = c$, then $u = \pm\sqrt{c}$.

Example: $(x + 3)^2 = 16$

$$x + 3 = \pm 4$$

$$x = -3 \pm 4$$

$$x = 1 \quad \text{or} \quad x = -7$$

Completing the Square: If $x^2 + bx = c$, then

$$x^2 + bx + \left(\frac{b}{2}\right)^2 = c + \left(\frac{b}{2}\right)^2$$

$$\left(x + \frac{b}{2}\right)^2 = c + \frac{b^2}{4}.$$

Example: $x^2 + 6x = 5$

$$x^2 + 6x + 3^2 = 5 + 3^2$$

$$(x + 3)^2 = 14$$

$$x + 3 = \pm\sqrt{14}$$

$$x = -3 \pm \sqrt{14}$$

Quadratic Formula: If $ax^2 + bx + c = 0$, then $x = \dfrac{-b \pm \sqrt{b^2 - 4ac}}{2a}$.

Example: $2x^2 + 3x - 1 = 0$

$$x = \frac{-3 \pm \sqrt{3^2 - 4(2)(-1)}}{2(2)} = \frac{-3 \pm \sqrt{17}}{4}$$

What you should learn

- Solve quadratic equations by factoring.
- Solve quadratic equations by extracting square roots.
- Solve quadratic equations by completing the square.
- Use the Quadratic Formula to solve quadratic equations.
- Use quadratic equations to model and solve real-life problems.

Why you should learn it

Knowing how to solve quadratic equations algebraically can help you solve real-life problems, such as Exercise 86 on page 207, where you determine the annual per capita consumption of bottled water.

Myrleen Ferguson Cate/PhotoEdit

Example 1 Solving a Quadratic Equation by Factoring

Solve each quadratic equation by factoring.

a. $6x^2 = 3x$ **b.** $9x^2 - 6x + 1 = 0$

Solution

a.

$6x^2 = 3x$	Write original equation.
$6x^2 - 3x = 0$	Write in general form.
$3x(2x - 1) = 0$	Factor.
$3x = 0 \implies x = 0$	Set 1st factor equal to 0.
$2x - 1 = 0 \implies x = \frac{1}{2}$	Set 2nd factor equal to 0.

b.

$9x^2 - 6x + 1 = 0$	Write original equation.
$(3x - 1)^2 = 0$	Factor.
$3x - 1 = 0 \implies x = \frac{1}{3}$	Set repeated factor equal to 0.

Throughout the text, when solving equations, be sure to check your solutions either *algebraically* by substituting in the original equation or *graphically*.

Check

a.

$6x^2 = 3x$	Write original equation.
$6(0)^2 \stackrel{?}{=} 3(0)$	Substitute 0 for x.
$0 = 0$	Solution checks. ✓
$6\left(\frac{1}{2}\right)^2 \stackrel{?}{=} 3\left(\frac{1}{2}\right)$	Substitute $\frac{1}{2}$ for x.
$\frac{6}{4} = \frac{3}{2}$	Solution checks. ✓

b.

$9x^2 - 6x + 1 = 0$	Write original equation.
$9\left(\frac{1}{3}\right)^2 - 6\left(\frac{1}{3}\right) + 1 \stackrel{?}{=} 0$	Substitute $\frac{1}{3}$ for x.
$1 - 2 + 1 \stackrel{?}{=} 0$	Simplify.
$0 = 0$	Solution checks. ✓

Similarly, you can check your solutions graphically using the graphs in Figure 2.26.

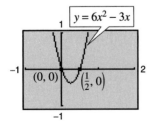

(a)

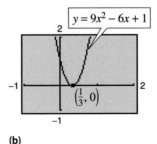

(b)

Figure 2.26

 CHECKPOINT   Now try Exercise 7.

STUDY TIP

Quadratic equations always have two solutions. From the graph in Figure 2.26(b), it looks like there is only one solution to the equation $9x^2 - 6x + 1 = 0$.

Because the equation is a perfect square trinomial, its two factors are identical. As a result, the equation has two *repeated* solutions.

Solving a quadratic equation by extracting square roots is an efficient method to use when the quadratic equation can be written in the form $ax^2 + c = 0$.

Example 2   Extracting Square Roots

Solve each quadratic equation.

a. $4x^2 = 12$ **b.** $(x - 3)^2 = 7$ **c.** $(2x - 1)^2 = -9$

Solution

a. $4x^2 = 12$ Write original equation.

    $x^2 = 3$ Divide each side by 4.

    $x = \pm\sqrt{3}$ Take square root of each side.

This equation has two solutions: $x = \pm\sqrt{3} \approx \pm 1.73$.

b. $(x - 3)^2 = 7$ Write original equation.

    $x - 3 = \pm\sqrt{7}$ Take square root of each side.

    $x = 3 \pm\sqrt{7}$ Add 3 to each side.

This equation has two solutions: $x = 3 + \sqrt{7} \approx 5.65$ and $x = 3 - \sqrt{7} \approx 0.35$.

c. $(2x - 1)^2 = -9$ Write original equation.

    $2x - 1 = \pm\sqrt{-9}$ Take square root of each side.

    $2x - 1 = \pm 3i$ Write in i-form.

    $x = \frac{1}{2} \pm \frac{3}{2}i$ Solve for x.

This equation has two complex solutions: $x = \frac{1}{2} \pm \frac{3}{2}i$.

The graphs of $y = 4x^2 - 12$, $y = (x - 3)^2 - 7$, and $y = (2x - 1)^2 + 9$, shown in Figure 2.27, verify the solutions.

STUDY TIP

When you take the square root of a variable expression, you must account for both positive and negative solutions.

TECHNOLOGY TIP

Note that the solutions shown in Example 2 are listed in *exact* form and as decimal approximations. Most graphing utilities produce decimal approximations of solutions rather than exact forms. For instance, if you solve the equations in Example 2 using a graphing utility, you will obtain $x \approx \pm 1.73$ in part (a) and $x \approx 5.65$ and $x \approx 0.35$ in part (b). Some graphing utilities have symbolic algebra programs that *can* list the exact form of a solution.

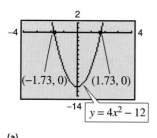

(a)

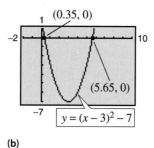

(b)

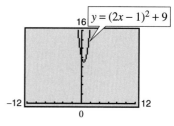

(c)

Figure 2.27

✓**CHECKPOINT**   Now try Exercise 19.

Completing the square is best suited for quadratic equations in general form $ax^2 + bx + c = 0$ with $a = 1$ and b an even number (see page 195). If the leading coefficient of the quadratic is not 1, divide each side of the equation by this coefficient before completing the square, as shown in Example 4.

Example 3   Completing the Square: Leading Coefficient Is 1

Solve $x^2 + 2x - 6 = 0$ by completing the square.

Solution

$$x^2 + 2x - 6 = 0 \qquad \text{Write original equation.}$$

$$x^2 + 2x = 6 \qquad \text{Add 6 to each side.}$$

$$x^2 + 2x + 1^2 = 6 + 1^2 \qquad \text{Add } 1^2 \text{ to each side.}$$

(Half of 2)²

$$(x + 1)^2 = 7 \qquad \text{Simplify.}$$

$$x + 1 = \pm\sqrt{7} \qquad \text{Take square root of each side.}$$

$$x = -1 \pm \sqrt{7} \qquad \text{Solutions}$$

Using a calculator, the two solutions are $x \approx 1.65$ and $x \approx -3.65$, which agree with the graphical solutions shown in Figure 2.28.

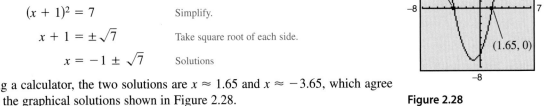

Figure 2.28

✔**CHECKPOINT**   Now try Exercise 23.

Example 4   Completing the Square: Leading Coefficient Is Not 1

Solve $2x^2 + 8x + 3 = 0$ by completing the square.

Solution

$$2x^2 + 8x + 3 = 0 \qquad \text{Write original equation.}$$

$$2x^2 + 8x = -3 \qquad \text{Subtract 3 from each side.}$$

$$x^2 + 4x = -\frac{3}{2} \qquad \text{Divide each side by 2.}$$

$$x^2 + 4x + 2^2 = -\frac{3}{2} + 2^2 \qquad \text{Add } 2^2 \text{ to each side.}$$

(Half of 4)²

$$(x + 2)^2 = \frac{5}{2} \qquad \text{Simplify.}$$

$$x + 2 = \pm\sqrt{\frac{5}{2}} \qquad \text{Take square root of each side.}$$

$$x + 2 = \pm\frac{\sqrt{10}}{2} \qquad \text{Rationalize denominator.}$$

$$x = -2 \pm \frac{\sqrt{10}}{2} \qquad \text{Solutions}$$

Using a calculator, the two solutions are $x \approx -0.42$ and $x \approx -3.58$, which agree with the graphical solutions shown in Figure 2.29.

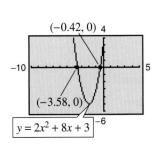

Figure 2.29

✔**CHECKPOINT**   Now try Exercise 27.

Example 5   Completing the Square: Leading Coefficient Is Not 1

Solve $3x^2 - 4x - 5 = 0$ by completing the square.

Solution

$$3x^2 - 4x - 5 = 0 \qquad \text{Write original equation.}$$

$$3x^2 - 4x = 5 \qquad \text{Add 5 to each side.}$$

$$x^2 - \frac{4}{3}x = \frac{5}{3} \qquad \text{Divide each side by 3.}$$

$$x^2 - \frac{4}{3}x + \left(-\frac{2}{3}\right)^2 = \frac{5}{3} + \left(-\frac{2}{3}\right)^2 \qquad \text{Add } \left(-\frac{2}{3}\right)^2 \text{ to each side.}$$

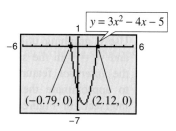

$$\left(\text{Half of } -\frac{4}{3}\right)^2$$

$$\left(x - \frac{2}{3}\right)^2 = \frac{19}{9} \qquad \text{Simplify.}$$

$$x - \frac{2}{3} = \pm\frac{\sqrt{19}}{3} \qquad \text{Take square root of each side.}$$

$$x = \frac{2}{3} \pm \frac{\sqrt{19}}{3} \qquad \text{Solutions}$$

Using a calculator, the two solutions are $x \approx 2.12$ and $x \approx -0.79$, which agree with the graphical solutions shown in Figure 2.30.

$$y = 3x^2 - 4x - 5$$

(−0.79, 0)   (2.12, 0)

Figure 2.30

✓CHECKPOINT   Now try Exercise 31.

Often in mathematics you are taught the long way of solving a problem first. Then, the longer method is used to develop shorter techniques. The long way stresses understanding and the short way stresses efficiency.

For instance, you can think of completing the square as a "long way" of solving a quadratic equation. When you use the method of completing the square to solve a quadratic equation, you must complete the square for *each* equation separately. In the derivation on the following page, you complete the square *once* in a general setting to obtain the Quadratic Formula, which is a shortcut for solving a quadratic equation.

Applications

A common application of quadratic equations involves an object that is falling (or projected into the air). The general equation that gives the height of such an object is called a **position equation,** and on *Earth's* surface it has the form

$$s = -16t^2 + v_0 t + s_0.$$

In this equation, s represents the height of the object (in feet), v_0 represents the initial velocity of the object (in feet per second), s_0 represents the initial height of the object (in feet), and t represents the time (in seconds). Note that this position equation ignores air resistance.

STUDY TIP

In the position equation

$$s = -16t^2 + v_0 t + s_0$$

the initial velocity v_0 is positive when the object is rising and negative when the object is falling.

Example 9   Falling Time

A construction worker on the 24th floor of a building project (see Figure 2.34) accidentally drops a wrench and yells, "Look out below!" Could a person at ground level hear this warning in time to get out of the way?

Solution

Assume that each floor of the building is 10 feet high, so that the wrench is dropped from a height of 235 feet (the construction worker's hand is 5 feet below the ceiling of the 24th floor). Because sound travels at about 1100 feet per second, it follows that a person at ground level hears the warning within 1 second of the time the wrench is dropped. To set up a mathematical model for the height of the wrench, use the position equation

$$s = -16t^2 + v_0 t + s_0. \qquad \text{Position equation}$$

Because the object is dropped rather than thrown, the initial velocity is $v_0 = 0$ feet per second. So, with an initial height of $s_0 = 235$ feet, you have the model

$$s = -16t^2 + (0)t + 235 = -16t^2 + 235.$$

After falling for 1 second, the height of the wrench is $-16(1)^2 + 235 = 219$ feet. After falling for 2 seconds, the height of the wrench is $-16(2)^2 + 235 = 171$ feet. To find the number of seconds it takes the wrench to hit the ground, let the height s be zero and solve the equation for t.

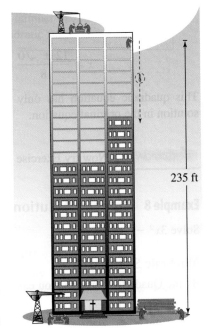

235 ft

Figure 2.34

$$s = -16t^2 + 235 \qquad \text{Write position equation.}$$

$$0 = -16t^2 + 235 \qquad \text{Substitute 0 for } s.$$

$$16t^2 = 235 \qquad \text{Add } 16t^2 \text{ to each side.}$$

$$t^2 = \frac{235}{16} \qquad \text{Divide each side by 16.}$$

$$t = \frac{\sqrt{235}}{4} \approx 3.83 \qquad \text{Extract positive square root.}$$

The wrench will take about 3.83 seconds to hit the ground. If the person hears the warning 1 second after the wrench is dropped, the person still has almost 3 more seconds to get out of the way.

✓CHECKPOINT   Now try Exercise 81.

Example 10   Quadratic Modeling: Internet Use

From 1996 to 2003, the numbers of hours h spent annually per person using the Internet in the United States closely followed the quadratic model

$$h = -0.81t^2 + 39.5t - 200, \quad 6 \le t \le 13$$

where t represents the year, with $t = 6$ corresponding to 1996. The numbers of hours per year are shown graphically in Figure 2.35. According to this model, in which year did the number of hours spent per person reach or surpass 150? (Source: Veronis Suhler Stevenson)

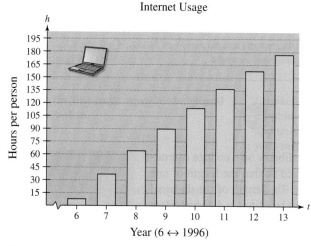

Internet Usage

Figure 2.35

Solution

To find when the number of hours spent per person reached 150, you need to solve the equation

$$-0.81t^2 + 39.5t - 200 = 150.$$

To begin, write the equation in general form.

$$-0.81t^2 + 39.5t - 350 = 0$$

Then apply the Quadratic Formula.

$$t = \frac{-39.5 \pm \sqrt{(39.5)^2 - 4(-0.81)(-350)}}{2(-0.81)}$$

$$\approx 11.64 \text{ or } 37.13$$

Choose the smaller value $t = 11.64$. Because $t = 6$ corresponds to 1996, it follows that $t = 11.64$ must correspond to some time in 2001. So, the number of hours spent annually per person using the Internet reached 150 during 2001.

✔CHECKPOINT   Now try Exercise 85.

TECHNOLOGY TIP   You can solve Example 10 with your graphing utility by graphing the two functions $y_1 = -0.81x^2 + 39.5x - 200$ and $y_2 = 150$ in the same viewing window and finding their point of intersection. You should obtain $x \approx 11.64$, which verifies the answer obtained algebraically.

In Ex
any, o
61.

—

—

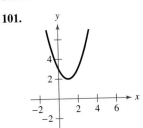
y

63.

—

—

y

65.

—
−1

y

Think
equati
correc

67. −

69. −

71. 5,

73. 1

75. 2

77. Ge
loi
flo

(a)

(b)

(c)

78. Ge
squ
of
be
ba:

89. Flying Speed Two planes leave simultaneously from Chicago's O'Hare Airport, one flying due north and the other due east. The northbound plane is flying 50 miles per hour faster than the eastbound plane. After 3 hours the planes are 2440 miles apart. Find the speed of each plane. (*Hint:* Draw a diagram.)

90. Flying Distance A chartered airplane flies to three cities whose locations form the vertices of a right triangle (see figure). The total flight distance (from Indianapolis to Peoria to Springfield and back to Indianapolis) is approximately 448 miles. It is 195 miles between Indianapolis and Peoria. Approximate the other two distances.

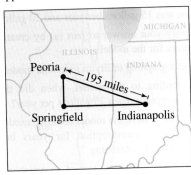

Synthesis

True or False? **In Exercises 91–94, determine whether the statement is true or false. Justify your answer.**

91. The quadratic equation $-3x^2 - x = 10$ has two real solutions.

92. If $(2x - 3)(x + 5) = 8$, then $2x - 3 = 8$ or $x + 5 = 8$.

93. A quadratic equation with real coefficients can have one real solution and one imaginary solution.

94. A quadratic equation with real coefficients can have one repeated imaginary solution.

95. Exploration Solve $3(x + 4)^2 + (x + 4) - 2 = 0$ in two ways.

(a) Let $u = x + 4$, and solve the resulting equation for u. Then find the corresponding values of x that are the solutions of the original equation.

(b) Expand and collect like terms in the original equation, and solve the resulting equation for x.

(c) Which method is easier? Explain.

96. Exploration Given that a and b are nonzero real numbers, determine the solutions of the equations.

(a) $ax^2 + bx = 0$ (b) $ax^2 - ax = 0$

97. Proof Given that the solutions of a quadratic equation are $x = \left(-b \pm \sqrt{b^2 - 4ac}\right)/(2a)$, show that the sum of the solutions is $S = -b/a$.

98. Proof Given that the solutions of a quadratic equation are $x = \left(-b \pm \sqrt{b^2 - 4ac}\right)/(2a)$, show that the product of the solutions is $P = c/a$.

99. Writing On a graphing utility, store the value 5 in A, -2 in B, and 1 in C. Use the graphing utility to graph $y = C(x - A)(x - B)$. Explain how the values of A and B can be determined from the graph. Now store any other nonzero value in C. Does the value of C affect the x-intercepts of the graph? Explain. Find values of A, B, and C such that the graph opens downward and has x-intercepts at $(-5, 0)$ and $(0, 0)$. Summarize your findings.

100. Exploration Is it possible for a quadratic equation to have only one x-intercept? Explain.

Library of Parent Functions **In Exercises 101 and 102, determine which function the graph represents.**

101.   102.

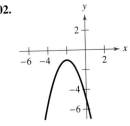

101.	102.
(a) $y = (x + 1)^2 + 2$	(a) $y = -(x - 2)^2 - 1$
(b) $y = (x - 2)^2 + 1$	(b) $y = -(x + 2)^2 + 1$
(c) $y = (x + 2)^2 + 1$	(c) $y = -x^2 - 2x + 1$
(d) $y = x^2 - x + 2$	(d) $y = -(x + 2)^2 - 1$
(e) $y = (x - 1)^2 + 2$	(e) $y = -(x - 1)^2 + 2$

Skills Review

In Exercises 103–106, completely factor the expression over the real numbers.

103. $x^5 - 27x^2$ **104.** $x^3 - 5x^2 - 14x$

105. $x^3 + 5x^2 - 2x - 10$ **106.** $5(x + 5)x^{1/3} + 4x^{4/3}$

In Exercises 107–112, determine whether y is a function of x.

107. $5x + 8y = -1$ **108.** $-x^2 + y^2 = 2$

109. $x + y^2 = 10$ **110.** $-2y = \sqrt{x + 6}$

111. $y = |x - 3|$ **112.** $|y| = 1 - x$

113. Make a Decision To work an extended application analyzing the population of the United States, visit this textbooks's *Online Study Center*. (Data Source: U.S. Census Bureau)

2.5 Solving Other Types of Equations Algebraically

Polynomial Equations

In this section, the techniques for solving equations are extended to nonlinear and nonquadratic equations. At this point in the text, you have only four basic methods for solving nonlinear equations—*factoring*, *extracting square roots*, *completing the square*, and the *Quadratic Formula*. So the main goal of this section is to learn to *rewrite* nonlinear equations in a form to which you can apply one of these methods.

Example 1 shows how to use factoring to solve a **polynomial equation,** which is an equation that can be written in the general form

$$a_n x^n + a_{n-1} x^{n-1} + \cdots + a_2 x^2 + a_1 x + a_0 = 0.$$

Example 1 Solving a Polynomial Equation by Factoring

Solve $3x^4 = 48x^2$.

Solution

First write the polynomial equation in general form with zero on one side, factor the other side, and then set each factor equal to zero and solve.

$3x^4 = 48x^2$	Write original equation.
$3x^4 - 48x^2 = 0$	Write in general form.
$3x^2(x^2 - 16) = 0$	Factor out common factor.
$3x^2(x + 4)(x - 4) = 0$	Factor completely.
$3x^2 = 0 \implies x = 0$	Set 1st factor equal to 0.
$x + 4 = 0 \implies x = -4$	Set 2nd factor equal to 0.
$x - 4 = 0 \implies x = 4$	Set 3rd factor equal to 0.

You can check these solutions by substituting in the original equation, as follows.

Check

$3(0)^4 \overset{?}{=} 48(0)^2$	Substitute 0 for x.
$0 = 0$	0 checks. ✓
$3(-4)^4 \overset{?}{=} 48(-4)^2$	Substitute -4 for x.
$768 = 768$	-4 checks. ✓
$3(4)^4 \overset{?}{=} 48(4)^2$	Substitute 4 for x.
$768 = 768$	4 checks. ✓

So, you can conclude that the solutions are $x = 0$, $x = -4$, and $x = 4$.

✓*CHECKPOINT*   Now try Exercise 1.

What you should learn

- Solve polynomial equations of degree three or greater.
- Solve equations involving radicals.
- Solve equations involving fractions or absolute values.
- Use polynomial equations and equations involving radicals to model and to solve real-life problems.

Why you should learn it

Polynomial equations, radical equations, and absolute value equations can be used to model and solve real-life problems. For instance, in Exercise 79 on page 217, a radical equation can be used to model the total monthly cost of airplane flights between Chicago and Denver.

© Ralf-Finn Hestoft/Corbis

STUDY TIP

A common mistake that is made in solving an equation such as that in Example 1 is to divide each side of the equation by the variable factor x^2. This loses the solution $x = 0$. When solving an equation, always write the equation in general form, then factor the equation and set each factor equal to zero. Do not divide each side of an equation by a variable factor in an attempt to simplify the equation.

80. *Demand* The demand equation for a video game is modeled by

$$p = 40 - \sqrt{0.01x + 1}$$

where x is the number of units demanded per day and p is the price per unit. Approximate the demand when the price is $37.55.

81. *Demand* The demand equation for a high-definition television set is modeled by

$$p = 800 - \sqrt{0.01x + 1}$$

where x is the number of units demanded per month and p is the price per unit. Approximate the demand when the price is $750.

82. *Baseball* A baseball diamond has the shape of a square in which the distance from home plate to second base is approximately $127\frac{1}{2}$ feet. Approximate the distance between the bases.

83. *Saturated Steam* The temperature T (in degrees Fahrenheit) of saturated steam increases as pressure increases. This relationship is approximated by the model

$$T = 75.82 - 2.11x + 43.51\sqrt{x}, \quad 5 \le x \le 40$$

where x is the absolute pressure (in pounds per square inch).

(a) Use a graphing utility to graph the function over the specified domain.

(b) The temperature of steam at sea level ($x = 14.696$) is 212°F. Evaluate the model at this pressure and verify the result graphically.

(c) Use the model to approximate the pressure for a steam temperature of 240°F.

84. *Meteorology* A meteorologist is positioned 100 feet from the point at which a weather balloon is launched. When the balloon is at height h, the distance d (in feet) between the meteorologist and the balloon is $d = \sqrt{100^2 + h^2}$.

(a) Use a graphing utility to graph the equation. Use the *trace* feature to approximate the value of h when $d = 200$.

(b) Complete the table. Use the table to approximate the value of h when $d = 200$.

h	160	165	170	175	180	185
d						

(c) Find h algebraically when $d = 200$.

(d) Compare the results of each method. In each case, what information did you gain that wasn't revealed by another solution method?

Synthesis

True or False? **In Exercises 85 and 86, determine whether the statement is true or false. Justify your answer.**

85. An equation can never have more than one extraneous solution.

86. When solving an absolute value equation, you will always have to check more than one solution.

Think About It **In Exercises 87–92, find an equation having the given solutions. (There are many correct answers.)**

87. $\pm\sqrt{2}, 4$

88. $2, \pm\sqrt{5}$

89. $2, -1, \frac{1}{2}, -3$

90. $-1, \frac{3}{2}, \pm 2$

91. $\pm 2, \pm i$

92. $\pm 4i, \pm 6$

Think About It **In Exercises 93 and 94, find x such that the distance between the points is 13.**

93. $(1, 2), (x, -10)$

94. $(-8, 0), (x, 5)$

In Exercises 95 and 96, consider an equation of the form $x + |x - a| = b$, where a and b are constants.

95. Find a and b when the solution of the equation is $x = 9$. (There are many correct answers.)

96. *Writing* Write a short paragraph listing the steps required to solve this equation involving absolute values and explain why it is important to check your solutions.

In Exercises 97 and 98, consider an equation of the form $x + \sqrt{x - a} = b$, where a and b are constants.

97. Find a and b when the solution of the equation is $x = 20$. (There are many correct answers.)

98. *Writing* Write a short paragraph listing the steps required to solve this equation involving radicals and explain why it is important to check your solutions.

Skills Review

In Exercises 99–102, simplify the expression.

99. $\dfrac{8}{3x} + \dfrac{3}{2x}$

100. $\dfrac{2}{x^2 - 4} - \dfrac{1}{x^2 - 3x + 2}$

101. $\dfrac{2}{z + 2} - \left(3 - \dfrac{2}{z}\right)$

102. $25y^2 \div \dfrac{xy}{5}$

In Exercises 103 and 104, find all real solutions of the equation.

103. $x^2 - 22x + 121 = 0$

104. $x(x - 20) + 3(x - 20) = 0$

2.6 Solving Inequalities Algebraically and Graphically

Properties of Inequalities

Simple inequalities were reviewed in Section P.1. There, the inequality symbols $<$, $\le$, $>$, and $\ge$ were used to compare two numbers and to denote subsets of real numbers. For instance, the simple inequality $x \ge 3$ denotes all real numbers x that are greater than or equal to 3.

In this section, you will study inequalities that contain more involved statements such as

$$5x - 7 > 3x + 9 \qquad \text{and} \qquad -3 \le 6x - 1 < 3.$$

As with an equation, you **solve an inequality** in the variable x by finding all values of x for which the inequality is true. These values are **solutions** of the inequality and are said to **satisfy** the inequality. For instance, the number 9 is a solution of the first inequality listed above because

$$5(9) - 7 > 3(9) + 9$$

$$38 > 36.$$

On the other hand, the number 7 is not a solution because

$$5(7) - 7 \not> 3(7) + 9$$

$$28 \not> 30.$$

The set of all real numbers that are solutions of an inequality is the **solution set** of the inequality.

The set of all points on the real number line that represent the solution set is the **graph of the inequality.** Graphs of many types of inequalities consist of intervals on the real number line.

The procedures for solving linear inequalities in one variable are much like those for solving linear equations. To isolate the variable, you can make use of the **properties of inequalities.** These properties are similar to the properties of equality, but there are two important exceptions. When each side of an inequality is multiplied or divided by a negative number, *the direction of the inequality symbol must be reversed* in order to maintain a true statement. Here is an example.

$$-2 < 5 \qquad \text{Original inequality}$$

$$(-3)(-2) > (-3)(5) \qquad \text{Multiply each side by } -3 \text{ and reverse the inequality.}$$

$$6 > -15 \qquad \text{Simplify.}$$

Two inequalities that have the same solution set are **equivalent inequalities.** For instance, the inequalities

$$x + 2 < 5 \qquad \text{and} \qquad x < 3$$

are equivalent. To obtain the second inequality from the first, you can subtract 2 from each side of the inequality. The properties listed at the top of the next page describe operations that can be used to create equivalent inequalities.

What you should learn

- Use properties of inequalities to solve linear inequalities.
- Solve inequalities involving absolute values.
- Solve polynomial inequalities.
- Solve rational inequalities.
- Use inequalities to model and solve real-life problems.

Why you should learn it

An inequality can be used to determine when a real-life quantity exceeds a given level. For instance, Exercises 85–88 on page 230 show how to use linear inequalities to determine when the number of hours per person spent playing video games exceeded the number of hours per person spent reading newspapers.

Image Source/Superstock

Prerequisite Skills

To review techniques for solving linear inequalities, see Appendix D.

Polynomial Inequalities

To solve a polynomial inequality such as $x^2 - 2x - 3 < 0$, use the f[act that] polynomial can change signs only at its zeros (the x-values that [make the] polynomial equal to zero). Between two consecutive zeros, a polynomi[al is] entirely positive or entirely negative. This means that when the real [zeros of a] polynomial are put in order, they divide the real number line into i[ntervals in] which the polynomial has no sign changes. These zeros are the **critical [numbers]** of the inequality, and the resulting open intervals are the **test interv[als for the]** inequality. For instance, the polynomial above factors as

$$x^2 - 2x - 3 = (x + 1)(x - 3)$$

and has two zeros, $x = -1$ and $x = 3$, which divide the real numbe[r line into] three test intervals: $(-\infty, -1)$, $(-1, 3)$, and $(3, \infty)$. To solve the [inequality] $x^2 - 2x - 3 < 0$, you need to test only one value in each test interva[l.]

Finding Test Intervals for a Polynomial

To determine the intervals on which the values of a polynomial are [entirely] negative or entirely positive, use the following steps.

1. Find all real zeros of the polynomial, and arrange the zeros i[n] increasing order. The zeros of a polynomial are its critical nu[mbers.]

2. Use the critical numbers to determine the test intervals.

3. Choose one representative x-value in each test interval and e[valuate] the polynomial at that value. If the value of the polynomial i[s nega]tive, the polynomial will have negative values for *every* x-va[lue in the] interval. If the value of the polynomial is positive, the polyn[omial] will have positive values for *every* x-value in the interval.

Example 5 Investigating Polynomial Behavior

To determine the intervals on which $x^2 - 3$ is entirely negative and th[ose on which] it is entirely positive, factor the quadratic as $x^2 - 3 = (x + \sqrt{3})(x[- \sqrt{3})$. The] critical numbers occur at $x = -\sqrt{3}$ and $x = \sqrt{3}$. So, the test inte[rvals for the] quadratic are $(-\infty, -\sqrt{3})$, $(-\sqrt{3}, \sqrt{3})$, and $(\sqrt{3}, \infty)$. In each [test interval,] choose a representative x-value and evaluate the polynomial, as show[n.]

Interval	x-Value	Value of Polynomial	Sign of Pol[ynomial]
$(-\infty, -\sqrt{3})$	$x = -3$	$(-3)^2 - 3 = 6$	Positi[ve]
$(-\sqrt{3}, \sqrt{3})$	$x = 0$	$(0)^2 - 3 = -3$	Negat[ive]
$(\sqrt{3}, \infty)$	$x = 5$	$(5)^2 - 3 = 22$	Positi[ve]

The polynomial has negative values for every x in the interval $(-[\sqrt{3}, \sqrt{3})$ and] positive values for every x in the intervals $(-\infty, -\sqrt{3})$ and $(\sqrt{3}, \infty)$. [This] is shown graphically in Figure 2.53.

✓CHECKPOINT Now try Exercise 49.

Inequalities Involving Absolute Values

Solving an Absolute Value Inequality

Let x be a variable or an algebraic expression and let a be a real nur

1. The solutions of $|x| < a$ are all values of x that lie between

   $$|x| < a \quad \text{if and only if} \quad -a < x < a.$$

2. The solutions of $|x| > a$ are all values of x that are less than

   $$|x| > a \quad \text{if and only if} \quad x < -a \quad \text{or} \quad x > a.$$

These rules are also valid if $<$ is replaced by $\leq$ and $>$ is replaced by

Example 4   Solving Absolute Value Inequalities

Solve each inequality.

a. $|x - 5| < 2$ **b.** $|x - 5| > 2$

Algebraic Solution

a. $|x - 5| < 2$ Write original inequality.

$-2 < x - 5 < 2$ Write double inequality.

$3 < x < 7$ Add 5 to each part.

The solution set is all real numbers that are greater than 3 *and* le than 7. The interval notation for this solution set is $(3, 7)$. T number line graph of this solution set is shown in Figure 2.50.

b. The absolute value inequality $|x - 5| > 2$ is equivalent to t following compound inequality: $x - 5 < -2$ or $x - 5 > 2$.

Solve first inequality: $x - 5 < -2$ Write first inequality.

$x < 3$ Add 5 to each side.

Solve second inequality: $x - 5 > 2$ Write second inequality.

$x > 7$ Add 5 to each side.

The solution set is all real numbers that are less than 3 *or* grea than 7. The interval notation for this solution set $(-\infty, 3) \cup (7, \infty)$. The symbol $\cup$ is called a *union* symbol an used to denote the combining of two sets. The number line grapl this solution set is shown in Figure 2.51.

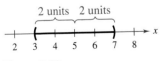

Figure 2.50

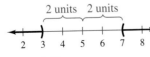

Figure 2.51

✓CHECKPOINT   Now try Exercise 31.

11. ***Hooke's Law*** Hooke's Law states that the force F required to compress or stretch a spring (within its elastic limits) is proportional to the distance d that the spring is compressed or stretched from its original length. That is, $F = kd$, where k is the measure of the stiffness of the spring and is called the *spring constant*. The table shows the elongation d in centimeters of a spring when a force of F kilograms is applied.

Force, F	Elongation, d
20	1.4
40	2.5
60	4.0
80	5.3
100	6.6

(a) Sketch a scatter plot of the data.

(b) Find the equation of the line that seems to best fit the data.

(c) Use the *regression* feature of a graphing utility to find a linear model for the data. Compare this model with the model from part (b).

(d) Use the model from part (c) to estimate the elongation of the spring when a force of 55 kilograms is applied.

12. ***Cell Phones*** The average lengths L of cellular phone calls in minutes from 1999 to 2004 are shown in the table. (Source: Cellular Telecommunications & Internet Association)

Year	Average length, L (in minutes)
1999	2.38
2000	2.56
2001	2.74
2002	2.73
2003	2.87
2004	3.05

(a) Use a graphing utility to create a scatter plot of the data, with $t = 9$ corresponding to 1999.

(b) Use the *regression* feature of a graphing utility to find a linear model for the data. Let t represent the year, with $t = 9$ corresponding to 1999.

(c) Use a graphing utility to plot the data and graph the model in the same viewing window. Is the model a good fit? Explain.

(d) Use the model to predict the average lengths of cellular phone calls for the years 2010 and 2015. Do your answers seem reasonable? Explain.

13. ***Sports*** The mean salaries S (in thousands of dollars) for professional football players in the United States from 2000 to 2004 are shown in the table. (Source: National Collegiate Athletic Assn.)

Year	Mean salary, S (in thousands of dollars)
2000	787
2001	986
2002	1180
2003	1259
2004	1331

(a) Use a graphing utility to create a scatter plot of the data, with $t = 0$ corresponding to 2000.

(b) Use the *regression* feature of a graphing utility to find a linear model for the data. Let t represent the year, with $t = 0$ corresponding to 2000.

(c) Use a graphing utility to plot the data and graph the model in the same viewing window. Is the model a good fit? Explain.

(d) Use the model to predict the mean salaries for professional football players in 2005 and 2010. Do the results seem reasonable? Explain.

(e) What is the slope of your model? What does it tell you about the mean salaries of professional football players?

14. ***Teacher's Salaries*** The mean salaries S (in thousands of dollars) of public school teachers in the United States from 1999 to 2004 are shown in the table. (Source: Educational Research Service)

Year	Mean salary, S (in thousands of dollars)
1999	41.4
2000	42.2
2001	43.7
2002	43.8
2003	45.0
2004	45.6

(a) Use a graphing utility to create a scatter plot of the data, with $t = 9$ corresponding to 1999.

(b) Use the *regression* feature of a graphing utility to find a linear model for the data. Let t represent the year, with $t = 9$ corresponding to 1999.

(c) Use a graphing utility to plot the data and graph the model in the same viewing window. Is the model a good fit? Explain.

(d) Use the model to predict the mean salaries for teachers in 2005 and 2010. Do the results seem reasonable? Explain.

15. Cable Television The average monthly cable television bills *C* (in dollars) for a basic plan from 1990 to 2004 are shown in the table. (Source: Kagan Research, LLC)

Year	Monthly bill, C (in dollars)
1990	16.78
1991	18.10
1992	19.08
1993	19.39
1994	21.62
1995	23.07
1996	24.41
1997	26.48
1998	27.81
1999	28.92
2000	30.37
2001	32.87
2002	34.71
2003	36.59
2004	38.23

(a) Use a graphing utility to create a scatter plot of the data, with $t = 0$ corresponding to 1990.

(b) Use the *regression* feature of a graphing utility to find a linear model for the data and to identify the correlation coefficient. Let *t* represent the year, with $t = 0$ corresponding to 1990.

(c) Graph the model with the data in the same viewing window.

(d) Is the model a good fit for the data? Explain.

(e) Use the model to predict the average monthly cable bills for the years 2005 and 2010.

(f) Do you believe the model would be accurate to predict the average monthly cable bills for future years? Explain.

16. State Population The projected populations *P* (in thousands) for selected years for New Jersey based on the 2000 census are shown in the table. (Source: U.S. Census Bureau)

Year	Population, P (in thousands)
2005	8745
2010	9018
2015	9256
2020	9462
2025	9637
2030	9802

(a) Use a graphing utility to create a scatter plot of the data, with $t = 5$ corresponding to 2005.

(b) Use the *regression* feature of a graphing utility to find a linear model for the data. Let *t* represent the year, with $t = 5$ corresponding to 2005.

(c) Use a graphing utility to plot the data and graph the model in the same viewing window. Is the model a good fit? Explain.

(d) Use the model to predict the population of New Jersey in 2050. Does the result seem reasonable? Explain.

17. State Population The projected populations *P* (in thousands) for selected years for Wyoming based on the 2000 census are shown in the table. (Source: U.S. Census Bureau)

Year	Population, P (in thousands)
2005	507
2010	520
2015	528
2020	531
2025	529
2030	523

(a) Use a graphing utility to create a scatter plot of the data, with $t = 5$ corresponding to 2005.

(b) Use the *regression* feature of a graphing utility to find a linear model for the data. Let *t* represent the year, with $t = 5$ corresponding to 2005.

(c) Use a graphing utility to plot the data and graph the model in the same viewing window. Is the model a good fit? Explain.

(d) Use the model to predict the population of Wyoming in 2050. Does the result seem reasonable? Explain.

18. Advertising and Sales The table shows the advertising expenditures *x* and sales volumes *y* for a company for seven randomly selected months. Both are measured in thousands of dollars.

Month	Advertising expenditures, x	Sales volume, y
1	2.4	202
2	1.6	184
3	2.0	220
4	2.6	240
5	1.4	180
6	1.6	164
7	2.0	186

(a) Use the *regression* feature of a graphing utility to find a linear model for the data and to identify the correlation coefficient.

(b) Use a graphing utility to plot the data and graph the model in the same viewing window.

(c) Interpret the slope of the model in the context of the problem.

(d) Use the model to estimate sales for advertising expenditures of $1500.

19. *Number of Stores* The table shows the numbers T of Target stores from 1997 to 2006. (Source: Target Corp.)

Year	Number of stores, T
1997	1130
1998	1182
1999	1243
2000	1307
2001	1381
2002	1475
2003	1553
2004	1308
2005	1400
2006	1505

(a) Use the *regression* feature of a graphing utility to find a linear model for the data and to identify the correlation coefficient. Let t represent the year, with $t = 7$ corresponding to 1997.

(b) Use a graphing utility to plot the data and graph the model in the same viewing window.

(c) Interpret the slope of the model in the context of the problem.

(d) Use the model to find the year in which the number of Target stores will exceed 1800.

(e) Create a table showing the actual values of T and the values of T given by the model. How closely does the model fit the data?

20. *Sports* The following ordered pairs (t, T) represent the Olympic year t and the winning time T (in minutes) in the women's 400-meter freestyle swimming event. (Source: *The World Almanac* 2005)

(1948, 5.30)	(1968, 4.53)	(1988, 4.06)
(1952, 5.20)	(1972, 4.32)	(1992, 4.12)
(1956, 4.91)	(1976, 4.16)	(1996, 4.12)
(1960, 4.84)	(1980, 4.15)	(2000, 4.10)
(1964, 4.72)	(1984, 4.12)	(2004, 4.09)

(a) Use the *regression* feature of a graphing utility to find a linear model for the data. Let t represent the year, with $t = 0$ corresponding to 1950.

(b) What information is given by the sign of the slope of the model?

(c) Use a graphing utility to plot the data and graph the model in the same viewing window.

(d) Create a table showing the actual values of y and the values of y given by the model. How closely does the model fit the data?

(e) Can the model be used to predict the winning times in the future? Explain.

Synthesis

True or False? **In Exercises 21 and 22, determine whether the statement is true or false. Justify your answer.**

21. A linear regression model with a positive correlation will have a slope that is greater than 0.

22. If the correlation coefficient for a linear regression model is close to -1, the regression line cannot be used to describe the data.

23. *Writing* A linear mathematical model for predicting prize winnings at a race is based on data for 3 years. Write a paragraph discussing the potential accuracy or inaccuracy of such a model.

24. *Research Project* Use your school's library, the Internet, or some other reference source to locate data that you think describes a linear relationship. Create a scatter plot of the data and find the least squares regression line that represents the points. Interpret the slope and y-intercept in the context of the data. Write a summary of your findings.

Skills Review

In Exercises 25–28, evaluate the function at each value of the independent variable and simplify.

25. $f(x) = 2x^2 - 3x + 5$

   (a) $f(-1)$ (b) $f(w + 2)$

26. $g(x) = 5x^2 - 6x + 1$

   (a) $g(-2)$ (b) $g(z - 2)$

27. $h(x) = \begin{cases} 1 - x^2, & x \le 0 \\ 2x + 3, & x > 0 \end{cases}$

   (a) $h(1)$ (b) $h(0)$

28. $k(x) = \begin{cases} 5 - 2x, & x < -1 \\ x^2 + 4, & x \ge -1 \end{cases}$

   (a) $k(-3)$ (b) $k(-1)$

In Exercises 29–34, solve the equation algebraically. Check your solution graphically.

29. $6x + 1 = -9x - 8$

30. $3(x - 3) = 7x + 2$

31. $8x^2 - 10x - 3 = 0$

32. $10x^2 - 23x - 5 = 0$

33. $2x^2 - 7x + 4 = 0$

34. $2x^2 - 8x + 5 = 0$

What Did You Learn?

Key Terms

extraneous solution, *p. 167*

mathematical modeling, *p. 167*

zero of a function, *p. 177*

point of intersection, *p. 180*

imaginary unit *i*, *p. 187*

complex number, *p. 187*

imaginary number, *p. 187*

complex conjugates, *p. 190*

quadratic equation, *p. 195*

Quadratic Formula, *p. 195*

polynomial equation, *p. 209*

equation of quadratic type, *p. 210*

solution set of an inequality, *p. 219*

equivalent inequalities, *p. 219*

critical numbers, *p. 223*

test intervals, *p. 223*

positive correlation, *p. 233*

negative correlation, *p. 233*

Key Concepts

2.1 ■ Solve and use linear equations

1. To solve an equation in *x* means to find all values of *x* for which the equation is true.

2. An equation that is true for every real number in the domain of the variable is called an identity.

3. An equation that is true for just some (or even none) of the real numbers in the domain of the variable is called a conditional equation.

4. To form a mathematical model, begin by using a verbal description of the problem to form a verbal model. Then, after assigning labels to the quantities in the verbal model, write the algebraic equation.

2.2 ■ Find intercepts, zeros, and solutions of equations

1. The point $(a, 0)$ is an *x*-intercept and the point $(0, b)$ is a *y*-intercept of the graph of $y = f(x)$.

2. The number *a* is a zero of the function *f*.

3. The number *a* is a solution of the equation $f(x) = 0$.

2.3 ■ Perform operations with complex numbers and plot complex numbers

1. If *a* and *b* are real numbers and $i = \sqrt{-1}$, the number $a + bi$ is a complex number written in standard form.

2. Add: $(a + bi) + (c + di) = (a + c) + (b + d)i$

   Subtract: $(a + bi) - (c + di) = (a - c) + (b - d)i$

   Multiply: $(a + bi)(c + di) = (ac - bd) + (ad + bc)i$

   Divide: $\dfrac{a + bi}{c + di}\left(\dfrac{c - di}{c - di}\right) = \dfrac{ac + bd}{c^2 + d^2} + \left(\dfrac{bc - ad}{c^2 + d^2}\right)i$

3. The complex plane consists of a real (horizontal) axis and an imaginary (vertical) axis. The point that corresponds to the complex number $a + bi$ is (a, b).

2.4 ■ Solve quadratic equations

1. Methods for solving quadratic equations include factoring, extracting square roots, completing the square, and using the Quadratic Formula.

2. Quadratic equations can have two real solutions, one repeated real solution, or two complex solutions.

2.5 ■ Solve other types of equations

1. To solve a polynomial equation, factor if possible. Then use the methods used in solving linear and quadratic equations.

2. To solve an equation involving a radical, isolate the radical on one side of the equation, and raise each side to an appropriate power.

3. To solve an equation with a fraction, multiply each term by the LCD, then solve the resulting equation.

4. To solve an equation involving an absolute value, isolate the absolute value term on one side of the equation. Then set up two equations, one where the absolute value term is positive and one where the absolute value term is negative. Solve both equations.

2.6 ■ Solve inequalities

1. To solve an inequality involving an absolute value, rewrite the inequality as a double inequality or as a compound inequality.

2. To solve a polynomial inequality, write the polynomial in general form, find all the real zeros (critical numbers) of the polynomial, and test the intervals bounded by the critical numbers to determine the intervals that are solutions to the polynomial inequality.

3. To solve a rational inequality, find the *x*-values for which the rational expression is 0 or undefined (critical numbers) and test the intervals bounded by the critical numbers to determine the intervals that are solutions to the rational inequality.

2.7 ■ Use scatter plots and find linear models

1. A scatter plot is a graphical representation of data written as a set of ordered pairs.

2. The best-fitting linear model can be found using the *linear regression* feature of a graphing utility or a computer program.

Review Exercises

See www.CalcChat.com for worked-out solutions to odd-numbered exercises.

2.1 In Exercises 1 and 2, determine whether each value of x is a solution of the equation.

Equation   *Values*

1. $6 + \dfrac{3}{x - 4} = 5$ (a) $x = 5$ (b) $x = 0$

(c) $x = -2$ (d) $x = 1$

2. $6 + \dfrac{2}{x + 3} = \dfrac{6x + 1}{3}$ (a) $x = -3$ (b) $x = 3$

(c) $x = 0$ (d) $x = -\frac{2}{3}$

In Exercises 3–12, solve the equation (if possible). Then use a graphing utility to verify your solution.

3. $\dfrac{18}{x} = \dfrac{10}{x - 4}$

4. $\dfrac{2}{x} = \dfrac{5}{x - 2}$

5. $\dfrac{5}{x - 2} = \dfrac{13}{2x - 3}$

6. $\dfrac{10}{x + 1} = \dfrac{12}{3x - 2}$

7. $14 + \dfrac{2}{x - 1} = 10$

8. $10 + \dfrac{2}{x - 1} = 4$

9. $6 - \dfrac{11}{x} = 3 + \dfrac{7}{x}$

10. $2 - \dfrac{1}{x} = 4 + \dfrac{3}{x}$

11. $\dfrac{9x}{3x - 1} - \dfrac{4}{3x + 1} = 3$

12. $\dfrac{5}{x - 5} + \dfrac{1}{x + 5} = \dfrac{2}{x^2 - 25}$

13. *Profit* In October, a greeting card company's total profit was 12% more than it was in September. The total profit for the two months was $689,000. Find the profit for each month.

14. *Mixture Problem* A car radiator contains 10 liters of a 30% antifreeze solution. How many liters will have to be replaced with pure antifreeze if the resulting solution is to be 50% antifreeze?

15. *Height* To obtain the height of a tree, you measure the tree's shadow and find that it is 8 meters long. You also measure the shadow of a two-meter lamppost and find that it is 75 centimeters long.

(a) Draw a diagram that illustrates the problem. Let h represent the height of the tree.

(b) Find the height of the tree in meters.

16. *Investment* You invest $12,000 in a fund paying $2\frac{1}{2}\%$ simple interest and $10,000 in a fund with a variable interest rate. At the end of the year, you were notified that the total interest for both funds was $870. Find the equivalent simple interest rate on the variable-rate fund.

17. *Meteorology* The average daily temperature for the month of January in Juneau, Alaska is 25.7°F. What is Juneau's average daily temperature for the month of January in degrees Celsius? (Source: U.S. National Oceanic and Atmospheric Administration)

18. *Geometry* A basketball and a baseball have circumferences of 30 inches and $9\frac{1}{4}$ inches, respectively. Find the volume of each.

2.2 In Exercises 19–22, find the x- and y-intercepts of the graph of the equation.

19. $-x + y = 3$

20. $x - 5y = 20$

21. $y = x^2 - 9x + 8$

22. $y = 25 - x^2$

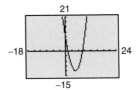

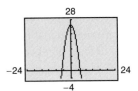

In Exercises 23–28, use a graphing utility to approximate any solutions of the equation. [Remember to write the equation in the form $f(x) = 0$.]

23. $5(x - 2) - 1 = 0$

24. $12 - 5(x - 7) = 0$

25. $3x^3 - 2x + 4 = 0$

26. $\frac{1}{3}x^3 - x + 4 = 0$

27. $x^4 - 3x + 1 = 0$

28. $6 - \frac{1}{2}x^2 + \frac{5}{6}x^4 = 0$

In Exercises 29–32, use a graphing utility to approximate any points of intersection of the graphs of the equations. Check your results algebraically.

29. $3x + 5y = -7$
    $-x - 2y = 3$

30. $x - y = 3$
    $2x + y = 12$

31. $x^2 + 2y = 14$
    $3x + 4y = 1$

32. $y = -x + 7$
    $y = 2x^3 - x + 9$

2.3 In Exercises 33–36, write the complex number in standard form.

33. $6 + \sqrt{-25}$

34. $-\sqrt{-12} + 3$

35. $-2i^2 + 7i$

36. $-i^2 - 4i$

In Exercises 37–48, perform the operations and write the result in standard form.

37. $(7 + 5i) + (-4 + 2i)$

38. $\left(\dfrac{\sqrt{2}}{2} - \dfrac{\sqrt{2}}{2}i \right) - \left(\dfrac{\sqrt{2}}{2} + \dfrac{\sqrt{2}}{2}i \right)$

39. $5i(13 - 8i)$

40. $(1 + 6i)(5 - 2i)$

41. $(\sqrt{-16} + 3)(\sqrt{-25} - 2)$

42. $(5 - \sqrt{-4})(5 + \sqrt{-4})$

43. $\sqrt{-9} + 3 + \sqrt{-36}$

44. $7 - \sqrt{-81} + \sqrt{-49}$

45. $(10 - 8i)(2 - 3i)$

46. $i(6 + i)(3 - 2i)$

47. $(3 + 7i)^2 + (3 - 7i)^2$

48. $(4 - i)^2 - (4 + i)^2$

In Exercises 49–52, write the quotient in standard form.

49. $\dfrac{6 + i}{i}$

50. $\dfrac{4}{-3i}$

51. $\dfrac{3 + 2i}{5 + i}$

52. $\dfrac{1 - 7i}{2 + 3i}$

In Exercises 53 and 54, determine the complex number shown in the complex plane.

53.
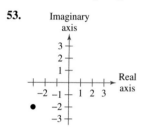

54.
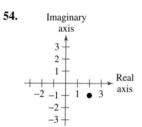

In Exercises 55–60, plot the complex number in the complex plane.

55. $2 - 5i$

56. $-1 + 4i$

57. $-6i$

58. $7i$

59. 3

60. -2

2.4 In Exercises 61–86, solve the equation using any convenient method. Use a graphing utility to verify your solution(s).

61. $(2x - 1)(x + 3) = 0$

62. $(2x - 5)(x + 2) = 0$

63. $(3x - 2)(x - 5) = 0$

64. $(3x - 1)(2x + 1) = 0$

65. $6x = 3x^2$

66. $16x^2 = 25$

67. $x^2 - 4x = 5$

68. $x^2 - 3x = 54$

69. $x^2 - 3x = 4$

70. $x^2 - 5x = 6$

71. $2x^2 - x - 3 = 0$

72. $2x^2 - x - 10 = 0$

73. $15 + x - 2x^2 = 0$

74. $1 + x - 2x^2 = 0$

75. $(x + 4)^2 = 18$

76. $(x + 1)^2 = 24$

77. $x^2 - 12x + 30 = 0$

78. $x^2 + 6x - 3 = 0$

79. $2x^2 + 9x - 5 = 0$

80. $4x^2 + x - 5 = 0$

81. $-x^2 - x + 15 = 0$

82. $2 - 3x - 2x^2 = 0$

83. $x^2 + 4x + 10 = 0$

84. $x^2 + 6x - 1 = 0$

85. $2x^2 - 6x + 21 = 0$

86. $2x^2 - 8x + 11 = 0$

87. *Medical Costs* The average costs per day C (in dollars) for hospital care from 1997 to 2003 in the U.S. can be approximated by the model $C = 6.00t^2 - 62.9t + 1182$, $7 \le t \le 13$, where t is the year, with $t = 7$ corresponding to 1997.   (Source: Health Forum)

(a) Use a graphing utility to graph the model in an appropriate viewing window.

(b) Use the *zoom* and *trace* features of a graphing utility to estimate when the cost per day reached $1250.

(c) Algebraically find when the cost per day reached $1250.

(d) According to the model, when will the cost per day reach $1500 and $2000?

(e) Do your answers seem reasonable? Explain.

88. *Auto Parts* The sales S (in millions of dollars) for Advanced Auto Parts from 2000 to 2006 can be approximated by the model $S = -8.45t^2 + 439.0t + 2250$, $0 \le t \le 6$, where t is the year, with $t = 0$ corresponding to 2000.   (Source: Value Line)

(a) Use a graphing utility to graph the model in an appropriate viewing window.

(b) Use the *zoom* and *trace* features of a graphing utility to estimate when the sales reached 3.5 billion dollars.

(c) Algebraically find when the sales reached 3.5 billion dollars.

(d) According to the model, when, if ever, will the sales reach 5.0 billion dollars? If sales will not reach that amount, explain why not.

2.5 In Exercises 89–116, find all solutions of the equation algebraically. Use a graphing utility to verify the solutions graphically.

89. $3x^3 - 26x^2 + 16x = 0$

90. $36x^3 - x = 0$

91. $5x^4 - 12x^3 = 0$

92. $4x^3 - 6x^2 = 0$

93. $x^4 - x^2 - 12 = 0$

94. $x^4 - 4x^2 - 5 = 0$

95. $2x^4 - 22x^2 = -56$

96. $3x^4 + 18x^2 = -24$

97. $\sqrt{x + 4} = 3$

98. $\sqrt{x - 2} - 8 = 0$

99. $2\sqrt{x} - 5 = 0$

100. $\sqrt{3x - 2} = 4 - x$

101. $\sqrt{2x + 3} + \sqrt{x - 2} = 2$

102. $5\sqrt{x} - \sqrt{x - 1} = 6$

103. $(x - 1)^{2/3} - 25 = 0$

104. $(x + 2)^{3/4} = 27$

105. $(x + 4)^{1/2} + 5x(x + 4)^{3/2} = 0$

106. $8x^2(x^2 - 4)^{1/3} + (x^2 - 4)^{4/3} = 0$

107. $\dfrac{x}{8} + \dfrac{3}{8} = \dfrac{1}{2x}$

108. $\dfrac{3x}{2} = \dfrac{1}{x} - \dfrac{5}{2}$

109. $3\left(1 - \dfrac{1}{5t}\right) = 0$

110. $\dfrac{1}{x - 2} = 3$

111. $\dfrac{4}{(x - 4)^2} = 1$

112. $\dfrac{1}{(t + 1)^2} = 1$

113. $|x - 5| = 10$

114. $|2x + 3| = 7$

115. $|x^2 - 3| = 2x$

116. $|x^2 - 6| = x$

117. *Cost Sharing*   A group of farmers agree to share equally in the cost of a \$48,000 piece of machinery. If they can find two more farmers to join the group, each person's share of the cost will decrease by \$4000. How many farmers are presently in the group?

118. *Average Speed*   You drove 56 miles one way on a service call. On the return trip, your average speed was 8 miles per hour greater and the trip took 10 fewer minutes. What was your average speed on the return trip?

119. *Mutual Funds*   A deposit of \$1000 in a mutual fund reaches a balance of \$1196.95 after 6 years. What annual interest rate on a certificate of deposit compounded monthly would yield an equivalent return?

120. *Mutual Funds*   A deposit of \$1500 in a mutual fund reaches a balance of \$2465.43 after 10 years. What annual interest rate on a certificate of deposit compounded quarterly would yield an equivalent return?

121. *City Population*   The populations P (in millions) of New York City from 2000 to 2004 can be modeled by the equation

$$P = 18.310 + 0.1989\sqrt{t}, \quad 0 \le t \le 4$$

where t is the year, with $t = 0$ corresponding to 2000.
(Source: U.S. Census Bureau)

(a) Use the *table* feature of a graphing utility to find the population of New York City for each year from 2000 to 2004.

(b) Use a graphing utility to graph the model in an appropriate viewing window.

(c) Use the *zoom* and *trace* features of a graphing utility to find when the population reached 18.5 million.

(d) Algebraically confirm your approximation in part (b).

(e) According to the model, when will the population reach 19 million? Does this answer seem reasonable?

(f) Do you believe the population will ever reach 20 million? Explain your reasoning.

122. *School Enrollment*   The numbers of students N (in millions) enrolled in school at all levels in the United States from 1999 to 2003 can be modeled by the equation

$$N = \sqrt{23.649t^2 - 420.19t + 7090.1}, \quad 9 \le t \le 13$$

where t is the year, with $t = 9$ corresponding to 1999.
(Source: U.S. Census Bureau)

(a) Use the *table* feature of a graphing utility to find the number of students enrolled for each year from 1999 to 2003.

(b) Use a graphing utility to graph the model in an appropriate viewing window.

(c) Use the *zoom* and *trace* features of a graphing utility to find when school enrollment reached 74 million.

(d) Algebraically confirm your approximation in part (c).

(e) According to the model, when will the enrollment reach 75 million? Does this answer seem reasonable?

(f) Do you believe the enrollment population will ever reach 100 million? Explain your reasoning.

2.6 In Exercises 123–144, solve the inequality and sketch the solution on the real number line. Use a graphing utility to verify your solution graphically.

123. $8x - 3 < 6x + 15$

124. $9x - 8 \le 7x + 16$

125. $\frac{1}{2}(3 - x) > \frac{1}{3}(2 - 3x)$

126. $4(5 - 2x) \ge \frac{1}{2}(8 - x)$

127. $-2 < -x + 7 \le 10$

128. $-6 \le 3 - 2(x - 5) < 14$

129. $|x - 2| < 1$

130. $|x| \le 4$

131. $\left|x - \frac{3}{2}\right| \ge \frac{3}{2}$

132. $|x - 3| > 4$

133. $4|3 - 2x| \le 16$

134. $|x + 9| + 7 > 19$

135. $x^2 - 2x \ge 3$

136. $x^2 - 6x - 27 < 0$

137. $4x^2 - 23x \le 6$

138. $6x^2 + 5x < 4$

139. $x^3 - 16x \ge 0$

140. $12x^3 - 20x^2 < 0$

141. $\dfrac{x - 5}{3 - x} < 0$

142. $\dfrac{2}{x + 1} \le \dfrac{3}{x - 1}$

143. $\dfrac{3x + 8}{x - 3} \le 4$

144. $\dfrac{x + 8}{x + 5} - 2 < 0$

In Exercises 145–148, find the domain of x in the expression.

145. $\sqrt{x - 4}$

146. $\sqrt{x^2 - 25}$

147. $\sqrt[3]{2 - 3x}$

148. $\sqrt[3]{4x^2 - 1}$

149. Accuracy of Measurement You stop at a self-service gas station to buy 15 gallons of 87-octane gasoline at $2.59 a gallon. The gas pump is accurate to within $\frac{1}{10}$ of a gallon. How much might you be overcharged or undercharged?

150. Meteorology An electronic device is to be operated in an environment with relative humidity h in the interval defined by $|h - 50| \le 30$. What are the minimum and maximum relative humidities for the operation of this device?

2.7

151. Education The following ordered pairs give the entrance exam scores x and the grade-point averages y after 1 year of college for 10 students.

(75, 2.3), (82, 3.0), (90, 3.6), (65, 2.0), (70, 2.1), (88, 3.5), (93, 3.9), (69, 2.0), (80, 2.8), (85, 3.3)

(a) Create a scatter plot of the data.

(b) Does the relationship between x and y appear to be approximately linear? Explain.

152. Stress Test A machine part was tested by bending it x centimeters 10 times per minute until it failed (y equals the time to failure in hours). The results are given as the following ordered pairs.

(3, 61), (6, 56), (9, 53), (12, 55), (15, 48), (18, 35), (21, 36), (24, 33), (27, 44), (30, 23)

(a) Create a scatter plot of the data.

(b) Does the relationship between x and y appear to be approximately linear? If not, give some possible explanations.

153. Falling Object In an experiment, students measured the speed s (in meters per second) of a ball t seconds after it was released. The results are shown in the table.

Time, t	Speed, s
0	0
1	11.0
2	19.4
3	29.2
4	39.4

(a) Sketch a scatter plot of the data.

(b) Find the equation of the line that seems to best fit the data.

(c) Use the *regression* feature of a graphing utility to find a linear model for the data. Compare this model with the model from part (b).

(d) Use the model from part (c) to estimate the speed of the ball after 2.5 seconds.

154. Sports The following ordered pairs (x, y) represent the Olympic year x and the winning time y (in minutes) in the men's 400-meter freestyle swimming event. (Source: The World Almanac 2005)

(1964, 4.203) (1980, 3.855) (1996, 3.800)
(1968, 4.150) (1984, 3.854) (2000, 3.677)
(1972, 4.005) (1988, 3.783) (2004, 3.718)
(1976, 3.866) (1992, 3.750)

(a) Use the *regression* feature of a graphing utility to find a linear model for the data and to identify the correlation coefficient. Let x represent the year, with $x = 4$ corresponding to 1964.

(b) Use a graphing utility to create a scatter plot of the data.

(c) Graph the model with the data in the same viewing window.

(d) Is the model a good fit for the data? Explain.

(e) Is the model appropriate for predicting the winning times in future Olympics? Explain.

Synthesis

True or False? In Exercises 155–157, determine whether the statement is true or false. Justify your answer.

155. The graph of a function may have two distinct y-intercepts.

156. The sum of two complex numbers cannot be a real number.

157. The sign of the slope of a regression line is always positive.

158. Writing In your own words, explain the difference between an identity and a conditional equation.

159. Writing Describe the relationship among the x-intercepts of a graph, the zeros of a function, and the solutions of an equation.

160. Consider the linear equation $ax + b = 0$.

(a) What is the sign of the solution if $ab > 0$?

(b) What is the sign of the solution if $ab < 0$?

161. Error Analysis Describe the error.
$$\sqrt{-6}\sqrt{-6} = \sqrt{(-6)(-6)} = \sqrt{36} = 6$$

162. Error Analysis Describe the error.
$$-i(\sqrt{-4} - 1) = -i(4i - 1)$$
$$= -4i^2 - i$$
$$= 4 - i$$

163. Write each of the powers of i as i, $-i$, 1, or -1.
(a) i^{40} (b) i^{25} (c) i^{50} (d) i^{67}

2 Chapter Test

See www.CalcChat.com for worked-out solutions to odd-numbered exercises.

Take this test as you would take a test in class. After you are finished, check your work against the answers given in the back of the book.

In Exercises 1 and 2, solve the equation (if possible). Then use a graphing utility to verify your solution.

1. $\dfrac{12}{x} - 7 = -\dfrac{27}{x} + 6$

2. $\dfrac{4}{3x - 2} - \dfrac{9x}{3x + 2} = -3$

In Exercises 3–6, perform the operations and write the result in standard form.

3. $(-8 - 3i) + (-1 - 15i)$

4. $\left(10 + \sqrt{-20}\right) - \left(4 - \sqrt{-14}\right)$

5. $(2 + i)(6 - i)$

6. $(4 + 3i)^2 - (5 + i)^2$

In Exercises 7–9, write the quotient in standard form.

7. $\dfrac{8 + 5i}{6 - i}$

8. $\dfrac{5i}{2 + i}$

9. $(2i - 1) \div (3i + 2)$

10. Plot the complex number $3 - 2i$ in the complex plane.

In Exercises 11–14, use a graphing utility to approximate any solutions of the equation. [Remember to write the equation in the form $f(x) = 0$.]

11. $3x^2 - 6 = 0$

12. $8x^2 - 2 = 0$

13. $x^3 + 5x = 4x^2$

14. $x = x^3$

In Exercises 15–18, solve the equation using any convenient method. Use a graphing utility to verify the solutions graphically.

15. $x^2 - 10x + 9 = 0$

16. $x^2 + 12x - 2 = 0$

17. $4x^2 - 81 = 0$

18. $5x^2 + 14x - 3 = 0$

In Exercises 19–22, find all solutions of the equation algebraically. Use a graphing utility to verify the solutions graphically.

19. $3x^3 - 4x^2 - 12x + 16 = 0$

20. $x + \sqrt{22 - 3x} = 6$

21. $(x^2 + 6)^{2/3} = 16$

22. $|8x - 1| = 21$

In Exercises 23–26, solve the inequality and sketch the solution on the real number line. Use a graphing utility to verify your solution graphically.

23. $8x - 1 > 3x - 10$

24. $2|x - 8| < 10$

25. $6x^2 + 5x + 1 \geq 0$

26. $\dfrac{3 - 5x}{2 + 3x} < -2$

27. The table shows the numbers of cellular phone subscribers S (in millions) in the United States from 1999 through 2004, where t represents the year, with $t = 9$ corresponding to 1999. Use the *regression* feature of a graphing utility to find a linear model for the data and to identify the correlation coefficient. Use the model to find the year in which the number of subscribers exceeded 200 million. (Source: Cellular Telecommunications & Internet Association)

Year, t	Subscribers, S
9	86.0
10	109.5
11	128.4
12	140.8
13	158.7
14	182.1

Table for 27

P–2 Cumulative Test

See www.CalcChat.com for worked-out solutions to odd-numbered exercises.

Take this test to review the material in Chapters P–2. After you are finished, check your work against the answers in the back of the book.

In Exercises 1–3, simplify the expression.

1. $\dfrac{14x^2y^{-3}}{32x^{-1}y^2}$

2. $8\sqrt{60} - 2\sqrt{135} - \sqrt{15}$

3. $\sqrt{28x^4y^3}$

In Exercises 4–6, perform the operation and simplify the result.

4. $4x - [2x + 5(2 - x)]$

5. $(x - 2)(x^2 + x - 3)$

6. $\dfrac{2}{x + 3} - \dfrac{1}{x + 1}$

In Exercises 7–9, factor the expression completely.

7. $25 - (x - 2)^2$

8. $x - 5x^2 - 6x^3$

9. $54 - 16x^3$

10. Find the midpoint of the line segment connecting the points $\left(-\frac{7}{2}, 4\right)$ and $\left(\frac{5}{2}, -8\right)$. Then find the distance between the points.

11. Write the standard form of the equation of a circle with center $\left(-\frac{1}{2}, -8\right)$ and a radius of 4.

In Exercises 12–14, use point plotting to sketch the graph of the equation.

12. $x - 3y + 12 = 0$

13. $y = x^2 - 9$

14. $y = \sqrt{4 - x}$

In Exercises 15–17, (a) write the general form of the equation of the line that satisfies the given conditions and (b) find three additional points through which the line passes.

15. The line contains the points $(-5, 8)$ and $(-1, 4)$.

16. The line contains the point $\left(-\frac{1}{2}, 1\right)$ and has a slope of -2.

17. The line has an undefined slope and contains the point $\left(-\frac{3}{7}, \frac{1}{8}\right)$.

18. Find the equation of the line that passes through the point $(2, 3)$ and is (a) parallel to and (b) perpendicular to the line $6x - y = 4$.

In Exercises 19 and 20, evaluate the function at each value of the independent variable and simplify.

19. $f(x) = \dfrac{x}{x - 2}$

   (a) $f(5)$ (b) $f(2)$ (c) $f(5 + 4s)$

20. $f(x) = \begin{cases} 3x - 8, & x < 0 \\ x^2 + 4, & x \ge 0 \end{cases}$

   (a) $f(-8)$ (b) $f(0)$ (c) $f(4)$

In Exercises 21–24, find the domain of the function.

21. $f(x) = (x + 2)(3x - 4)$

22. $f(t) = \sqrt{5 + 7t}$

23. $g(s) = \sqrt{9 - s^2}$

24. $h(x) = \dfrac{4}{5x + 2}$

25. Determine if the function given by $g(x) = 3x - x^3$ is even, odd, or neither.

26. Does the graph at the right represent y as a function of x? Explain.

27. Use a graphing utility to graph the function $f(x) = 2|x - 5| - |x + 5|$. Then determine the open intervals over which the function is increasing, decreasing, or constant.

28. Compare the graph of each function with the graph of $f(x) = \sqrt[3]{x}$.

   (a) $r(x) = \dfrac{1}{2}\sqrt[3]{x}$ (b) $h(x) = \sqrt[3]{x} + 2$ (c) $g(x) = -\sqrt[3]{x + 2}$

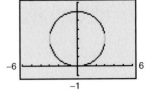

Figure for 26

In Exercises 29–32, evaluate the indicated function for

$$f(x) = x^2 + 2 \quad \text{and} \quad g(x) = 4x + 1.$$

29. $(f + g)(x)$

30. $(g - f)(x)$

31. $(g \circ f)(x)$

32. $(fg)(x)$

33. Determine whether $h(x) = 5x - 2$ has an inverse function. If so, find it.

34. Plot the complex number $-5 + 4i$ in the complex plane.

In Exercises 35–38, use a graphing utility to approximate the solutions of the equation. [Remember to write the equation in the form $f(x) = 0$.]

35. $4x^3 - 12x^2 + 8x = 0$

36. $\dfrac{5}{x} = \dfrac{10}{x - 3}$

37. $|3x + 4| - 2 = 0$

38. $\sqrt{x^2 + 1} + x - 9 = 0$

In Exercises 39–42, solve the inequality and graph the solution on the real number line. Use a graphing utility to verify your solution graphically.

39. $\dfrac{x}{5} - 6 \le -\dfrac{x}{2} + 6$

40. $2x^2 + x \ge 15$

41. $|7 + 8x| > 5$

42. $\dfrac{2(x - 2)}{x + 1} \le 0$

43. A soccer ball has a volume of about 370.7 cubic inches. Find the radius of the soccer ball (accurate to three decimal places).

44. A rectangular plot of land with a perimeter of 546 feet has a width of x.

   (a) Write the area A of the plot as a function of x.

   (b) Use a graphing utility to graph the area function. What is the domain of the function?

   (c) Approximate the dimensions of the plot when the area is 15,000 square feet.

45. The total sales S (in millions of dollars) for 7-Eleven, Inc. from 1998 through 2004 are shown in the table.   (Source: 7-Eleven, Inc.)

   (a) Use the *regression* feature of a graphing utility to find a linear model for the data and to identify the correlation coefficient. Let t represent the year, with $t = 8$ corresponding to 1998.

   (b) Use a graphing utility to plot the data and graph the model in the same viewing window.

   (c) Use the model to predict the sales for 7-Eleven, Inc. in 2008 and 2010.

   (d) In your opinion, is the model appropriate for predicting future sales? Explain.

Year	Sales, S
1998	7,258
1999	8,252
2000	9,346
2001	9,782
2002	10,110
2003	11,116
2004	12,283

Table for 45

Proofs in Mathematics

Biconditional Statements

Recall from the Proofs in Mathematics in Chapter 1 that a conditional statement is a statement of the form "if p, then q." A statement of the form "p if and only if q" is called a **biconditional statement.** A biconditional statement, denoted by

$p \leftrightarrow q$ Biconditional statement

is the conjunction of the conditional statement $p \rightarrow q$ and its converse $q \rightarrow p$.

A biconditional statement can be either true or false. To be true, *both* the conditional statement and its converse must be true.

Example 1   Analyzing a Biconditional Statement

Consider the statement $x = 3$ if and only if $x^2 = 9$.

a. Is the statement a biconditional statement?   **b.** Is the statement true?

Solution

a. The statement is a biconditional statement because it is of the form "p if and only if q."
b. The statement can be rewritten as the following conditional statement and its converse.

Conditional statement: If $x = 3$, then $x^2 = 9$.
Converse: If $x^2 = 9$, then $x = 3$.

The first of these statements is true, but the second is false because x could also equal -3. So, the biconditional statement is false.

Knowing how to use biconditional statements is an important tool for reasoning in mathematics.

Example 2   Analyzing a Biconditional Statement

Determine whether the biconditional statement is true or false. If it is false, provide a counterexample.

A number is divisible by 5 if and only if it ends in 0.

Solution

The biconditional statement can be rewritten as the following conditional statement and its converse.

Conditional statement: If a number is divisible by 5, then it ends in 0.
Converse: If a number ends in 0, then it is divisible by 5.

The conditional statement is false. A counterexample is the number 15, which is divisible by 5 but does not end in 0. So, the biconditional statement is false.

Progressive Summary (Chapters P–2)

This chart outlines the topics that have been covered so far in this text.
Progressive Summary charts appear after Chapters 2, 4, and 7. In each
progressive summary, new topics encountered for the first time appear in red.

Algebraic Functions	Transcendental Functions	Other Topics
Polynomial, Rational, Radical		
■ **Rewriting**	■ **Rewriting**	■ **Rewriting**
Polynomial form ↔ Factored form		
Operations with polynomials		
Rationalize denominators		
Simplify rational expressions		
Exponent form ↔ Radical form		
Operations with complex numbers		
■ **Solving**	■ **Solving**	■ **Solving**

Solving

Equation	Strategy
Linear	Isolate variable
Quadratic	Factor, set to zero
	Extract square roots
	Complete the square
	Quadratic Formula
Polynomial	Factor, set to zero
	Rational Zero Test
Rational	Multiply by LCD
Radical	Isolate, raise to power
Absolute Value	Isolate, form two equations

■ **Analyzing**   ■ **Analyzing**   ■ **Analyzing**

Graphically	Algebraically
Intercepts	Domain, Range
Symmetry	Transformations
Slope	Composition
Asymptotes	

Numerically

Table of values

Chapter 3

3.1 Quadratic Functions

3.2 Polynomial Functions of Higher Degree

3.3 Real Zeros of Polynomial Functions

3.4 The Fundamental Theorem of Algebra

3.5 Rational Functions and Asymptotes

3.6 Graphs of Rational Functions

3.7 Quadratic Models

Selected Applications

Polynomial and rational functions have many real-life applications. The applications listed below represent a small sample of the applications in this chapter.

■ Automobile Aerodynamics, Exercise 58, page 261

■ Revenue, Exercise 93, page 274

■ U.S. Population, Exercise 91, page 289

■ Profit, Exercise 64, page 297

■ Data Analysis, Exercises 41 and 42, page 306

■ Wildlife, Exercise 43, page 307

■ Comparing Models, Exercise 85, page 316

■ Media, Exercise 18, page 322

Polynomial and Rational Functions

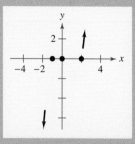
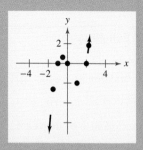
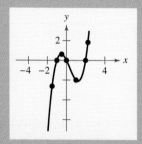

Polynomial and rational functions are two of the most common types of functions used in algebra and calculus. In Chapter 3, you will learn how to graph these types of functions and how to find zeros of these functions.

David Madison/Getty Images

Aerodynamics is crucial in creating racecars. Two types of racecars designed and built by NASCAR teams are short track cars, as shown in the photo, and super-speedway (long track) cars. Both types of racecars are designed either to allow for as much downforce as possible or to reduce the amount of drag on the racecar.

3.1 Quadratic Functions

The Graph of a Quadratic Function

In this and the next section, you will study the graphs of polynomial functions.

Definition of Polynomial Function

Let n be a nonnegative integer and let $a_n, a_{n-1}, \ldots, a_2, a_1, a_0$ be real numbers with $a_n \neq 0$. The function given by

$$f(x) = a_n x^n + a_{n-1} x^{n-1} + \cdots + a_2 x^2 + a_1 x + a_0$$

is called a **polynomial function in x of degree n.**

Polynomial functions are classified by degree. For instance, the polynomial function

$$f(x) = a \qquad \text{Constant function}$$

has degree 0 and is called a **constant function.** In Chapter 1, you learned that the graph of this type of function is a horizontal line. The polynomial function

$$f(x) = mx + b, \quad m \neq 0 \qquad \text{Linear function}$$

has degree 1 and is called a **linear function.** You also learned in Chapter 1 that the graph of the linear function $f(x) = mx + b$ is a line whose slope is m and whose y-intercept is $(0, b)$. In this section, you will study second-degree polynomial functions, which are called **quadratic functions.**

Definition of Quadratic Function

Let a, b, and c be real numbers with $a \neq 0$. The function given by

$$f(x) = ax^2 + bx + c \qquad \text{Quadratic function}$$

is called a **quadratic function.**

Often real-life data can be modeled by quadratic functions. For instance, the table at the right shows the height h (in feet) of a projectile fired from a height of 6 feet with an initial velocity of 256 feet per second at any time t (in seconds). A quadratic model for the data in the table is $h(t) = -16t^2 + 256t + 6$ for $0 \leq t \leq 16$.

The graph of a quadratic function is a special type of U-shaped curve called a **parabola.** Parabolas occur in many real-life applications, especially those involving reflective properties, such as satellite dishes or flashlight reflectors. You will study these properties in a later chapter.

All parabolas are symmetric with respect to a line called the **axis of symmetry,** or simply the **axis** of the parabola. The point where the axis intersects the parabola is called the **vertex** of the parabola.

What you should learn

- Analyze graphs of quadratic functions.
- Write quadratic functions in standard form and use the results to sketch graphs of functions.
- Find minimum and maximum values of quadratic functions in real-life applications.

Why you should learn it

Quadratic functions can be used to model the design of a room. For instance, Exercise 53 on page 260 shows how the size of an indoor fitness room with a running track can be modeled.

Dwight Cendrowski

t	h
0	6
2	454
4	774
6	966
8	1030
10	966
12	774
14	454
16	6

Library of Parent Functions: Quadratic Function

The simplest type of *quadratic function* is $f(x) = ax^2$, also known as the *squaring function* when $a = 1$. The basic characteristics of a quadratic function are summarized below. A review of quadratic functions can be found in the *Study Capsules*.

Graph of $f(x) = ax^2$, $a > 0$
Domain: $(-\infty, \infty)$
Range: $[0, \infty)$
Intercept: $(0, 0)$
Decreasing on $(-\infty, 0)$
Increasing on $(0, \infty)$
Even function
Axis of symmetry: $x = 0$
Relative minimum or vertex: $(0, 0)$

Graph of $f(x) = ax^2$, $a < 0$
Domain: $(-\infty, \infty)$
Range: $(-\infty, 0]$
Intercept: $(0, 0)$
Increasing on $(-\infty, 0)$
Decreasing on $(0, \infty)$
Even function
Axis of symmetry: $x = 0$
Relative maximum or vertex: $(0, 0)$

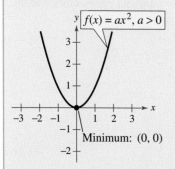

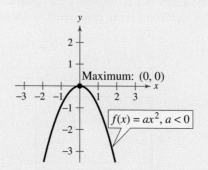

For the general quadratic form $f(x) = ax^2 + bx + c$, if the leading coefficient a is positive, the parabola opens upward; and if the leading coefficient a is negative, the parabola opens downward. Later in this section you will learn ways to find the coordinates of the vertex of a parabola.

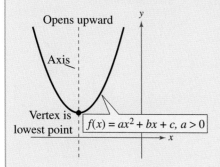

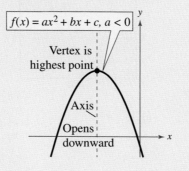

When sketching the graph of $f(x) = ax^2$, it is helpful to use the graph of $y = x^2$ as a reference, as discussed in Section 1.5. There you saw that when $a > 1$, the graph of $y = af(x)$ is a vertical stretch of the graph of $y = f(x)$. When $0 < a < 1$, the graph of $y = af(x)$ is a vertical shrink of the graph of $y = f(x)$. This is demonstrated again in Example 1.

Example 1 Graphing Simple Quadratic Functions

Describe how the graph of each function is related to the graph of $y = x^2$.

a. $f(x) = \dfrac{1}{3}x^2$ **b.** $g(x) = 2x^2$

c. $h(x) = -x^2 + 1$ **d.** $k(x) = (x + 2)^2 - 3$

Solution

a. Compared with $y = x^2$, each output of f "shrinks" by a factor of $\frac{1}{3}$. The result is a parabola that opens upward and is broader than the parabola represented by $y = x^2$, as shown in Figure 3.1.

b. Compared with $y = x^2$, each output of g "stretches" by a factor of 2, creating a narrower parabola, as shown in Figure 3.2.

c. With respect to the graph of $y = x^2$, the graph of h is obtained by a *reflection* in the x-axis and a vertical shift one unit *upward*, as shown in Figure 3.3.

d. With respect to the graph of $y = x^2$, the graph of k is obtained by a horizontal shift two units *to the left* and a vertical shift three units *downward*, as shown in Figure 3.4.

STUDY TIP

In Example 1, note that the coefficient a determines how widely the parabola given by $f(x) = ax^2$ opens. If $|a|$ is small, the parabola opens more widely than if $|a|$ is large.

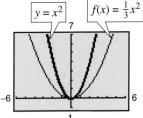

Figure 3.1

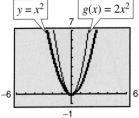

Figure 3.2

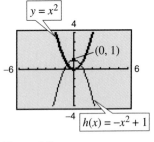

Figure 3.3

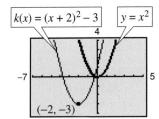

Figure 3.4

Prerequisite Skills

If you have difficulty with this example, review shifting, reflecting, and stretching of graphs in Section 1.5.

✓CHECKPOINT   Now try Exercise 5.

Recall from Section 1.5 that the graphs of $y = f(x \pm c)$, $y = f(x) \pm c$, $y = -f(x)$, and $y = f(-x)$ are rigid transformations of the graph of $y = f(x)$.

$y = f(x \pm c)$ Horizontal shift $y = -f(x)$ Reflection in x-axis

$y = f(x) \pm c$ Vertical shift $y = f(-x)$ Reflection in y-axis

The Standard Form of a Quadratic Function

The equation in Example 1(d) is written in the **standard form**

$$f(x) = a(x - h)^2 + k.$$

This form is especially convenient for sketching a parabola because it identifies the vertex of the parabola as (h, k).

Standard Form of a Quadratic Function

The quadratic function given by

$$f(x) = a(x - h)^2 + k, \qquad a \neq 0$$

is in **standard form.** The graph of f is a parabola whose axis is the vertical line $x = h$ and whose vertex is the point (h, k). If $a > 0$, the parabola opens upward, and if $a < 0$, the parabola opens downward.

Example 2   Identifying the Vertex of a Quadratic Function

Describe the graph of $f(x) = 2x^2 + 8x + 7$ and identify the vertex.

Solution

Write the quadratic function in standard form by completing the square. Recall that the first step is to factor out any coefficient of x^2 that is not 1.

$f(x) = 2x^2 + 8x + 7$ Write original function.

$= (2x^2 + 8x) + 7$ Group x-terms.

$= 2(x^2 + 4x) + 7$ Factor 2 out of x-terms.

$= 2(x^2 + 4x + 4 - 4) + 7$ Add and subtract $(4/2)^2 = 4$ within parentheses to complete the square.

$$\left(\frac{4}{2}\right)^2$$

$= 2(x^2 + 4x + 4) - 2(4) + 7$ Regroup terms.

$= 2(x + 2)^2 - 1$ Write in standard form.

From the standard form, you can see that the graph of f is a parabola that opens upward with vertex $(-2, -1)$, as shown in Figure 3.5. This corresponds to a left shift of two units and a downward shift of one unit relative to the graph of $y = 2x^2$.

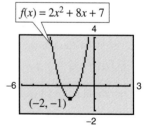

Figure 3.5

✓CHECKPOINT   Now try Exercise 13.

To find the x-intercepts of the graph of $f(x) = ax^2 + bx + c$, solve the equation $ax^2 + bx + c = 0$. If $ax^2 + bx + c$ does not factor, you can use the Quadratic Formula to find the x-intercepts, or a graphing utility to approximate the x-intercepts. Remember, however, that a parabola may not have x-intercepts.

Exploration

Use a graphing utility to graph $y = ax^2$ with $a = -2, -1, -0.5, 0.5, 1$, and 2. How does changing the value of a affect the graph?

Use a graphing utility to graph $y = (x - h)^2$ with $h = -4, -2, 2$, and 4. How does changing the value of h affect the graph?

Use a graphing utility to graph $y = x^2 + k$ with $k = -4, -2, 2$, and 4. How does changing the value of k affect the graph?

Prerequisite Skills

If you have difficulty with this example, review the process of completing the square for an algebraic expression in Section 2.4, paying special attention to problems in which $a \neq 1$.

Example 3   Identifying x-Intercepts of a Quadratic Function

Describe the graph of $f(x) = -x^2 + 6x - 8$ and identify any x-intercepts.

Solution

$$f(x) = -x^2 + 6x - 8 \qquad \text{Write original function.}$$

$$= -(x^2 - 6x) - 8 \qquad \text{Factor } -1 \text{ out of } x\text{-terms.}$$

$$= -(x^2 - 6x + 9 - 9) - 8 \qquad \begin{array}{l}\text{Because } b = 6, \text{ add and subtract} \\ (6/2)^2 = 9 \text{ within parentheses.}\end{array}$$

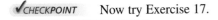

$$\left(\frac{6}{2}\right)^2$$

$$= -(x^2 - 6x + 9) - (-9) - 8 \qquad \text{Regroup terms.}$$

$$= -(x - 3)^2 + 1 \qquad \text{Write in standard form.}$$

The graph of f is a parabola that opens downward with vertex $(3, 1)$, as shown in Figure 3.6. The x-intercepts are determined as follows.

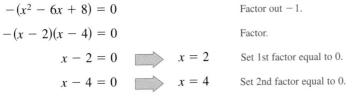

Figure 3.6

$$-(x^2 - 6x + 8) = 0 \qquad \text{Factor out } -1.$$

$$-(x - 2)(x - 4) = 0 \qquad \text{Factor.}$$

$$x - 2 = 0 \quad \Longrightarrow \quad x = 2 \qquad \text{Set 1st factor equal to 0.}$$

$$x - 4 = 0 \quad \Longrightarrow \quad x = 4 \qquad \text{Set 2nd factor equal to 0.}$$

So, the x-intercepts are $(2, 0)$ and $(4, 0)$, as shown in Figure 3.6.

✔CHECKPOINT   Now try Exercise 17.

Example 4   Writing the Equation of a Parabola in Standard Form

Write the standard form of the equation of the parabola whose vertex is $(1, 2)$ and that passes through the point $(3, -6)$.

Solution

Because the vertex of the parabola is $(h, k) = (1, 2)$, the equation has the form

$$f(x) = a(x - 1)^2 + 2. \qquad \text{Substitute for } h \text{ and } k \text{ in standard form.}$$

Because the parabola passes through the point $(3, -6)$, it follows that $f(3) = -6$. So, you obtain

$$-6 = a(3 - 1)^2 + 2$$

$$-6 = 4a + 2$$

$$-2 = a.$$

The equation in standard form is $f(x) = -2(x - 1)^2 + 2$. You can confirm this answer by graphing $f(x) = -2(x - 1)^2 + 2$ with a graphing utility, as shown in Figure 3.7 Use the *zoom* and *trace* features or the *maximum* and *value* features to confirm that its vertex is $(1, 2)$ and that it passes through the point $(3, -6)$.

✔CHECKPOINT   Now try Exercise 29.

STUDY TIP

In Example 4, there are infinitely many different parabolas that have a vertex at $(1, 2)$. Of these, however, the only one that passes through the point $(3, -6)$ is the one given by

$$f(x) = -2(x - 1)^2 + 2.$$

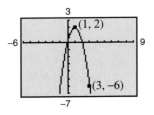

Figure 3.7

Finding Minimum and Maximum Values

Many applications involve finding the maximum or minimum value of a quadratic function. By completing the square of the quadratic function $f(x) = ax^2 + bx + c$, you can rewrite the function in standard form.

$$f(x) = a\left(x + \frac{b}{2a}\right)^2 + \left(c - \frac{b^2}{4a}\right) \qquad \text{Standard form}$$

You can see that the vertex occurs at $x = -b/(2a)$, which implies the following.

Minimum and Maximum Values of Quadratic Functions

1. If $a > 0$, f has a *minimum* value at $x = -\dfrac{b}{2a}$.

2. If $a < 0$, f has a *maximum* value at $x = -\dfrac{b}{2a}$.

Example 5   The Maximum Height of a Baseball

A baseball is hit at a point 3 feet above the ground at a velocity of 100 feet per second and at an angle of 45° with respect to the ground. The path of the baseball is given by the function $f(x) = -0.0032x^2 + x + 3$, where $f(x)$ is the height of the baseball (in feet) and x is the horizontal distance from home plate (in feet). What is the maximum height reached by the baseball?

TECHNOLOGY TIP

Note in the graphical solution for Example 5, that when using the *zoom* and *trace* features, you might have to change the y-scale in order to avoid a graph that is "too flat."

Algebraic Solution

For this quadratic function, you have

$$f(x) = ax^2 + bx + c = -0.0032x^2 + x + 3$$

which implies that $a = -0.0032$ and $b = 1$. Because the function has a maximum when $x = -b/(2a)$, you can conclude that the baseball reaches its maximum height when it is x feet from home plate, where x is

$$x = -\frac{b}{2a} = -\frac{1}{2(-0.0032)}$$

$$= 156.25 \text{ feet.}$$

At this distance, the maximum height is

$$f(156.25) = -0.0032(156.25)^2 + 156.25 + 3$$

$$= 81.125 \text{ feet.}$$

✓CHECKPOINT   Now try Exercise 55.

Graphical Solution

Use a graphing utility to graph $y = -0.0032x^2 + x + 3$ so that you can see the important features of the parabola. Use the *maximum* feature (see Figure 3.8) or the *zoom* and *trace* features (see Figure 3.9) of the graphing utility to approximate the maximum height on the graph to be $y \approx 81.125$ feet at $x \approx 156.25$.

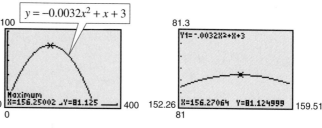

Figure 3.8   **Figure 3.9**

TECHNOLOGY SUPPORT   For instructions on how to use the *maximum*, the *minimum*, the *table*, and the *zoom* and *trace* features, see Appendix A; for specific keystrokes, go to this textbook's *Online Study Center*.

Example 6   Cost

A soft drink manufacturer has daily production costs of

$$C(x) = 70,000 - 120x + 0.055x^2$$

where C is the total cost (in dollars) and x is the number of units produced. Estimate numerically the number of units that should be produced each day to yield a minimum cost.

Solution

Enter the function $y = 70,000 - 120x + 0.055x^2$ into your graphing utility. Then use the *table* feature of the graphing utility to create a table. Set the table to start at $x = 0$ and set the table step to 100. By scrolling through the table you can see that the minimum cost is between 1000 units and 1200 units, as shown in Figure 3.10. You can improve this estimate by starting the table at $x = 1000$ and setting the table step to 10. From the table in Figure 3.11, you can see that approximately 1090 units should be produced to yield a minimum cost of $4545.50.

 CHECKPOINT   Now try Exercise 57.

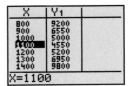

Figure 3.10

X	Y1	
1060	4598	
1070	4569.5	
1080	4552	
1090	4545.5	
1100	4550	
1110	4565.5	
1120	4592	

X=1090

Figure 3.11

Example 7   Grants

The numbers g of grants awarded from the National Endowment for the Humanities fund from 1999 to 2003 can be approximated by the model

$$g(t) = -99.14t^2 + 2,201.1t - 10,896, \qquad 9 \le t \le 13$$

where t represents the year, with $t = 9$ corresponding to 1999. Using this model, determine the year in which the number of grants awarded was greatest.
(Source: U.S. National Endowment for the Arts)

Algebraic Solution

Use the fact that the maximum point of the parabola occurs when $t = -b/(2a)$. For this function, you have $a = -99.14$ and $b = 2201.1$. So,

$$t = -\frac{b}{2a}$$

$$= -\frac{2201.1}{2(-99.14)}$$

$$\approx 11.1$$

From this t-value and the fact that $t = 9$ represents 1999, you can conclude that the greatest number of grants were awarded during 2001.

 CHECKPOINT   Now try Exercise 61.

Graphical Solution

Use a graphing utility to graph

$$y = -99.14x^2 + 2,201.1x - 10,896$$

for $9 \le x \le 13$, as shown in Figure 3.12. Use the *maximum* feature (see Figure 3.12) or the *zoom* and *trace* features (see Figure 3.13) of the graphing utility to approximate the maximum point of the parabola to be $x \approx 11.1$. So, you can conclude that the greatest number of grants were awarded during 2001.

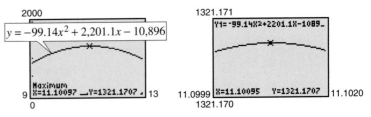

Figure 3.12   **Figure 3.13**

3.1 Exercises

See www.CalcChat.com for worked-out solutions to odd-numbered exercises.

Vocabulary Check

Fill in the blanks.

1. A polynomial function of degree n and leading coefficient a_n is a function of the form
$$f(x) = a_n x^n + a_{n-1} x^{n-1} + \cdots + a_2 x^2 + a_1 x + a_0, \quad a_n \neq 0$$
where n is a _____ and $a_n, a_{n-1}, \ldots, a_2, a_1, a_0$ are _____ numbers.

2. A _____ function is a second-degree polynomial function, and its graph is called a _____ .

3. The graph of a quadratic function is symmetric about its _____ .

4. If the graph of a quadratic function opens upward, then its leading coefficient is _____ and the vertex of the graph is a _____ .

5. If the graph of a quadratic function opens downward, then its leading coefficient is _____ and the vertex of the graph is a _____ .

In Exercises 1–4, match the quadratic function with its graph. [The graphs are labeled (a), (b), (c), and (d).]

(a)
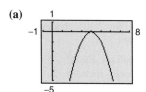

(b)
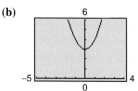

(c)
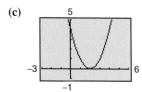

(d)
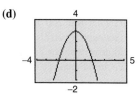

1. $f(x) = (x - 2)^2$
2. $f(x) = 3 - x^2$
3. $f(x) = x^2 + 3$
4. $f(x) = -(x - 4)^2$

In Exercises 5 and 6, use a graphing utility to graph each function in the same viewing window. Describe how the graph of each function is related to the graph of $y = x^2$.

5. (a) $y = \frac{1}{2}x^2$
   (b) $y = \frac{1}{2}x^2 - 1$
   (c) $y = \frac{1}{2}(x + 3)^2$
   (d) $y = -\frac{1}{2}(x + 3)^2 - 1$

6. (a) $y = \frac{3}{2}x^2$
   (b) $y = \frac{3}{2}x^2 + 1$
   (c) $y = \frac{3}{2}(x - 3)^2$
   (d) $y = -\frac{3}{2}(x - 3)^2 + 1$

In Exercises 7–20, sketch the graph of the quadratic function. Identify the vertex and x-intercept(s). Use a graphing utility to verify your results.

7. $f(x) = 25 - x^2$
8. $f(x) = x^2 - 7$
9. $f(x) = \frac{1}{2}x^2 - 4$
10. $f(x) = 16 - \frac{1}{4}x^2$

11. $f(x) = (x + 4)^2 - 3$
12. $f(x) = (x - 6)^2 + 3$
13. $h(x) = x^2 - 8x + 16$
14. $g(x) = x^2 + 2x + 1$
15. $f(x) = x^2 - x + \frac{5}{4}$
16. $f(x) = x^2 + 3x + \frac{1}{4}$
17. $f(x) = -x^2 + 2x + 5$
18. $f(x) = -x^2 - 4x + 1$
19. $h(x) = 4x^2 - 4x + 21$
20. $f(x) = 2x^2 - x + 1$

In Exercises 21–26, use a graphing utility to graph the quadratic function. Identify the vertex and x-intercept(s). Then check your results algebraically by writing the quadratic function in standard form.

21. $f(x) = -(x^2 + 2x - 3)$
22. $f(x) = -(x^2 + x - 30)$
23. $g(x) = x^2 + 8x + 11$
24. $f(x) = x^2 + 10x + 14$
25. $f(x) = -2x^2 + 16x - 31$
26. $f(x) = -4x^2 + 24x - 41$

In Exercises 27 and 28, write an equation for the parabola in standard form. Use a graphing utility to graph the equation and verify your result.

27.
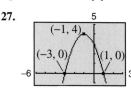

28.
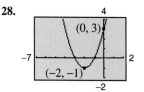

In Exercises 29–34, write the standard form of the quadratic function that has the indicated vertex and whose graph passes through the given point. Verify your result with a graphing utility.

29. Vertex: $(-2, 5)$;   Point: $(0, 9)$

30. Vertex: $(4, 1)$;   Point: $(6, -7)$

31. Vertex: $(1, -2)$;   Point: $(-1, 14)$

32. Vertex: $(-4, -1)$;   Point: $(-2, 4)$

33. Vertex: $\left(\frac{1}{2}, 1\right)$;   Point: $\left(-2, -\frac{21}{5}\right)$

34. Vertex: $\left(-\frac{1}{4}, -1\right)$;   Point: $\left(0, -\frac{17}{16}\right)$

Graphical Reasoning **In Exercises 35–38, determine the *x*-intercept(s) of the graph visually. How do the *x*-intercepts correspond to the solutions of the quadratic equation when $y = 0$?**

35.

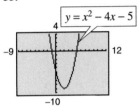

$y = x^2 - 4x - 5$

36.

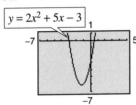

$y = 2x^2 + 5x - 3$

37.

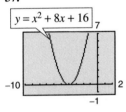

$y = x^2 + 8x + 16$

38.

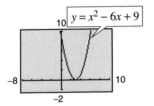

$y = x^2 - 6x + 9$

In Exercises 39–44, use a graphing utility to graph the quadratic function. Find the *x*-intercepts of the graph and compare them with the solutions of the corresponding quadratic equation when $y = 0$.

39. $y = x^2 - 4x$

40. $y = -2x^2 + 10x$

41. $y = 2x^2 - 7x - 30$

42. $y = 4x^2 + 25x - 21$

43. $y = -\frac{1}{2}(x^2 - 6x - 7)$

44. $y = \frac{7}{10}(x^2 + 12x - 45)$

In Exercises 45–48, find two quadratic functions, one that opens upward and one that opens downward, whose graphs have the given *x*-intercepts. (There are many correct answers.)

45. $(-1, 0), (3, 0)$

46. $(0, 0), (10, 0)$

47. $(-3, 0), \left(-\frac{1}{2}, 0\right)$

48. $\left(-\frac{5}{2}, 0\right), (2, 0)$

In Exercises 49–52, find two positive real numbers whose product is a maximum.

49. The sum is 110.

50. The sum is S.

51. The sum of the first and twice the second is 24.

52. The sum of the first and three times the second is 42.

53. *Geometry* An indoor physical fitness room consists of a rectangular region with a semicircle on each end. The perimeter of the room is to be a 200-meter single-lane running track.

(a) Draw a diagram that illustrates the problem. Let x and y represent the length and width of the rectangular region, respectively.

(b) Determine the radius of the semicircular ends of the track. Determine the distance, in terms of y, around the inside edge of the two semicircular parts of the track.

(c) Use the result of part (b) to write an equation, in terms of x and y, for the distance traveled in one lap around the track. Solve for y.

(d) Use the result of part (c) to write the area A of the rectangular region as a function of x.

(e) Use a graphing utility to graph the area function from part (d). Use the graph to approximate the dimensions that will produce a rectangle of maximum area.

54. *Numerical, Graphical, and Analytical Analysis* A rancher has 200 feet of fencing to enclose two adjacent rectangular corrals (see figure). Use the following methods to determine the dimensions that will produce a maximum enclosed area.

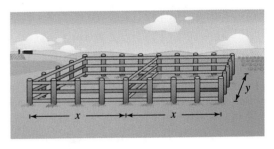

(a) Write the area A of the corral as a function of x.

(b) Use the *table* feature of a graphing utility to create a table showing possible values of x and the corresponding areas A of the corral. Use the table to estimate the dimensions that will produce the maximum enclosed area.

(c) Use a graphing utility to graph the area function. Use the graph to approximate the dimensions that will produce the maximum enclosed area.

(d) Write the area function in standard form to find algebraically the dimensions that will produce the maximum area.

(e) Compare your results from parts (b), (c), and (d).

55. Height of a Ball　The height y (in feet) of a punted football is approximated by

$$y = -\frac{16}{2025}x^2 + \frac{9}{5}x + \frac{3}{2}$$

where x is the horizontal distance (in feet) from where the football is punted.

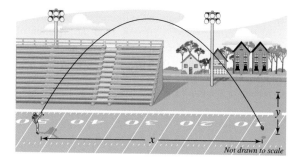

Not drawn to scale

(a) Use a graphing utility to graph the path of the football.

(b) How high is the football when it is punted? (*Hint:* Find y when $x = 0$.)

(c) What is the maximum height of the football?

(d) How far from the punter does the football strike the ground?

56. Path of a Diver　The path of a diver is approximated by

$$y = -\frac{4}{9}x^2 + \frac{24}{9}x + 12$$

where y is the height (in feet) and x is the horizontal distance (in feet) from the end of the diving board (see figure). What is the maximum height of the diver? Verify your answer using a graphing utility.

57. Cost　A manufacturer of lighting fixtures has daily production costs of

$$C(x) = 800 - 10x + 0.25x^2$$

where C is the total cost (in dollars) and x is the number of units produced. Use the *table* feature of a graphing utility to determine how many fixtures should be produced each day to yield a minimum cost.

58. Automobile Aerodynamics　The number of horsepower H required to overcome wind drag on a certain automobile is approximated by

$$H(s) = 0.002s^2 + 0.05s - 0.029, \quad 0 \le s \le 100$$

where s is the speed of the car (in miles per hour).

(a) Use a graphing utility to graph the function.

(b) Graphically estimate the maximum speed of the car if the power required to overcome wind drag is not to exceed 10 horsepower. Verify your result algebraically.

59. Revenue　The total revenue R (in thousands of dollars) earned from manufacturing and selling hand-held video games is given by

$$R(p) = -25p^2 + 1200p$$

where p is the price per unit (in dollars).

(a) Find the revenue when the price per unit is $20, $25, and $30.

(b) Find the unit price that will yield a maximum revenue.

(c) What is the maximum revenue?

(d) Explain your results.

60. Revenue　The total revenue R (in dollars) earned by a dog walking service is given by

$$R(p) = -12p^2 + 150p$$

where p is the price charged per dog (in dollars).

(a) Find the revenue when the price per dog is $4, $6, and $8.

(b) Find the price that will yield a maximum revenue.

(c) What is the maximum revenue?

(d) Explain your results.

61. Graphical Analysis　From 1960 to 2004, the annual per capita consumption C of cigarettes by Americans (age 18 and older) can be modeled by

$$C(t) = 4306 - 3.4t - 1.32t^2, \quad 0 \le t \le 44$$

where t is the year, with $t = 0$ corresponding to 1960. (Source: U.S. Department of Agriculture)

(a) Use a graphing utility to graph the model.

(b) Use the graph of the model to approximate the year when the maximum annual consumption of cigarettes occurred. Approximate the maximum average annual consumption. Beginning in 1966, all cigarette packages were required by law to carry a health warning. Do you think the warning had any effect? Explain.

(c) In 2000, the U.S. population (age 18 and older) was 209,117,000. Of those, about 48,306,000 were smokers. What was the average annual cigarette consumption *per smoker* in 2000? What was the average daily cigarette consumption *per smoker*?

62. Data Analysis The factory sales S of VCRs (in millions of dollars) in the United States from 1990 to 2004 can be modeled by $S = -28.40t^2 + 218.1t + 2435$, for $0 \le t \le 14$, where t is the year, with $t = 0$ corresponding to 1990. (Source: Consumer Electronics Association)

(a) According to the model, when did the maximum value of factory sales of VCRs occur?

(b) According to the model, what was the value of the factory sales in 2004? Explain your result.

(c) Would you use the model to predict the value of the factory sales for years beyond 2004? Explain.

Synthesis

True or False? In Exercises 63 and 64, determine whether the statement is true or false. Justify your answer.

63. The function $f(x) = -12x^2 - 1$ has no x-intercepts.

64. The graphs of $f(x) = -4x^2 - 10x + 7$ and $g(x) = 12x^2 + 30x + 1$ have the same axis of symmetry.

Library of Parent Functions In Exercises 65 and 66, determine which equation(s) may be represented by the graph shown. (There may be more than one correct answer.)

65. (a) $f(x) = -(x - 4)^2 + 2$

(b) $f(x) = -(x + 2)^2 + 4$

(c) $f(x) = -(x + 2)^2 - 4$

(d) $f(x) = -x^2 - 4x - 8$

(e) $f(x) = -(x - 2)^2 - 4$

(f) $f(x) = -x^2 + 4x - 8$

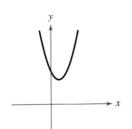

66. (a) $f(x) = (x - 1)^2 + 3$

(b) $f(x) = (x + 1)^2 + 3$

(c) $f(x) = (x - 3)^2 + 1$

(d) $f(x) = x^2 + 2x + 4$

(e) $f(x) = (x + 3)^2 + 1$

(f) $f(x) = x^2 + 6x + 10$

Think About It In Exercises 67–70, find the value of b such that the function has the given maximum or minimum value.

67. $f(x) = -x^2 + bx - 75$; Maximum value: 25

68. $f(x) = -x^2 + bx - 16$; Maximum value: 48

69. $f(x) = x^2 + bx + 26$; Minimum value: 10

70. $f(x) = x^2 + bx - 25$; Minimum value: -50

71. Profit The profit P (in millions of dollars) for a recreational vehicle retailer is modeled by a quadratic function of the form $P = at^2 + bt + c$, where t represents the year. If you were president of the company, which of the following models would you prefer? Explain your reasoning.

(a) a is positive and $t \ge -b/(2a)$.

(b) a is positive and $t \le -b/(2a)$.

(c) a is negative and $t \ge -b/(2a)$.

(d) a is negative and $t \le -b/(2a)$.

72. Writing The parabola in the figure below has an equation of the form $y = ax^2 + bx - 4$. Find the equation of this parabola in two different ways, by hand and with technology (graphing utility or computer software). Write a paragraph describing the methods you used and comparing the results of the two methods.

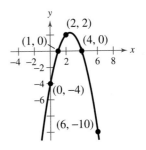

Skills Review

In Exercises 73–76, determine algebraically any point(s) of intersection of the graphs of the equations. Verify your results using the *intersect* feature of a graphing utility.

73. $x + y = 8$
$-\frac{2}{3}x + y = 6$

74. $y = 3x - 10$
$y = \frac{1}{4}x + 1$

75. $y = 9 - x^2$
$y = x + 3$

76. $y = x^3 + 2x - 1$
$y = -2x + 15$

In Exercises 77–80, perform the operation and write the result in standard form.

77. $(6 - i) - (2i + 11)$

78. $(2i + 5)^2 - 21$

79. $(3i + 7)(-4i + 1)$

80. $(4 - i)^3$

81. Make a Decision To work an extended application analyzing the height of a basketball after it has been dropped, visit this textbook's *Online Study Center*.

3.2 Polynomial Functions of Higher Degree

Graphs of Polynomial Functions

You should be able to sketch accurate graphs of polynomial functions of degrees 0, 1, and 2. The graphs of polynomial functions of degree greater than 2 are more difficult to sketch by hand. However, in this section you will learn how to recognize some of the basic features of the graphs of polynomial functions. Using these features along with point plotting, intercepts, and symmetry, you should be able to make reasonably accurate sketches *by hand*.

The graph of a polynomial function is **continuous.** Essentially, this means that the graph of a polynomial function has no breaks, holes, or gaps, as shown in Figure 3.14. Informally, you can say that a function is continuous if its graph can be drawn with a pencil without lifting the pencil from the paper.

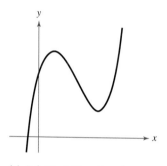

(a) Polynomial functions have continuous graphs.

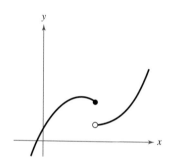

(b) Functions with graphs that are not continuous are not polynomial functions.

Figure 3.14

Another feature of the graph of a polynomial function is that it has only smooth, rounded turns, as shown in Figure 3.15(a). It cannot have a sharp turn such as the one shown in Figure 3.15(b).

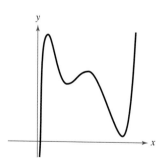

(a) Polynomial functions have graphs with smooth, rounded turns.

Figure 3.15

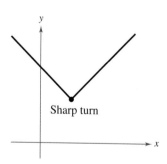

Sharp turn

(b) Functions with graphs that have sharp turns are not polynomial functions.

What you should learn

- Use transformations to sketch graphs of polynomial functions.
- Use the Leading Coefficient Test to determine the end behavior of graphs of polynomial functions.
- Find and use zeros of polynomial functions as sketching aids.
- Use the Intermediate Value Theorem to help locate zeros of polynomial functions.

Why you should learn it

You can use polynomial functions to model various aspects of nature, such as the growth of a red oak tree, as shown in Exercise 94 on page 274.

Leonard Lee Rue III/Earth Scenes

Library of Parent Functions: Polynomial Function

The graphs of polynomial functions of degree 1 are lines, and those of functions of degree 2 are parabolas. The graphs of all polynomial functions are smooth and continuous. A polynomial function of degree n has the form

$$f(x) = a_n x^n + a_{n-1} x^{n-1} + \cdots + a_2 x^2 + a_1 x + a_0$$

where n is a positive integer and $a_n \neq 0$. The polynomial functions that have the simplest graphs are monomials of the form $f(x) = x^n$, where n is an integer greater than zero. If n is even, the graph is similar to the graph of $f(x) = x^2$ and touches the axis at the x-intercept. If n is odd, the graph is similar to the graph of $f(x) = x^3$ and crosses the axis at the x-intercept. The greater the value of n, the flatter the graph near the origin. The basic characteristics of the *cubic function* $f(x) = x^3$ are summarized below. A review of polynomial functions can be found in the *Study Capsules*.

Graph of $f(x) = x^3$

Domain: $(-\infty, \infty)$
Range: $(-\infty, \infty)$
Intercept: $(0, 0)$
Increasing on $(-\infty, \infty)$
Odd function
Origin symmetry

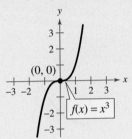

Exploration

Use a graphing utility to graph $y = x^n$ for $n = 2, 4,$ and 8. (Use the viewing window $-1.5 \le x \le 1.5$ and $-1 \le y \le 6$.) Compare the graphs. In the interval $(-1, 1)$, which graph is on the bottom? Outside the interval $(-1, 1)$, which graph is on the bottom?
  Use a graphing utility to graph $y = x^n$ for $n = 3, 5,$ and 7. (Use the viewing window $-1.5 \le x \le 1.5$ and $-4 \le y \le 4$.) Compare the graphs. In the intervals $(-\infty, -1)$ and $(0, 1)$, which graph is on the bottom? In the intervals $(-1, 0)$ and $(1, \infty)$, which graph is on the bottom?

Example 1   Transformations of Monomial Functions

Sketch the graphs of (a) $f(x) = -x^5$, (b) $g(x) = x^4 + 1$, and (c) $h(x) = (x + 1)^4$.

Solution

a. Because the degree of $f(x) = -x^5$ is odd, the graph is similar to the graph of $y = x^3$. Moreover, the negative coefficient reflects the graph in the x-axis, as shown in Figure 3.16.

b. The graph of $g(x) = x^4 + 1$ is an upward shift of one unit of the graph of $y = x^4$, as shown in Figure 3.17.

c. The graph of $h(x) = (x + 1)^4$ is a left shift of one unit of the graph of $y = x^4$, as shown in Figure 3.18.

Prerequisite Skills

If you have difficulty with this example, review shifting and reflecting of graphs in Section 1.5.

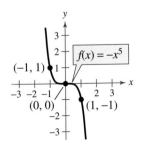

Figure 3.16

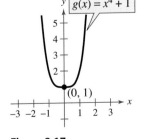

Figure 3.17

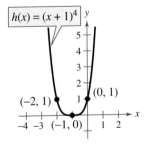

Figure 3.18

✔CHECKPOINT   Now try Exercise 9.

The Leading Coefficient Test

In Example 1, note that all three graphs eventually rise or fall without bound as x moves to the right. Whether the graph of a polynomial eventually rises or falls can be determined by the polynomial function's degree (even or odd) and by its leading coefficient, as indicated in the **Leading Coefficient Test.**

Leading Coefficient Test

As x moves without bound to the left or to the right, the graph of the polynomial function $f(x) = a_n x^n + \cdots + a_1 x + a_0$, $a_n \neq 0$, eventually rises or falls in the following manner.

1. When n is odd:

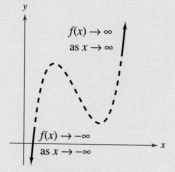

If the leading coefficient is positive ($a_n > 0$), the graph falls to the left and rises to the right.

If the leading coefficient is negative ($a_n < 0$), the graph rises to the left and falls to the right.

2. When n is even:

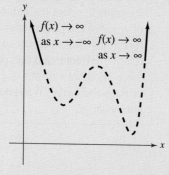
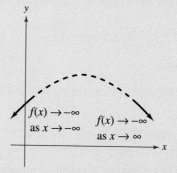

If the leading coefficient is positive ($a_n > 0$), the graph rises to the left and right.

If the leading coefficient is negative ($a_n < 0$), the graph falls to the left and right.

Note that the dashed portions of the graphs indicate that the test determines only the right-hand and left-hand behavior of the graph.

As you continue to study polynomial functions and their graphs, you will notice that the degree of a polynomial plays an important role in determining other characteristics of the polynomial function and its graph.

Example 2 Applying the Leading Coefficient Test

Use the Leading Coefficient Test to describe the right-hand and left-hand behavior of the graph of each polynomial function.

a. $f(x) = -x^3 + 4x$ **b.** $f(x) = x^4 - 5x^2 + 4$ **c.** $f(x) = x^5 - x$

Solution

a. Because the degree is odd and the leading coefficient is negative, the graph rises to the left and falls to the right, as shown in Figure 3.19.

b. Because the degree is even and the leading coefficient is positive, the graph rises to the left and right, as shown in Figure 3.20.

c. Because the degree is odd and the leading coefficient is positive, the graph falls to the left and rises to the right, as shown in Figure 3.21.

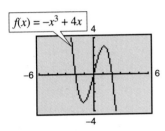

Figure 3.19

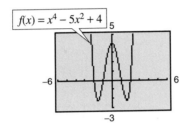

Figure 3.20

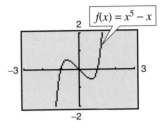

Figure 3.21

 CHECKPOINT   Now try Exercise 15.

In Example 2, note that the Leading Coefficient Test only tells you whether the graph *eventually* rises or falls to the right or left. Other characteristics of the graph, such as intercepts and minimum and maximum points, must be determined by other tests.

Zeros of Polynomial Functions

It can be shown that for a polynomial function f of degree n, the following statements are true.

1. The function f has at most n real zeros. (You will study this result in detail in Section 3.4 on the Fundamental Theorem of Algebra.)

2. The graph of f has at most $n - 1$ relative **extrema** (relative **minima** or **maxima**).

Recall that a **zero** of a function f is a number x for which $f(x) = 0$. Finding the zeros of polynomial functions is one of the most important problems in algebra. You have already seen that there is a strong interplay between graphical and algebraic approaches to this problem. Sometimes you can use information about the graph of a function to help find its zeros. In other cases, you can use information about the zeros of a function to find a good viewing window.

Exploration

For each of the graphs in Example 2, count the number of zeros of the polynomial function and the number of relative extrema, and compare these numbers with the degree of the polynomial. What do you observe?

> **Real Zeros of Polynomial Functions**
>
> If f is a polynomial function and a is a real number, the following statements are equivalent.
>
> **1.** $x = a$ is a *zero* of the function f.
> **2.** $x = a$ is a *solution* of the polynomial equation $f(x) = 0$.
> **3.** $(x - a)$ is a *factor* of the polynomial $f(x)$.
> **4.** $(a, 0)$ is an *x-intercept* of the graph of f.

> **TECHNOLOGY SUPPORT**
>
> For instructions on how to use the *zero* or *root* feature, see Appendix A; for specific keystrokes, go to this textbook's *Online Study Center.*

Finding zeros of polynomial functions is closely related to factoring and finding x-intercepts, as demonstrated in Examples 3, 4, and 5.

Example 3   Finding Zeros of a Polynomial Function

Find all real zeros of $f(x) = x^3 - x^2 - 2x$.

Algebraic Solution

$$f(x) = x^3 - x^2 - 2x \qquad \text{Write original function.}$$
$$0 = x^3 - x^2 - 2x \qquad \text{Substitute 0 for } f(x).$$
$$0 = x(x^2 - x - 2) \qquad \text{Remove common monomial factor.}$$
$$0 = x(x - 2)(x + 1) \qquad \text{Factor completely.}$$

So, the real zeros are $x = 0$, $x = 2$, and $x = -1$, and the corresponding x-intercepts are $(0, 0)$, $(2, 0)$, and $(-1, 0)$.

Check

$$(0)^3 - (0)^2 - 2(0) = 0 \qquad x = 0 \text{ is a zero. } ✓$$
$$(2)^3 - (2)^2 - 2(2) = 0 \qquad x = 2 \text{ is a zero. } ✓$$
$$(-1)^3 - (-1)^2 - 2(-1) = 0 \qquad x = -1 \text{ is a zero. } ✓$$

✓ *CHECKPOINT*   Now try Exercise 33.

Graphical Solution

Use a graphing utility to graph $y = x^3 - x^2 - 2x$. In Figure 3.22, the graph appears to have the x-intercepts $(0, 0)$, $(2, 0)$, and $(-1, 0)$. Use the *zero* or *root* feature, or the *zoom* and *trace* features, of the graphing utility to verify these intercepts. Note that this third-degree polynomial has two relative extrema, at $(-0.55, 0.63)$ and $(1.22, -2.11)$.

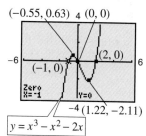

Figure 3.22

Example 4   Analyzing a Polynomial Function

Find all real zeros and relative extrema of $f(x) = -2x^4 + 2x^2$.

Solution

$$0 = -2x^4 + 2x^2 \qquad \text{Substitute 0 for } f(x).$$
$$0 = -2x^2(x^2 - 1) \qquad \text{Remove common monomial factor.}$$
$$0 = -2x^2(x - 1)(x + 1) \qquad \text{Factor completely.}$$

So, the real zeros are $x = 0$, $x = 1$, and $x = -1$, and the corresponding x-intercepts are $(0, 0)$, $(1, 0)$, and $(-1, 0)$, as shown in Figure 3.23. Using the *minimum* and *maximum* features of a graphing utility, you can approximate the three relative extrema to be $(-0.71, 0.5)$, $(0, 0)$, and $(0.71, 0.5)$.

✓ *CHECKPOINT*   Now try Exercise 45.

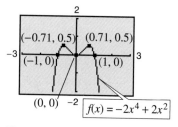

Figure 3.23

Repeated Zeros

For a polynomial function, a factor of $(x - a)^k$, $k > 1$, yields a **repeated zero** $x = a$ of **multiplicity** k.

1. If k is odd, the graph *crosses* the x-axis at $x = a$.
2. If k is even, the graph *touches* the x-axis (but does not cross the x-axis) at $x = a$.

STUDY TIP

In Example 4, note that because k is even, the factor $-2x^2$ yields the repeated zero $x = 0$. The graph touches (but does not cross) the x-axis at $x = 0$, as shown in Figure 3.23.

Example 5   Finding Zeros of a Polynomial Function

Find all real zeros of $f(x) = x^5 - 3x^3 - x^2 - 4x - 1$.

Solution

Use a graphing utility to obtain the graph shown in Figure 3.24. From the graph, you can see that there are three zeros. Using the *zero* or *root* feature, you can determine that the zeros are approximately $x \approx -1.86$, $x \approx -0.25$, and $x \approx 2.11$. It should be noted that this fifth-degree polynomial factors as

$$f(x) = x^5 - 3x^3 - x^2 - 4x - 1 = (x^2 + 1)(x^3 - 4x - 1).$$

The three zeros obtained above are the zeros of the cubic factor $x^3 - 4x - 1$ (the quadratic factor $x^2 + 1$ has two complex zeros and so no *real* zeros).

✓CHECKPOINT   Now try Exercise 47.

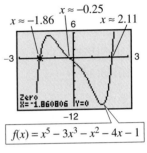

Figure 3.24

Example 6   Finding a Polynomial Function with Given Zeros

Find polynomial functions with the following zeros. (There are many correct solutions.)

a. $-\dfrac{1}{2}, 3, 3$ **b.** $3, 2 + \sqrt{11}, 2 - \sqrt{11}$

Prerequisite Skills

If you have difficulty with Example 6(b), review special products in Section P.3.

Solution

a. Note that the zero $x = -\frac{1}{2}$ corresponds to either $\left(x + \frac{1}{2}\right)$ or $(2x + 1)$. To avoid fractions, choose the second factor and write

$$f(x) = (2x + 1)(x - 3)^2$$

$$= (2x + 1)(x^2 - 6x + 9) = 2x^3 - 11x^2 + 12x + 9.$$

b. For each of the given zeros, form a corresponding factor and write

$$f(x) = (x - 3)\big[x - \big(2 + \sqrt{11}\big)\big]\big[x - \big(2 - \sqrt{11}\big)\big]$$

$$= (x - 3)\big[(x - 2) - \sqrt{11}\big]\big[(x - 2) + \sqrt{11}\big]$$

$$= (x - 3)\big[(x - 2)^2 - \big(\sqrt{11}\big)^2\big]$$

$$= (x - 3)(x^2 - 4x + 4 - 11)$$

$$= (x - 3)(x^2 - 4x - 7) = x^3 - 7x^2 + 5x + 21.$$

✓CHECKPOINT   Now try Exercise 55.

Exploration

Use a graphing utility to graph

$$y_1 = x + 2$$

$$y_2 = (x + 2)(x - 1).$$

Predict the shape of the curve $y = (x + 2)(x - 1)(x - 3)$, and verify your answer with a graphing utility.

Note in Example 6 that there are many polynomial functions with the indicated zeros. In fact, multiplying the functions by any real number does not change the zeros of the function. For instance, multiply the function from part (b) by $\frac{1}{2}$ to obtain $f(x) = \frac{1}{2}x^3 - \frac{7}{2}x^2 + \frac{5}{2}x + \frac{21}{2}$. Then find the zeros of the function. You will obtain the zeros 3, $2 + \sqrt{11}$, and $2 - \sqrt{11}$, as given in Example 6.

Example 7 Sketching the Graph of a Polynomial Function

Sketch the graph of $f(x) = 3x^4 - 4x^3$ by hand.

Solution

1. *Apply the Leading Coefficient Test.*   Because the leading coefficient is positive and the degree is even, you know that the graph eventually rises to the left and to the right (see Figure 3.25).

2. *Find the Real Zeros of the Polynomial.*   By factoring

$$f(x) = 3x^4 - 4x^3 = x^3(3x - 4)$$

you can see that the real zeros of f are $x = 0$ (of odd multiplicity 3) and $x = \frac{4}{3}$ (of odd multiplicity 1). So, the x-intercepts occur at $(0, 0)$ and $\left(\frac{4}{3}, 0\right)$. Add these points to your graph, as shown in Figure 3.25.

3. *Plot a Few Additional Points.*   To sketch the graph by hand, find a few additional points, as shown in the table. Be sure to choose points between the zeros and to the left and right of the zeros. Then plot the points (see Figure 3.26).

x	-1	0.5	1	1.5
$f(x)$	7	-0.31	-1	1.69

4. *Draw the Graph.*   Draw a continuous curve through the points, as shown in Figure 3.26. Because both zeros are of odd multiplicity, you know that the graph should cross the x-axis at $x = 0$ and $x = \frac{4}{3}$. If you are unsure of the shape of a portion of the graph, plot some additional points.

TECHNOLOGY TIP

It is easy to make mistakes when entering functions into a graphing utility. So, it is important to have an understanding of the basic shapes of graphs and to be able to graph simple polynomials *by hand*. For example, suppose you had entered the function in Example 7 as $y = 3x^5 - 4x^3$. By looking at the graph, what mathematical principles would alert you to the fact that you had made a mistake?

Exploration

Partner Activity   Multiply three, four, or five distinct linear factors to obtain the equation of a polynomial function of degree 3, 4, or 5. Exchange equations with your partner and sketch, *by hand*, the graph of the equation that your partner wrote. When you are finished, use a graphing utility to check each other's work.

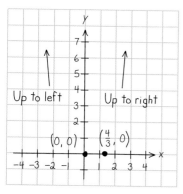

Figure 3.25

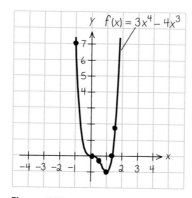

Figure 3.26

✓**CHECKPOINT**   Now try Exercise 71.

Example 8   Sketching the Graph of a Polynomial Function

Sketch the graph of $f(x) = -2x^3 + 6x^2 - \frac{9}{2}x$.

Solution

1. *Apply the Leading Coefficient Test.* Because the leading coefficient is negative and the degree is odd, you know that the graph eventually rises to the left and falls to the right (see Figure 3.27).

2. *Find the Real Zeros of the Polynomial.* By factoring

$$f(x) = -2x^3 + 6x^2 - \frac{9}{2}x$$

$$= -\frac{1}{2}x(4x^2 - 12x + 9)$$

$$= -\frac{1}{2}x(2x - 3)^2$$

you can see that the real zeros of f are $x = 0$ (of odd multiplicity 1) and $x = \frac{3}{2}$ (of even multiplicity 2). So, the x-intercepts occur at $(0, 0)$ and $\left(\frac{3}{2}, 0\right)$. Add these points to your graph, as shown in Figure 3.27.

3. *Plot a Few Additional Points.* To sketch the graph by hand, find a few additional points, as shown in the table. Then plot the points (see Figure 3.28.)

x	-0.5	0.5	1	2
$f(x)$	4	-1	-0.5	-1

4. *Draw the Graph.* Draw a continuous curve through the points, as shown in Figure 3.28. As indicated by the multiplicities of the zeros, the graph crosses the x-axis at $(0, 0)$ and touches (but does not cross) the x-axis at $\left(\frac{3}{2}, 0\right)$.

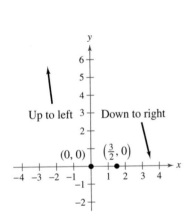

Figure 3.27

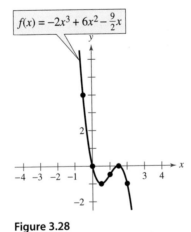

Figure 3.28

✔CHECKPOINT   Now try Exercise 73.

TECHNOLOGY TIP   Remember that when using a graphing utility to verify your graphs, you may need to adjust your viewing window in order to see all the features of the graph.

STUDY TIP

Observe in Example 8 that the sign of $f(x)$ is positive to the left of and negative to the right of the zero $x = 0$. Similarly, the sign of $f(x)$ is negative to the left and to the right of the zero $x = \frac{3}{2}$. This suggests that if a zero of a polynomial function is of *odd* multiplicity, then the sign of $f(x)$ changes from one side of the zero to the other side. If a zero is of *even* multiplicity, then the sign of $f(x)$ does not change from one side of the zero to the other side. The following table helps to illustrate this result.

x	-0.5	0	0.5
$f(x)$	4	0	-1
Sign	$+$		$-$

x	1	$\frac{3}{2}$	2
$f(x)$	-0.5	0	-1
Sign	$-$		$-$

This sign analysis may be helpful in graphing polynomial functions.

The Intermediate Value Theorem

The **Intermediate Value Theorem** concerns the existence of real zeros of polynomial functions. The theorem states that if $(a, f(a))$ and $(b, f(b))$ are two points on the graph of a polynomial function such that $f(a) \neq f(b)$, then for any number d between $f(a)$ and $f(b)$ there must be a number c between a and b such that $f(c) = d$. (See Figure 3.29.)

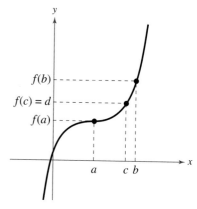

> **Intermediate Value Theorem**
>
> Let a and b be real numbers such that $a < b$. If f is a polynomial function such that $f(a) \neq f(b)$, then in the interval $[a, b]$, f takes on every value between $f(a)$ and $f(b)$.

Figure 3.29

This theorem helps you locate the real zeros of a polynomial function in the following way. If you can find a value $x = a$ at which a polynomial function is positive, and another value $x = b$ at which it is negative, you can conclude that the function has at least one real zero between these two values. For example, the function $f(x) = x^3 + x^2 + 1$ is negative when $x = -2$ and positive when $x = -1$. Therefore, it follows from the Intermediate Value Theorem that f must have a real zero somewhere between -2 and -1.

Example 9   Approximating the Zeros of a Function

Find three intervals of length 1 in which the polynomial $f(x) = 12x^3 - 32x^2 + 3x + 5$ is guaranteed to have a zero.

Graphical Solution

Use a graphing utility to graph

$$y = 12x^3 - 32x^2 + 3x + 5$$

as shown in Figure 3.30.

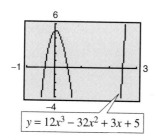

Figure 3.30

From the figure, you can see that the graph crosses the x-axis three times—between -1 and 0, between 0 and 1, and between 2 and 3. So, you can conclude that the function has zeros in the intervals $(-1, 0)$, $(0, 1)$, and $(2, 3)$.

✓CHECKPOINT   Now try Exercise 79.

Numerical Solution

Use the *table* feature of a graphing utility to create a table of function values. Scroll through the table looking for consecutive function values that differ in sign. For instance, from the table in Figure 3.31 you can see that $f(-1)$ and $f(0)$ differ in sign. So, you can conclude from the Intermediate Value Theorem that the function has a zero between -1 and 0. Similarly, $f(0)$ and $f(1)$ differ in sign, so the function has a zero between 0 and 1. Likewise, $f(2)$ and $f(3)$ differ in sign, so the function has a zero between 2 and 3. So, you can conclude that the function has zeros in the intervals $(-1, 0)$, $(0, 1)$, and $(2, 3)$.

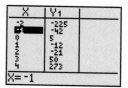

Figure 3.31

3.2 Exercises

See www.CalcChat.com for worked-out solutions to odd-numbered exercises.

Vocabulary Check

Fill in the blanks.

1. The graphs of all polynomial functions are _____ , which means that the graphs have no breaks, holes, or gaps.

2. The _____ is used to determine the left-hand and right-hand behavior of the graph of a polynomial function.

3. A polynomial function of degree n has at most _____ real zeros and at most _____ turning points, called _____ .

4. If $x = a$ is a zero of a polynomial function f, then the following statements are true.

   (a) $x = a$ is a _____ of the polynomial equation $f(x) = 0$.

   (b) _____ is a factor of the polynomial $f(x)$.

   (c) $(a, 0)$ is an _____ of the graph of f.

5. If a zero of a polynomial function is of even multiplicity, then the graph of f _____ the x-axis, and if the zero is of odd multiplicity, then the graph of f _____ the x-axis.

6. The _____ Theorem states that if f is a polynomial function such that $f(a) \neq f(b)$, then in the interval $[a, b]$, f takes on every value between $f(a)$ and $f(b)$.

In Exercises 1–8, match the polynomial function with its graph. [The graphs are labeled (a) through (h).]

(a)

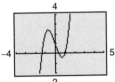

(b)

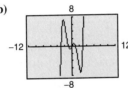

(c)

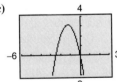

(d)

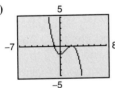

(e)

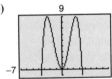

(f)

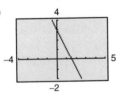

(g)

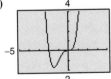

(h)

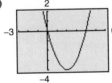

1. $f(x) = -2x + 3$

2. $f(x) = x^2 - 4x$

3. $f(x) = -2x^2 - 5x$

4. $f(x) = 2x^3 - 3x + 1$

5. $f(x) = -\frac{1}{4}x^4 + 3x^2$

6. $f(x) = -\frac{1}{3}x^3 + x^2 - \frac{4}{3}$

7. $f(x) = x^4 + 2x^3$

8. $f(x) = \frac{1}{5}x^5 - 2x^3 + \frac{9}{5}x$

In Exercises 9 and 10, sketch the graph of $y = x^n$ and each specified transformation.

9. $y = x^3$

   (a) $f(x) = (x - 2)^3$ (b) $f(x) = x^3 - 2$

   (c) $f(x) = -\frac{1}{2}x^3$ (d) $f(x) = (x - 2)^3 - 2$

10. $y = x^4$

   (a) $f(x) = (x + 5)^4$ (b) $f(x) = x^4 - 5$

   (c) $f(x) = 4 - x^4$ (d) $f(x) = \frac{1}{2}(x - 1)^4$

Graphical Analysis **In Exercises 11–14, use a graphing utility to graph the functions f and g in the same viewing window. Zoom out far enough so that the right-hand and left-hand behaviors of f and g appear identical. Show both graphs.**

11. $f(x) = 3x^3 - 9x + 1, \quad g(x) = 3x^3$

12. $f(x) = -\frac{1}{3}(x^3 - 3x + 2), \quad g(x) = -\frac{1}{3}x^3$

13. $f(x) = -(x^4 - 4x^3 + 16x), \quad g(x) = -x^4$

14. $f(x) = 3x^4 - 6x^2, \quad g(x) = 3x^4$

In Exercises 15–22, use the Leading Coefficient Test to describe the right-hand and left-hand behavior of the graph of the polynomial function. Use a graphing utility to verify your result.

15. $f(x) = 2x^4 - 3x + 1$ **16.** $h(x) = 1 - x^6$

17. $g(x) = 5 - \frac{7}{2}x - 3x^2$ **18.** $f(x) = \frac{1}{3}x^3 + 5x$

19. $f(x) = \dfrac{6x^5 - 2x^4 + 4x^2 - 5x}{3}$

20. $f(x) = \dfrac{3x^7 - 2x^5 + 5x^3 + 6x^2}{4}$

21. $h(t) = -\frac{2}{3}(t^2 - 5t + 3)$

22. $f(s) = -\frac{7}{8}(s^3 + 5s^2 - 7s + 1)$

In Exercises 23–32, find all the real zeros of the polynomial function. Determine the multiplicity of each zero. Use a graphing utility to verify your result.

23. $f(x) = x^2 - 25$ **24.** $f(x) = 49 - x^2$

25. $h(t) = t^2 - 6t + 9$ **26.** $f(x) = x^2 + 10x + 25$

27. $f(x) = x^2 + x - 2$ **28.** $f(x) = 2x^2 - 14x + 24$

29. $f(t) = t^3 - 4t^2 + 4t$ **30.** $f(x) = x^4 - x^3 - 20x^2$

31. $f(x) = \frac{1}{2}x^2 + \frac{5}{2}x - \frac{3}{2}$ **32.** $f(x) = \frac{5}{3}x^2 + \frac{8}{3}x - \frac{4}{3}$

Graphical Analysis In Exercises 33–44, (a) find the zeros algebraically, (b) use a graphing utility to graph the function, and (c) use the graph to approximate any zeros and compare them with those from part (a).

33. $f(x) = 3x^2 - 12x + 3$

34. $g(x) = 5x^2 - 10x - 5$

35. $g(t) = \frac{1}{2}t^4 - \frac{1}{2}$

36. $y = \frac{1}{4}x^3(x^2 - 9)$

37. $f(x) = x^5 + x^3 - 6x$

38. $g(t) = t^5 - 6t^3 + 9t$

39. $f(x) = 2x^4 - 2x^2 - 40$

40. $f(x) = 5x^4 + 15x^2 + 10$

41. $f(x) = x^3 - 4x^2 - 25x + 100$

42. $y = 4x^3 + 4x^2 - 7x + 2$

43. $y = 4x^3 - 20x^2 + 25x$

44. $y = x^5 - 5x^3 + 4x$

In Exercises 45–48, use a graphing utility to graph the function and approximate (accurate to three decimal places) any real zeros and relative extrema.

45. $f(x) = 2x^4 - 6x^2 + 1$

46. $f(x) = -\frac{3}{8}x^4 - x^3 + 2x^2 + 5$

47. $f(x) = x^5 + 3x^3 - x + 6$

48. $f(x) = -3x^3 - 4x^2 + x - 3$

In Exercises 49–58, find a polynomial function that has the given zeros. (There are many correct answers.)

49. $0, 4$ **50.** $-7, 2$

51. $0, -2, -3$ **52.** $0, 2, 5$

53. $4, -3, 3, 0$ **54.** $-2, -1, 0, 1, 2$

55. $1 + \sqrt{3}, 1 - \sqrt{3}$ **56.** $6 + \sqrt{3}, 6 - \sqrt{3}$

57. $2, 4 + \sqrt{5}, 4 - \sqrt{5}$ **58.** $4, 2 + \sqrt{7}, 2 - \sqrt{7}$

In Exercises 59–64, find a polynomial function with the given zeros, multiplicities, and degree. (There are many correct answers.)

59. Zero: -2, multiplicity: 2
Zero: -1, multiplicity: 1
Degree: 3

60. Zero: 3, multiplicity: 1
Zero: 2, multiplicity: 3
Degree: 4

61. Zero: -4, multiplicity: 2
Zero: 3, multiplicity: 2
Degree: 4

62. Zero: -5, multiplicity: 3
Zero: 0, multiplicity: 2
Degree: 5

63. Zero: -1, multiplicity: 2
Zero: -2, multiplicity: 1
Degree: 3
Rises to the left,
Falls to the right

64. Zero: -1, multiplicity: 2
Zero: 4, multiplicity: 2
Degree: 4
Falls to the left,
Falls to the right

In Exercises 65–68, sketch the graph of a polynomial function that satisfies the given conditions. If not possible, explain your reasoning. (There are many correct answers.)

65. Third-degree polynomial with two real zeros and a negative leading coefficient

66. Fourth-degree polynomial with three real zeros and a positive leading coefficient

67. Fifth-degree polynomial with three real zeros and a positive leading coefficient

68. Fourth-degree polynomial with two real zeros and a negative leading coefficient

In Exercises 69–78, sketch the graph of the function by (a) applying the Leading Coefficient Test, (b) finding the zeros of the polynomial, (c) plotting sufficient solution points, and (d) drawing a continuous curve through the points.

69. $f(x) = x^3 - 9x$ **70.** $g(x) = x^4 - 4x^2$

71. $f(x) = x^3 - 3x^2$ **72.** $f(x) = 3x^3 - 24x^2$

73. $f(x) = -x^4 + 9x^2 - 20$ **74.** $f(x) = -x^6 + 7x^3 + 8$

75. $f(x) = x^3 + 3x^2 - 9x - 27$

76. $h(x) = x^5 - 4x^3 + 8x^2 - 32$

77. $g(t) = -\frac{1}{4}t^4 + 2t^2 - 4$

78. $g(x) = \frac{1}{10}(x^4 - 4x^3 - 2x^2 + 12x + 9)$

In Exercises 79–82, (a) use the Intermediate Value Theorem and a graphing utility to find graphically any intervals of length 1 in which the polynomial function is guaranteed to have a zero, and (b) use the *zero* or *root* feature of the graphing utility to approximate the real zeros of the function. Verify your answers in part (a) by using the *table* feature of the graphing utility.

79. $f(x) = x^3 - 3x^2 + 3$ **80.** $f(x) = -2x^3 - 6x^2 + 3$

81. $g(x) = 3x^4 + 4x^3 - 3$ **82.** $h(x) = x^4 - 10x^2 + 2$

In Exercises 83–90, use a graphing utility to graph the function. Identify any symmetry with respect to the *x*-axis, *y*-axis, or origin. Determine the number of *x*-intercepts of the graph.

83. $f(x) = x^2(x + 6)$ **84.** $h(x) = x^3(x - 4)^2$

85. $g(t) = -\frac{1}{2}(t - 4)^2(t + 4)^2$

86. $g(x) = \frac{1}{8}(x + 1)^2(x - 3)^3$

87. $f(x) = x^3 - 4x$ **88.** $f(x) = x^4 - 2x^2$

89. $g(x) = \frac{1}{5}(x + 1)^2(x - 3)(2x - 9)$

90. $h(x) = \frac{1}{5}(x + 2)^2(3x - 5)^2$

91. *Numerical and Graphical Analysis* An open box is to be made from a square piece of material 36 centimeters on a side by cutting equal squares with sides of length *x* from the corners and turning up the sides (see figure).

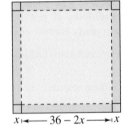
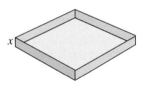

(a) Verify that the volume of the box is given by the function $V(x) = x(36 - 2x)^2$.

(b) Determine the domain of the function V.

(c) Use the *table* feature of a graphing utility to create a table that shows various box heights *x* and the corresponding volumes *V*. Use the table to estimate a range of dimensions within which the maximum volume is produced.

(d) Use a graphing utility to graph *V* and use the range of dimensions from part (c) to find the *x*-value for which $V(x)$ is maximum.

92. *Geometry* An open box with locking tabs is to be made from a square piece of material 24 inches on a side. This is done by cutting equal squares from the corners and folding along the dashed lines, as shown in the figure.

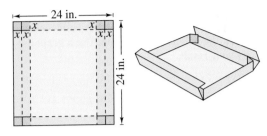

Figure for 92

(a) Verify that the volume of the box is given by the function $V(x) = 8x(6 - x)(12 - x)$.

(b) Determine the domain of the function V.

(c) Sketch the graph of the function and estimate the value of *x* for which $V(x)$ is maximum.

93. *Revenue* The total revenue *R* (in millions of dollars) for a company is related to its advertising expense by the function

$$R = 0.00001(-x^3 + 600x^2), \quad 0 \le x \le 400$$

where *x* is the amount spent on advertising (in tens of thousands of dollars). Use the graph of the function shown in the figure to estimate the point on the graph at which the function is increasing most rapidly. This point is called the **point of diminishing returns** because any expense above this amount will yield less return per dollar invested in advertising.

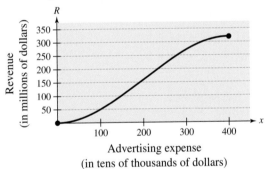

94. *Environment* The growth of a red oak tree is approximated by the function

$$G = -0.003t^3 + 0.137t^2 + 0.458t - 0.839$$

where *G* is the height of the tree (in feet) and *t* ($2 \le t \le 34$) is its age (in years). Use a graphing utility to graph the function and estimate the age of the tree when it is growing most rapidly. This point is called the **point of diminishing returns** because the increase in growth will be less with each additional year. (*Hint:* Use a viewing window in which $0 \le x \le 35$ and $0 \le y \le 60$.)

Data Analysis   In Exercises 95–98, use the table, which shows the median prices (in thousands of dollars) of new privately owned U.S. homes in the Northeast y_1 and in the South y_2 for the years 1995 through 2004. The data can be approximated by the following models.

$$y_1 = 0.3050t^3 - 6.949t^2 + 53.93t - 8.8$$

$$y_2 = 0.0330t^3 - 0.528t^2 + 8.35t + 65.2$$

In the models, t represents the year, with $t = 5$ corresponding to 1995.   (Sources: National Association of Realtors)

Year, t	y_1	y_2
5	126.7	97.7
6	127.8	103.4
7	131.8	109.6
8	135.9	116.2
9	139.0	120.3
10	139.4	128.3
11	146.5	137.4
12	164.3	147.3
13	190.5	157.1
14	220.0	169.0

95. Use a graphing utility to plot the data and graph the model for y_1 in the same viewing window. How closely does the model represent the data?

96. Use a graphing utility to plot the data and graph the model for y_2 in the same viewing window. How closely does the model represent the data?

97. Use the models to predict the median prices of new privately owned homes in both regions in 2010. Do your answers seem reasonable? Explain.

98. Use the graphs of the models in Exercises 95 and 96 to write a short paragraph about the relationship between the median prices of homes in the two regions.

Synthesis

True or False?   In Exercises 99–104, determine whether the statement is true or false. Justify your answer.

99. It is possible for a sixth-degree polynomial to have only one zero.

100. The graph of the function

$$f(x) = 2 + x - x^2 + x^3 - x^4 + x^5 + x^6 - x^7$$

rises to the left and falls to the right.

101. The graph of the function $f(x) = 2x(x - 1)^2(x + 3)^3$ crosses the x-axis at $x = 1$.

102. The graph of the function $f(x) = 2x(x - 1)^2(x + 3)^3$ touches, but does not cross, the x-axis.

103. The graph of the function $f(x) = -x^2(x + 2)^3(x - 4)^2$ crosses the x-axis at $x = -2$.

104. The graph of the function $f(x) = 2x(x - 1)^2(x + 3)^3$ rises to the left and falls to the right.

Library of Parent Functions   In Exercises 105–107, determine which polynomial function(s) may be represented by the graph shown. There may be more than one correct answer.

105. (a) $f(x) = x(x + 1)^2$
    (b) $f(x) = x(x - 1)^2$
    (c) $f(x) = x^2(x - 1)$
    (d) $f(x) = -x(x + 1)^2$
    (e) $f(x) = -x(x - 1)^2$

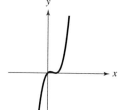

106. (a) $f(x) = x^2(x - 2)^2$
    (b) $f(x) = x^2(x + 2)^2$
    (c) $f(x) = x(x - 2)$
    (d) $f(x) = -x^2(x + 2)^2$
    (e) $f(x) = -x^2(x - 2)^2$

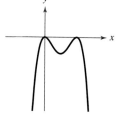

107. (a) $f(x) = (x - 1)^2(x + 2)^2$
    (b) $f(x) = (x - 1)(x + 2)$
    (c) $f(x) = (x + 1)^2(x - 2)^2$
    (d) $f(x) = -(x - 1)^2(x + 2)^2$
    (e) $f(x) = -(x + 1)^2(x - 2)^2$

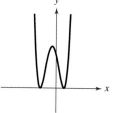

Skills Review

In Exercises 108–113, let $f(x) = 14x - 3$ and $g(x) = 8x^2$. Find the indicated value.

108. $(f + g)(-4)$

109. $(g - f)(3)$

110. $(fg)\left(-\dfrac{4}{7}\right)$

111. $\left(\dfrac{f}{g}\right)(-1.5)$

112. $(f \circ g)(-1)$

113. $(g \circ f)(0)$

In Exercises 114–117, solve the inequality and sketch the solution on the real number line. Use a graphing utility to verify your solution graphically.

114. $3(x - 5) < 4x - 7$

115. $2x^2 - x \geq 1$

116. $\dfrac{5x - 2}{x - 7} \leq 4$

117. $|x + 8| - 1 \geq 15$

The Rational Zero Test

The **Rational Zero Test** relates the possible rational zeros of a polynomial (having integer coefficients) to the leading coefficient and to the constant term of the polynomial.

The Rational Zero Test

If the polynomial

$$f(x) = a_n x^n + a_{n-1}x^{n-1} + \cdots + a_2 x^2 + a_1 x + a_0$$

has integer coefficients, every rational zero of f has the form

$$\text{Rational zero} = \frac{p}{q}$$

where p and q have no common factors other than 1, p is a factor of the constant term a_0, and q is a factor of the leading coefficient a_n.

To use the Rational Zero Test, first list all rational numbers whose numerators are factors of the constant term and whose denominators are factors of the leading coefficient.

$$\text{Possible rational zeros} = \frac{\text{factors of constant term}}{\text{factors of leading coefficient}}$$

Now that you have formed this list of *possible rational zeros*, use a trial-and-error method to determine which, if any, are actual zeros of the polynomial. Note that when the leading coefficient is 1, the possible rational zeros are simply the factors of the constant term. This case is illustrated in Example 7.

Example 7   Rational Zero Test with Leading Coefficient of 1

Find the rational zeros of $f(x) = x^3 + x + 1$.

Solution

Because the leading coefficient is 1, the possible rational zeros are simply the factors of the constant term.

   Possible rational zeros: ± 1

By testing these possible zeros, you can see that neither works.

$$f(1) = (1)^3 + 1 + 1 = 3$$

$$f(-1) = (-1)^3 + (-1) + 1 = -1$$

So, you can conclude that the polynomial has *no* rational zeros. Note from the graph of f in Figure 3.34 that f does have one real zero between -1 and 0. However, by the Rational Zero Test, you know that this real zero is *not* a rational number.

✓**CHECKPOINT**   Now try Exercise 49.

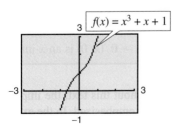

Figure 3.34

If the leading coefficient of a polynomial is not 1, the list of possible rational zeros can increase dramatically. In such cases, the search can be shortened in several ways.

1. A programmable calculator can be used to speed up the calculations.
2. A graphing utility can give a good estimate of the locations of the zeros.
3. The Intermediate Value Theorem, along with a table generated by a graphing utility, can give approximations of zeros.
4. The Factor Theorem and synthetic division can be used to test the possible rational zeros.

Finding the first zero is often the most difficult part. After that, the search is simplified by working with the lower-degree polynomial obtained in synthetic division.

Example 8   Using the Rational Zero Test

Find the rational zeros of $f(x) = 2x^3 + 3x^2 - 8x + 3$.

Solution

The leading coefficient is 2 and the constant term is 3.

Possible rational zeros:

$$\frac{\text{Factors of 3}}{\text{Factors of 2}} = \frac{\pm 1, \pm 3}{\pm 1, \pm 2} = \pm 1, \pm 3, \pm \frac{1}{2}, \pm \frac{3}{2}$$

By synthetic division, you can determine that $x = 1$ is a rational zero.

$$
\begin{array}{r|rrrr}
1 & 2 & 3 & -8 & 3 \\
  &   & 2 & 5 & -3 \\
\hline
  & 2 & 5 & -3 & 0 \\
\end{array}
$$

So, $f(x)$ factors as

$$f(x) = (x - 1)(2x^2 + 5x - 3) = (x - 1)(2x - 1)(x + 3)$$

and you can conclude that the rational zeros of f are $x = 1$, $x = \frac{1}{2}$, and $x = -3$, as shown in Figure 3.35.

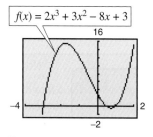

$f(x) = 2x^3 + 3x^2 - 8x + 3$

Figure 3.35

✓CHECKPOINT   Now try Exercise 51.

A graphing utility can help you determine which possible rational zeros to test, as demonstrated in Example 9.

Example 11 Finding the Zeros of a Polynomial Function

Find the real zeros of $f(x) = 6x^3 - 4x^2 + 3x - 2$.

Solution

The possible real zeros are as follows.

$$\frac{\text{Factors of 2}}{\text{Factors of 6}} = \frac{\pm 1, \pm 2}{\pm 1, \pm 2, \pm 3, \pm 6} = \pm 1, \pm\frac{1}{2}, \pm\frac{1}{3}, \pm\frac{1}{6}, \pm\frac{2}{3}, \pm 2$$

The original polynomial $f(x)$ has three variations in sign. The polynomial

$$f(-x) = 6(-x)^3 - 4(-x)^2 + 3(-x) - 2$$
$$= -6x^3 - 4x^2 - 3x - 2$$

has no variations in sign. As a result of these two findings, you can apply Descartes's Rule of Signs to conclude that there are three positive real zeros or one positive real zero, and no negative real zeros. Trying $x = 1$ produces the following.

$$\begin{array}{r|rrrr}
1 & 6 & -4 & 3 & -2 \\
  &   & 6 & 2 & 5 \\
\hline
  & 6 & 2 & 5 & 3
\end{array}$$

So, $x = 1$ is not a zero, but because the last row has all positive entries, you know that $x = 1$ is an upper bound for the real zeros. Therefore, you can restrict the search to zeros between 0 and 1. By trial and error, you can determine that $x = \frac{2}{3}$ is a zero. So,

$$f(x) = \left(x - \frac{2}{3}\right)(6x^2 + 3).$$

Because $6x^2 + 3$ has no real zeros, it follows that $x = \frac{2}{3}$ is the only real zero.

✓**CHECKPOINT**   Now try Exercise 75.

Before concluding this section, here are two additional hints that can help you find the real zeros of a polynomial.

1. If the terms of $f(x)$ have a common monomial factor, it should be factored out before applying the tests in this section. For instance, by writing

$$f(x) = x^4 - 5x^3 + 3x^2 + x = x(x^3 - 5x^2 + 3x + 1)$$

you can see that $x = 0$ is a zero of f and that the remaining zeros can be obtained by analyzing the cubic factor.

2. If you are able to find all but two zeros of $f(x)$, you can always use the Quadratic Formula on the remaining quadratic factor. For instance, if you succeeded in writing

$$f(x) = x^4 - 5x^3 + 3x^2 + x = x(x - 1)(x^2 - 4x - 1)$$

you can apply the Quadratic Formula to $x^2 - 4x - 1$ to conclude that the two remaining zeros are $x = 2 + \sqrt{5}$ and $x = 2 - \sqrt{5}$.

Exploration

Use a graphing utility to graph

$$y_1 = 6x^3 - 4x^2 + 3x - 2.$$

Notice that the graph intersects the x-axis at the point $\left(\frac{2}{3}, 0\right)$. How does this information relate to the real zero found in Example 11? Use a graphing utility to graph

$$y_2 = x^4 - 5x^3 + 3x^2 + x.$$

How many times does the graph intersect the x-axis? How many real zeros does y_2 have?

Exploration

Use a graphing utility to graph

$$y = x^3 + 4.9x^2 - 126x + 382.5$$

in the standard viewing window. From the graph, what do the real zeros appear to be? Discuss how the mathematical tools of this section might help you realize that the graph does not show all the important features of the polynomial function. Now use the *zoom* feature to find all the zeros of this function.

3.3 Exercises

See www.CalcChat.com for worked-out solutions to odd-numbered exercises.

Vocabulary Check

1. Two forms of the Division Algorithm are shown below. Identify and label each part.

$$f(x) = d(x)q(x) + r(x) \qquad \frac{f(x)}{d(x)} = q(x) + \frac{r(x)}{d(x)}$$

In Exercises 2–7, fill in the blanks.

2. The rational expression $p(x)/q(x)$ is called _____ if the degree of the numerator is greater than or equal to that of the denominator, and is called _____ if the degree of the numerator is less than that of the denominator.

3. An alternative method to long division of polynomials is called _____ , in which the divisor must be of the form $x - k$.

4. The test that gives a list of the possible rational zeros of a polynomial function is known as the _____ Test.

5. The theorem that can be used to determine the possible numbers of positive real zeros and negative real zeros of a function is called _____ of _____ .

6. The _____ states that if a polynomial $f(x)$ is divided by $x - k$, then the remainder is $r = f(k)$.

7. A real number b is an _____ for the real zeros of f if no zeros are greater than b, and is a _____ if no real zeros of f are less than b.

In Exercises 1–14, use long division to divide.

1. Divide $2x^2 + 10x + 12$ by $x + 3$.

2. Divide $5x^2 - 17x - 12$ by $x - 4$.

3. Divide $x^4 + 5x^3 + 6x^2 - x - 2$ by $x + 2$.

4. Divide $x^3 - 4x^2 - 17x + 6$ by $x - 3$.

5. Divide $4x^3 - 7x^2 - 11x + 5$ by $4x + 5$.

6. Divide $2x^3 - 3x^2 - 50x + 75$ by $2x - 3$.

7. Divide $7x^3 + 3$ by $x + 2$.

8. Divide $8x^4 - 5$ by $2x + 1$.

9. $(x + 8 + 6x^3 + 10x^2) \div (2x^2 + 1)$

10. $(1 + 3x^2 + x^4) \div (3 - 2x + x^2)$

11. $(x^3 - 9) \div (x^2 + 1)$ **12.** $(x^5 + 7) \div (x^3 - 1)$

13. $\dfrac{2x^3 - 4x^2 - 15x + 5}{(x - 1)^2}$ **14.** $\dfrac{x^4}{(x - 1)^3}$

In Exercises 15–24, use synthetic division to divide.

15. $(3x^3 - 17x^2 + 15x - 25) \div (x - 5)$

16. $(5x^3 + 18x^2 + 7x - 6) \div (x + 3)$

17. $(6x^3 + 7x^2 - x + 26) \div (x - 3)$

18. $(2x^3 + 14x^2 - 20x + 7) \div (x + 6)$

19. $(9x^3 - 18x^2 - 16x + 32) \div (x - 2)$

20. $(5x^3 + 6x + 8) \div (x + 2)$

21. $(x^3 + 512) \div (x + 8)$

22. $(x^3 - 729) \div (x - 9)$

23. $\dfrac{4x^3 + 16x^2 - 23x - 15}{x + \frac{1}{2}}$ **24.** $\dfrac{3x^3 - 4x^2 + 5}{x - \frac{3}{2}}$

Graphical Analysis In Exercises 25–28, use a graphing utility to graph the two equations in the same viewing window. Use the graphs to verify that the expressions are equivalent. Verify the results algebraically.

25. $y_1 = \dfrac{x^2}{x + 2}, \quad y_2 = x - 2 + \dfrac{4}{x + 2}$

26. $y_1 = \dfrac{x^2 + 2x - 1}{x + 3}, \quad y_2 = x - 1 + \dfrac{2}{x + 3}$

27. $y_1 = \dfrac{x^4 - 3x^2 - 1}{x^2 + 5}, \quad y_2 = x^2 - 8 + \dfrac{39}{x^2 + 5}$

28. $y_1 = \dfrac{x^4 + x^2 - 1}{x^2 + 1}, \quad y_2 = x^2 - \dfrac{1}{x^2 + 1}$

In Exercises 29–34, write the function in the form $f(x) = (x - k)q(x) + r(x)$ for the given value of k. Use a graphing utility to demonstrate that $f(k) = r$.

Function	Value of k
29. $f(x) = x^3 - x^2 - 14x + 11$	$k = 4$
30. $f(x) = 15x^4 + 10x^3 - 6x^2 + 14$	$k = -\frac{2}{3}$
31. $f(x) = x^3 + 3x^2 - 2x - 14$	$k = \sqrt{2}$
32. $f(x) = x^3 + 2x^2 - 5x - 4$	$k = -\sqrt{5}$
33. $f(x) = 4x^3 - 6x^2 - 12x - 4$	$k = 1 - \sqrt{3}$
34. $f(x) = -3x^3 + 8x^2 + 10x - 8$	$k = 2 + \sqrt{2}$

In Exercises 35–38, use the Remainder Theorem and synthetic division to evaluate the function at each given value. Use a graphing utility to verify your results.

35. $f(x) = 2x^3 - 7x + 3$

   (a) $f(1)$ (b) $f(-2)$ (c) $f\left(\tfrac{1}{2}\right)$ (d) $f(2)$

36. $g(x) = 2x^6 + 3x^4 - x^2 + 3$

   (a) $g(2)$ (b) $g(1)$ (c) $g(3)$ (d) $g(-1)$

37. $h(x) = x^3 - 5x^2 - 7x + 4$

   (a) $h(3)$ (b) $h(2)$ (c) $h(-2)$ (d) $h(-5)$

38. $f(x) = 4x^4 - 16x^3 + 7x^2 + 20$

   (a) $f(1)$ (b) $f(-2)$ (c) $f(5)$ (d) $f(-10)$

In Exercises 39–42, use synthetic division to show that x is a solution of the third-degree polynomial equation, and use the result to factor the polynomial completely. List all the real zeros of the function.

	Polynomial Equation	Value of x
39.	$x^3 - 7x + 6 = 0$	$x = 2$
40.	$x^3 - 28x - 48 = 0$	$x = -4$
41.	$2x^3 - 15x^2 + 27x - 10 = 0$	$x = \tfrac{1}{2}$
42.	$48x^3 - 80x^2 + 41x - 6 = 0$	$x = \tfrac{2}{3}$

In Exercises 43–48, (a) verify the given factors of the function f, (b) find the remaining factors of f, (c) use your results to write the complete factorization of f, and (d) list all real zeros of f. Confirm your results by using a graphing utility to graph the function.

	Function	Factor(s)
43.	$f(x) = 2x^3 + x^2 - 5x + 2$	$(x + 2)$
44.	$f(x) = 3x^3 + 2x^2 - 19x + 6$	$(x + 3)$
45.	$f(x) = x^4 - 4x^3 - 15x^2 + 58x - 40$	$(x - 5), (x + 4)$
46.	$f(x) = 8x^4 - 14x^3 - 71x^2 - 10x + 24$	$(x + 2), (x - 4)$
47.	$f(x) = 6x^3 + 41x^2 - 9x - 14$	$(2x + 1)$
48.	$f(x) = 2x^3 - x^2 - 10x + 5$	$(2x - 1)$

In Exercises 49–52, use the Rational Zero Test to list all possible rational zeros of f. Then find the rational zeros.

49. $f(x) = x^3 + 3x^2 - x - 3$

50. $f(x) = x^3 - 4x^2 - 4x + 16$

51. $f(x) = 2x^4 - 17x^3 + 35x^2 + 9x - 45$

52. $f(x) = 4x^5 - 8x^4 - 5x^3 + 10x^2 + x - 2$

In Exercises 53–60, find all real zeros of the polynomial function.

53. $f(z) = z^4 - z^3 - 2z - 4$

54. $f(x) = x^4 - x^3 - 29x^2 - x - 30$

55. $g(y) = 2y^4 + 7y^3 - 26y^2 + 23y - 6$

56. $h(x) = x^5 - x^4 - 3x^3 + 5x^2 - 2x$

57. $f(x) = 4x^4 - 55x^2 - 45x + 36$

58. $z(x) = 4x^4 - 43x^2 - 9x + 90$

59. $f(x) = 4x^5 + 12x^4 - 11x^3 - 42x^2 + 7x + 30$

60. $g(x) = 4x^5 + 8x^4 - 15x^3 - 23x^2 + 11x + 15$

Graphical Analysis **In Exercises 61–64, (a) use the *zero* or *root* feature of a graphing utility to approximate (accurate to the nearest thousandth) the zeros of the function, (b) determine one of the exact zeros and use synthetic division to verify your result, and (c) factor the polynomial completely.**

61. $h(t) = t^3 - 2t^2 - 7t + 2$

62. $f(s) = s^3 - 12s^2 + 40s - 24$

63. $h(x) = x^5 - 7x^4 + 10x^3 + 14x^2 - 24x$

64. $g(x) = 6x^4 - 11x^3 - 51x^2 + 99x - 27$

In Exercises 65–68, use Descartes's Rule of Signs to determine the possible numbers of positive and negative real zeros of the function.

65. $f(x) = 2x^4 - x^3 + 6x^2 - x + 5$

66. $f(x) = 3x^4 + 5x^3 - 6x^2 + 8x - 3$

67. $g(x) = 4x^3 - 5x + 8$

68. $g(x) = 2x^3 - 4x^2 - 5$

In Exercises 69–74, (a) use Descartes's Rule of Signs to determine the possible numbers of positive and negative real zeros of f, (b) list the possible rational zeros of f, (c) use a graphing utility to graph f so that some of the possible zeros in parts (a) and (b) can be disregarded, and (d) determine all the real zeros of f.

69. $f(x) = x^3 + x^2 - 4x - 4$

70. $f(x) = -3x^3 + 20x^2 - 36x + 16$

71. $f(x) = -2x^4 + 13x^3 - 21x^2 + 2x + 8$

72. $f(x) = 4x^4 - 17x^2 + 4$

73. $f(x) = 32x^3 - 52x^2 + 17x + 3$

74. $f(x) = 4x^3 + 7x^2 - 11x - 18$

Occasionally, throughout this text, you will be asked to round to a place value rather than to a number of decimal places.

In Exercises 75–78, use synthetic division to verify the upper and lower bounds of the real zeros of f. Then find the real zeros of the function.

75. $f(x) = x^4 - 4x^3 + 15$

Upper bound: $x = 4$;   Lower bound: $x = -1$

76. $f(x) = 2x^3 - 3x^2 - 12x + 8$

Upper bound: $x = 4$;   Lower bound: $x = -3$

77. $f(x) = x^4 - 4x^3 + 16x - 16$

Upper bound: $x = 5$;   Lower bound: $x = -3$

78. $f(x) = 2x^4 - 8x + 3$

Upper bound: $x = 3$;   Lower bound: $x = -4$

In Exercises 79–82, find the rational zeros of the polynomial function.

79. $P(x) = x^4 - \frac{25}{4}x^2 + 9 = \frac{1}{4}(4x^4 - 25x^2 + 36)$

80. $f(x) = x^3 - \frac{3}{2}x^2 - \frac{23}{2}x + 6 = \frac{1}{2}(2x^3 - 3x^2 - 23x + 12)$

81. $f(x) = x^3 - \frac{1}{4}x^2 - x + \frac{1}{4} = \frac{1}{4}(4x^3 - x^2 - 4x + 1)$

82. $f(z) = z^3 + \frac{11}{6}z^2 - \frac{1}{2}z - \frac{1}{3} = \frac{1}{6}(6z^3 + 11z^2 - 3z - 2)$

In Exercises 83–86, match the cubic function with the correct number of rational and irrational zeros.

(a) **Rational zeros: 0;   Irrational zeros: 1**

(b) **Rational zeros: 3;   Irrational zeros: 0**

(c) **Rational zeros: 1;   Irrational zeros: 2**

(d) **Rational zeros: 1;   Irrational zeros: 0**

83. $f(x) = x^3 - 1$

84. $f(x) = x^3 - 2$

85. $f(x) = x^3 - x$

86. $f(x) = x^3 - 2x$

In Exercises 87–90, the graph of $y = f(x)$ is shown. Use the graph as an aid to find all the real zeros of the function.

87. $y = 2x^4 - 9x^3 + 5x^2 + 3x - 1$

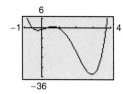

88. $y = x^4 - 5x^3 - 7x^2 + 13x - 2$

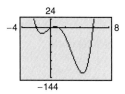

89. $y = -2x^4 + 17x^3 - 3x^2 - 25x - 3$

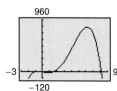

90. $y = -x^4 + 5x^3 - 10x - 4$

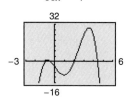

91. *U.S. Population*   The table shows the populations P of the United States (in millions) from 1790 to 2000.   (Source: U.S. Census Bureau)

Year	Population (in millions)
1790	3.9
1800	5.3
1810	7.2
1820	9.6
1830	12.9
1840	17.1
1850	23.2
1860	31.4
1870	39.8
1880	50.2
1890	63.0
1900	76.2
1910	92.2
1920	106.0
1930	123.2
1940	132.2
1950	151.3
1960	179.3
1970	203.3
1980	226.5
1990	248.7
2000	281.4

The population can be approximated by the equation

$$P = 0.0058t^3 + 0.500t^2 + 1.38t + 4.6, \quad -1 \le t \le 20$$

where t represents the year, with $t = -1$ corresponding to 1790, $t = 0$ corresponding to 1800, and so on.

(a) Use a graphing utility to graph the data and the equation in the same viewing window.

(b) How well does the model fit the data?

(c) Use the Remainder Theorem to evaluate the model for the year 2010. Do you believe this value is reasonable? Explain.

92. *Energy* The number of coal mines C in the United States from 1980 to 2004 can be approximated by the equation $C = 0.232t^3 - 2.11t^2 - 261.8t + 5699$, for $0 \le t \le 24$, where t is the year, with $t = 0$ corresponding to 1980. (Source: U.S. Energy Information Administration)

(a) Use a graphing utility to graph the model over the domain.

(b) Find the number of mines in 1980. Use the Remainder Theorem to find the number of mines in 1990.

(c) Could you use this model to predict the number of coal mines in the United States in the future? Explain.

93. *Geometry* A rectangular package sent by a delivery service can have a maximum combined length and girth (perimeter of a cross section) of 120 inches (see figure).

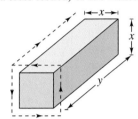

(a) Show that the volume of the package is given by the function $V(x) = 4x^2(30 - x)$.

(b) Use a graphing utility to graph the function and approximate the dimensions of the package that yield a maximum volume.

(c) Find values of x such that $V = 13,500$. Which of these values is a physical impossibility in the construction of the package? Explain.

94. *Automobile Emissions* The number of parts per million of nitric oxide emissions y from a car engine is approximated by the model $y = -5.05x^3 + 3,857x - 38,411.25$, for $13 \le x \le 18$, where x is the air-fuel ratio.

(a) Use a graphing utility to graph the model.

(b) It is observed from the graph that two air-fuel ratios produce 2400 parts per million of nitric oxide, with one being 15. Use the graph to approximate the second air-fuel ratio.

(c) Algebraically approximate the second air-fuel ratio that produces 2400 parts per million of nitric oxide. (*Hint:* Because you know that an air-fuel ratio of 15 produces the specified nitric oxide emission, you can use synthetic division.)

Synthesis

True or False? **In Exercises 95 and 96, determine whether the statement is true or false. Justify your answer.**

95. If $(7x + 4)$ is a factor of some polynomial function f, then $\frac{4}{7}$ is a zero of f.

96. $(2x - 1)$ is a factor of the polynomial
$$6x^6 + x^5 - 92x^4 + 45x^3 + 184x^2 + 4x - 48.$$

Think About It **In Exercises 97 and 98, the graph of a cubic polynomial function $y = f(x)$ with integer zeros is shown. Find the factored form of f.**

97.

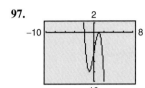

98.

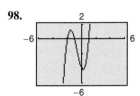

99. *Think About It* Let $y = f(x)$ be a quartic polynomial with leading coefficient $a = -1$ and $f(\pm 1) = f(\pm 2) = 0$. Find the factored form of f.

100. *Think About It* Let $y = f(x)$ be a cubic polynomial with leading coefficient $a = 2$ and $f(-2) = f(1) = f(2) = 0$. Find the factored form of f.

101. *Think About It* Find the value of k such that $x - 4$ is a factor of $x^3 - kx^2 + 2kx - 8$.

102. *Think About It* Find the value of k such that $x - 3$ is a factor of $x^3 - kx^2 + 2kx - 12$.

103. *Writing* Complete each polynomial division. Write a brief description of the pattern that you obtain, and use your result to find a formula for the polynomial division $(x^n - 1)/(x - 1)$. Create a numerical example to test your formula.

(a) $\dfrac{x^2 - 1}{x - 1} =$

(b) $\dfrac{x^3 - 1}{x - 1} =$

(c) $\dfrac{x^4 - 1}{x - 1} =$

104. *Writing* Write a short paragraph explaining how you can check polynomial division. Give an example.

Skills Review

In Exercises 105–108, use any convenient method to solve the quadratic equation.

105. $9x^2 - 25 = 0$

106. $16x^2 - 21 = 0$

107. $2x^2 + 6x + 3 = 0$

108. $8x^2 - 22x + 15 = 0$

In Exercises 109–112, find a polynomial function that has the given zeros. (There are many correct answers.)

109. $0, -12$

110. $1, -3, 8$

111. $0, -1, 2, 5$

112. $2 + \sqrt{3}, 2 - \sqrt{3}$

3.4 The Fundamental Theorem of Algebra

The Fundamental Theorem of Algebra

You know that an nth-degree polynomial can have at most n real zeros. In the complex number system, this statement can be improved. That is, in the complex number system, every nth-degree polynomial function has *precisely n zeros*. This important result is derived from the **Fundamental Theorem of Algebra,** first proved by the German mathematician Carl Friedrich Gauss (1777–1855).

> **The Fundamental Theorem of Algebra**
>
> If $f(x)$ is a polynomial of degree n, where $n > 0$, then f has at least one zero in the complex number system.

Using the Fundamental Theorem of Algebra and the equivalence of zeros and factors, you obtain the **Linear Factorization Theorem.**

> **Linear Factorization Theorem**   (See the proof on page 332.)
>
> If $f(x)$ is a polynomial of degree n, where $n > 0$, f has precisely n linear factors
>
> $$f(x) = a_n(x - c_1)(x - c_2) \cdots (x - c_n)$$
>
> where $c_1, c_2, \ldots, c_n$ are complex numbers.

Note that neither the Fundamental Theorem of Algebra nor the Linear Factorization Theorem tells you *how* to find the zeros or factors of a polynomial. Such theorems are called *existence theorems*. To find the zeros of a polynomial function, you still must rely on other techniques.

Remember that the n zeros of a polynomial function can be real or complex, and they may be repeated. Examples 1 and 2 illustrate several cases.

What you should learn

- Use the Fundamental Theorem of Algebra to determine the number of zeros of a polynomial function.
- Find all zeros of polynomial functions, including complex zeros.
- Find conjugate pairs of complex zeros.
- Find zeros of polynomials by factoring.

Why you should learn it

Being able to find zeros of polynomial functions is an important part of modeling real-life problems. For instance, Exercise 63 on page 297 shows how to determine whether a ball thrown with a given velocity can reach a certain height.

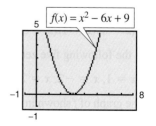

Jed Jacobsohn/Getty Images

Example 1 Real Zeros of a Polynomial Function

Counting multiplicity, confirm that the second-degree polynomial function

$$f(x) = x^2 - 6x + 9$$

has exactly *two* zeros: $x = 3$ and $x = 3$.

Solution

$$x^2 - 6x + 9 = (x - 3)^2 = 0$$

$$x - 3 = 0 \quad \Longrightarrow \quad x = 3 \qquad \text{Repeated solution}$$

The graph in Figure 3.38 touches the x-axis at $x = 3$.

✔ CHECKPOINT   Now try Exercise 1.

$f(x) = x^2 - 6x + 9$

Figure 3.38

3.5   Rational Functions and Asymptotes

Introduction to Rational Functions

A **rational function** can be written in the form

$$f(x) = \frac{N(x)}{D(x)}$$

where $N(x)$ and $D(x)$ are polynomials and $D(x)$ is not the zero polynomial.

In general, the *domain* of a rational function of x includes all real numbers except x-values that make the denominator zero. Much of the discussion of rational functions will focus on their graphical behavior near these x-values.

Example 1   Finding the Domain of a Rational Function

Find the domain of $f(x) = 1/x$ and discuss the behavior of f near any excluded x-values.

Solution

Because the denominator is zero when $x = 0$, the domain of f is all real numbers except $x = 0$. To determine the behavior of f near this excluded value, evaluate $f(x)$ to the left and right of $x = 0$, as indicated in the following tables.

x	-1	-0.5	-0.1	-0.01	-0.001	$\to 0$
$f(x)$	-1	-2	-10	-100	-1000	$\to -\infty$

x	$0 \leftarrow$	0.001	0.01	0.1	0.5	1
$f(x)$	$\infty \leftarrow$	1000	100	10	2	1

From the table, note that as x approaches 0 *from the left*, $f(x)$ decreases without bound. In contrast, as x approaches 0 *from the right*, $f(x)$ increases without bound. Because $f(x)$ decreases without bound from the left and increases without bound from the right, you can conclude that f is not continuous. The graph of f is shown in Figure 3.42.

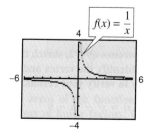

Figure 3.42

✓CHECKPOINT   Now try Exercise 1.

Exploration

Use the *table* and *trace* features of a graphing utility to verify that the function $f(x) = 1/x$ in Example 1 is not continuous.

TECHNOLOGY TIP

The graphing utility graphs in this section and the next section were created using the *dot* mode. A blue curve is placed behind the graphing utility's display to indicate where the graph should appear. You will learn more about how graphing utilities graph rational functions in the next section.

Values for which a rational function is undefined (the denominator is
result in a vertical asymptote or a hole in the graph, as shown in Example

Example 3 Finding Horizontal and Vertical Asymptotes and Holes

Find all horizontal and vertical asymptotes and holes in the graph of

$$f(x) = \frac{x^2 + x - 2}{x^2 - x - 6}.$$

Solution

For this rational function the degree of the numerator is *equal to* the degree
denominator. The leading coefficients of the numerator and denominator a
1, so the graph has the line $y = 1$ as a horizontal asymptote. To find any
asymptotes, first factor the numerator and denominator as follows.

$$f(x) = \frac{x^2 + x - 2}{x^2 - x - 6} = \frac{(x-1)(x+2)}{(x+2)(x-3)} = \frac{x-1}{x-3}, \quad x \neq -2$$

By setting the denominator $x - 3$ (of the simplified function) equal to ze
can determine that the graph has the line $x = 3$ as a vertical asymptote, as
in Figure 3.46. To find any holes in the graph, note that the function is un
at $x = -2$ and $x = 3$. Because $x = -2$ is not a vertical asymptote of th
tion, there is a hole in the graph at $x = -2$. To find the y-coordinate of th
substitute $x = -2$ into the simplified form of the function.

$$y = \frac{x-1}{x-3} = \frac{-2-1}{-2-3} = \frac{3}{5}$$

So, the graph of the rational function has a hole at $\left(-2, \frac{3}{5}\right)$.

✓CHECKPOINT   Now try Exercise 17.

Example 4 Finding a Function's Domain and Asymptotes

For the function f, find (a) the domain of f, (b) the vertical asymptote (
(c) the horizontal asymptote of f.

$$f(x) = \frac{3x^3 + 7x^2 + 2}{-4x^3 + 5}$$

Solution

a. Because the denominator is zero when $-4x^3 + 5 = 0$, solve this equ
   determine that the domain of f is all real numbers except $x = \sqrt[3]{\frac{5}{4}}$.

b. Because the denominator of f has a zero at $x = \sqrt[3]{\frac{5}{4}}$, and $\sqrt[3]{\frac{5}{4}}$ is not a
   the numerator, the graph of f has the vertical asymptote $x = \sqrt[3]{\frac{5}{4}} \approx$

c. Because the degrees of the numerator and denominator are the same
   leading coefficient of the numerator is 3 and the leading coefficie
   denominator is -4, the horizontal asymptote of f is $y = -\frac{3}{4}$.

✓CHECKPOINT   Now try Exercise 19.

Library of Parent Functions: Rational Function

A *rational function* $f(x)$ is the quotient of two polynomials,

$$f(x) = \frac{N(x)}{D(x)}.$$

A rational function is not defined at values of x for which $D(x) = 0$. Near
these values the graph of the rational function may increase or decrease
without bound. The simplest type of rational function is the *reciprocal
function* $f(x) = 1/x$. The basic characteristics of the reciprocal function
are summarized below. A review of rational functions can be found in the
Study Capsules.

Graph of $f(x) = \dfrac{1}{x}$

Domain: $(-\infty, 0) \cup (0, \infty)$

Range: $(-\infty, 0) \cup (0, \infty)$

No intercepts

Decreasing on $(-\infty, 0)$ and $(0, \infty)$

Odd function

Origin symmetry

Vertical asymptote: y-axis

Horizontal asymptote: x-axis

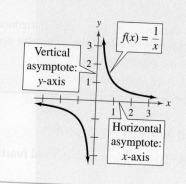

Horizontal and Vertical Asymptotes

In Example 1, the behavior of f near $x = 0$ is denoted as follows.

$$f(x) \to -\infty \text{ as } x \to 0^-$$

$f(x)$ decreases without bound as x approaches 0 from the left.

$$f(x) \to \infty \text{ as } x \to 0^+$$

$f(x)$ increases without bound as x approaches 0 from the right.

The line $x = 0$ is a **vertical asymptote** of the graph of f, as shown in the figure
above. The graph of f has a **horizontal asymptote**—the line $y = 0$. This means
the values of $f(x) = 1/x$ approach zero as x increases or decreases without bound.

$$f(x) \to 0 \text{ as } x \to -\infty$$

$f(x)$ approaches 0 as x decreases without bound.

$$f(x) \to 0 \text{ as } x \to \infty$$

$f(x)$ approaches 0 as x increases without bound.

Definition of Vertical and Horizontal Asymptotes

1. The line $x = a$ is a **vertical asymptote** of the graph of f if $f(x) \to \infty$
   or $f(x) \to -\infty$ as $x \to a$, either from the right or from the left.

2. The line $y = b$ is a **horizontal asymptote** of the graph of f if
   $f(x) \to b$ as $x \to \infty$ or $x \to -\infty$.

Figure 3.43 shows the horizontal and vertical asymptotes of the graphs of
three rational functions.

Exploration

Use a table of values to determine whether the functions in
Figure 3.43 are continuous.
If the graph of a function has
an asymptote, can you conclude
that the function is not
continuous? Explain.

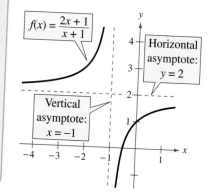

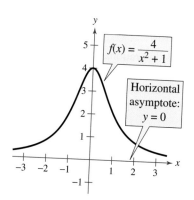

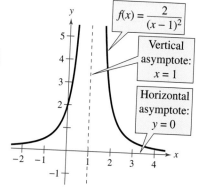

Figure 3.43

Vertical and Horizontal Asymptotes of a Rational Function

Let f be the rational function

$$f(x) = \frac{N(x)}{D(x)} = \frac{a_n x^n + a_{n-1} x^{n-1} + \cdots + a_1 x + a_0}{b_m x^m + b_{m-1} x^{m-1} + \cdots + b_1 x + b_0}$$

where $N(x)$ and $D(x)$ have no common factors.

1. The graph of f has *vertical* asymptotes at the zeros of $D(x)$.

2. The graph of f has at most one *horizontal* asymptote determine comparing the degrees of $N(x)$ and $D(x)$.

   a. If $n < m$, the graph of f has the line $y = 0$ (the x-axi horizontal asymptote.

   b. If $n = m$, the graph of f has the line $y = a_n/b_m$ as a ho asymptote, where a_n is the leading coefficient of the numer b_m is the leading coefficient of the denominator.

   c. If $n > m$, the graph of f has no horizontal asymptote.

Example 2 Finding Horizontal and Vertical Asymptotes

Find all horizontal and vertical asymptotes of the graph of each rationa

a. $f(x) = \dfrac{2x}{3x^2 + 1}$ **b.** $f(x) = \dfrac{2x^2}{x^2 - 1}$

Solution

a. For this rational function, the degree of the numerator is *less than* of the denominator, so the graph has the line $y = 0$ as a horizontal To find any vertical asymptotes, set the denominator equal to zer the resulting equation for x.

$$3x^2 + 1 = 0 \qquad \text{Set denominator}$$

Because this equation has no real solutions, you can conclude tha has no vertical asymptote. The graph of the function is shown in I

b. For this rational function, the degree of the numerator is *equal to* the denominator. The leading coefficient of the numerator is 2 and coefficient of the denominator is 1, so the graph has the line horizontal asymptote. To find any vertical asymptotes, set the equal to zero and solve the resulting equation for x.

$$x^2 - 1 = 0 \qquad \text{Set denominato}$$

$$(x + 1)(x - 1) = 0 \qquad \text{Factor.}$$

$$x + 1 = 0 \quad \Longrightarrow \quad x = -1 \qquad \text{Set 1st factor e}$$

$$x - 1 = 0 \quad \Longrightarrow \quad x = 1 \qquad \text{Set 2nd factor}$$

This equation has two real solutions, $x = -1$ and $x = 1$, so the lines $x = -1$ and $x = 1$ as vertical asymptotes, as shown in Fig

✔CHECKPOINT   Now try Exercise 13.

---

40. *Environment* In a pilot project, a rural township is given recycling bins for separating and storing recyclable products. The cost C (in dollars) for supplying bins to $p\%$ of the population is given by

$$C = \frac{25,000p}{100 - p}, \quad 0 \le p < 100.$$

(a) Find the cost of supplying bins to 15% of the population.

(b) Find the cost of supplying bins to 50% of the population.

(c) Find the cost of supplying bins to 90% of the population.

(d) Use a graphing utility to graph the cost function. Be sure to choose an appropriate viewing window. Explain why you chose the values that you used in your viewing window.

(e) According to this model, would it be possible to supply bins to 100% of the residents? Explain.

41. *Data Analysis* The endpoints of the interval over which distinct vision is possible are called the *near point* and *far point* of the eye (see figure). With increasing age these points normally change. The table shows the approximate near points y (in inches) for various ages x (in years).

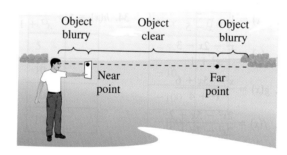

Age, x	Near point, y
16	3.0
32	4.7
44	9.8
50	19.7
60	39.4

(a) Find a rational model for the data. Take the reciprocals of the near points to generate the points $(x, 1/y)$. Use the *regression* feature of a graphing utility to find a linear model for the data. The resulting line has the form $1/y = ax + b$. Solve for y.

(b) Use the *table* feature of a graphing utility to create a table showing the predicted near point based on the model for each of the ages in the original table.

(c) Do you think the model can be used to predict the near point for a person who is 70 years old? Explain.

42. *Data Analysis* Consider a physics laboratory experiment designed to determine an unknown mass. A flexible metal meter stick is clamped to a table with 50 centimeters overhanging the edge (see figure). Known masses M ranging from 200 grams to 2000 grams are attached to the end of the meter stick. For each mass, the meter stick is displaced vertically and then allowed to oscillate. The average time t (in seconds) of one oscillation for each mass is recorded in the table.

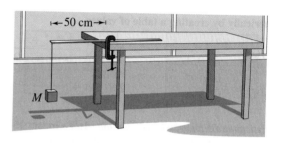

Mass, M	Time, t
200	0.450
400	0.597
600	0.712
800	0.831
1000	0.906
1200	1.003
1400	1.088
1600	1.126
1800	1.218
2000	1.338

A model for the data is given by

$$t = \frac{38M + 16,965}{10(M + 5000)}.$$

(a) Use the *table* feature of a graphing utility to create a table showing the estimated time based on the model for each of the masses shown in the table. What can you conclude?

(b) Use the model to approximate the mass of an object when the average time for one oscillation is 1.056 seconds.

43. *Wildlife*   The game commission introduces 100 deer into newly acquired state game lands. The population N of the herd is given by

$$N = \frac{20(5 + 3t)}{1 + 0.04t}, \quad t \geq 0$$

where t is the time in years.

(a) Use a graphing utility to graph the model.

(b) Find the populations when $t = 5$, $t = 10$, and $t = 25$.

(c) What is the limiting size of the herd as time increases? Explain.

44. *Defense*   The table shows the national defense outlays D (in billions of dollars) from 1997 to 2005. The data can be modeled by

$$D = \frac{1.493t^2 - 39.06t + 273.5}{0.0051t^2 - 0.1398t + 1}, \quad 7 \leq t \leq 15$$

where t is the year, with $t = 7$ corresponding to 1997. (Source: U.S. Office of Management and Budget)

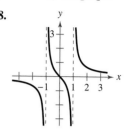

Year	Defense outlays (in billions of dollars)
1997	270.5
1998	268.5
1999	274.9
2000	294.5
2001	305.5
2002	348.6
2003	404.9
2004	455.9
2005	465.9

(a) Use a graphing utility to plot the data and graph the model in the same viewing window. How well does the model represent the data?

(b) Use the model to predict the national defense outlays for the years 2010, 2015, and 2020. Are the predictions reasonable?

(c) Determine the horizontal asymptote of the graph of the model. What does it represent in the context of the situation?

Synthesis

True or False?   In Exercises 45 and 46, determine whether the statement is true or false. Justify your answer.

45. A rational function can have infinitely many vertical asymptotes.

46. A rational function must have at least one vertical asymptote.

Library of Parent Functions   In Exercises 47 and 48, identify the rational function represented by the graph.

47.

48.

(a) $f(x) = \dfrac{x^2 - 9}{x^2 - 4}$ (a) $f(x) = \dfrac{x^2 - 1}{x^2 + 1}$

(b) $f(x) = \dfrac{x^2 - 4}{x^2 - 9}$ (b) $f(x) = \dfrac{x^2 + 1}{x^2 - 1}$

(c) $f(x) = \dfrac{x - 4}{x^2 - 9}$ (c) $f(x) = \dfrac{x}{x^2 - 1}$

(d) $f(x) = \dfrac{x - 9}{x^2 - 4}$ (d) $f(x) = \dfrac{x}{x^2 + 1}$

Think About It   In Exercises 49–52, write a rational function f that has the specified characteristics. (There are many correct answers.)

49. Vertical asymptote: $x = 2$

Horizontal asymptote: $y = 0$

Zero: $x = 1$

50. Vertical asymptote: $x = -1$

Horizontal asymptote: $y = 0$

Zero: $x = 2$

51. Vertical asymptotes: $x = -2, x = 1$

Horizontal asymptote: $y = 2$

Zeros: $x = 3, x = -3$

52. Vertical asymptotes: $x = -1, x = 2$

Horizontal asymptote: $y = -2$

Zeros: $x = -2, x = 3$

Skills Review

In Exercises 53–56, write the general form of the equation of the line that passes through the points.

53. $(3, 2), (0, -1)$ **54.** $(-6, 1), (4, -5)$

55. $(2, 7), (3, 10)$ **56.** $(0, 0), (-9, 4)$

In Exercises 57–60, divide using long division.

57. $(x^2 + 5x + 6) \div (x - 4)$

58. $(x^2 - 10x + 15) \div (x - 3)$

59. $(2x^4 + x^2 - 11) \div (x^2 + 5)$

60. $(4x^5 + 3x^3 - 10) \div (2x + 3)$

3.6   Graphs of Rational Functions

The Graph of a Rational Function

To sketch the graph of a rational function, use the following guidelines.

Guidelines for Graphing Rational Functions

Let $f(x) = N(x)/D(x)$, where $N(x)$ and $D(x)$ are polynomials.

1. Simplify f, if possible. Any restrictions on the domain of f not in the simplified function should be listed.

2. Find and plot the y-intercept (if any) by evaluating $f(0)$.

3. Find the zeros of the numerator (if any) by setting the numerator equal to zero. Then plot the corresponding x-intercepts.

4. Find the zeros of the denominator (if any) by setting the denominator equal to zero. Then sketch the corresponding vertical asymptotes using dashed vertical lines and plot the corresponding holes using open circles.

5. Find and sketch any other asymptotes of the graph using dashed lines.

6. Plot at least one point *between* and one point *beyond* each x-intercept and vertical asymptote.

7. Use smooth curves to complete the graph between and beyond the vertical asymptotes, excluding any points where f is not defined.

What you should learn

- Analyze and sketch graphs of rational functions.
- Sketch graphs of rational functions that have slant asymptotes.
- Use rational functions to model and solve real-life problems.

Why you should learn it

The graph of a rational function provides a good indication of the future behavior of a mathematical model. Exercise 86 on page 316 models the population of a herd of elk after their release onto state game lands.

Ed Reschke/Peter Arnold, Inc.

TECHNOLOGY TIP   Some graphing utilities have difficulty graphing rational functions that have vertical asymptotes. Often, the utility will connect parts of the graph that are not supposed to be connected. Notice that the graph in Figure 3.51(a) should consist of two *unconnected* portions—one to the left of $x = 2$ and the other to the right of $x = 2$. To eliminate this problem, you can try changing the *mode* of the graphing utility to *dot mode* [see Figure 3.51(b)]. The problem with this mode is that the graph is then represented as a collection of dots rather than as a smooth curve, as shown in Figure 3.51(c). In this text, a blue curve is placed behind the graphing utility's display to indicate where the graph should appear. [See Figure 3.51(c).]

TECHNOLOGY SUPPORT

For instructions on how to use the *connected* mode and the *dot* mode, see Appendix A; for specific keystrokes, go to this textbook's *Online Study Center*.

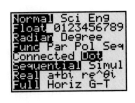

(a) *Connected* mode

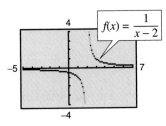

(b) **Mode** screen

(c) *Dot* mode

Figure 3.51

Example 1   Sketching the Graph of a Rational Function

Sketch the graph of $g(x) = \dfrac{3}{x-2}$ by hand.

Solution

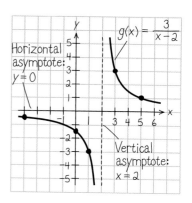

y-Intercept:	$\left(0, -\frac{3}{2}\right)$, because $g(0) = -\frac{3}{2}$
x-Intercept:	None, because $3 \neq 0$
Vertical Asymptote:	$x = 2$, zero of denominator
Horizontal Asymptote:	$y = 0$, because degree of $N(x) <$ degree of $D(x)$
Additional Points:	

x	-4	1	2	3	5
$g(x)$	-0.5	-3	Undefined	3	1

Figure 3.52

By plotting the intercept, asymptotes, and a few additional points, you can obtain the graph shown in Figure 3.52. Confirm this with a graphing utility.

✓CHECKPOINT   Now try Exercise 9.

Note that the graph of g in Example 1 is a vertical stretch and a right shift of the graph of

$$f(x) = \frac{1}{x}$$

because

$$g(x) = \frac{3}{x-2} = 3\left(\frac{1}{x-2}\right) = 3f(x-2).$$

Example 2   Sketching the Graph of a Rational Function

Sketch the graph of $f(x) = \dfrac{2x-1}{x}$ by hand.

Solution

y-Intercept:	None, because $x = 0$ is not in the domain
x-Intercept:	$\left(\frac{1}{2}, 0\right)$, because $2x - 1 = 0$
Vertical Asymptote:	$x = 0$, zero of denominator
Horizontal Asymptote:	$y = 2$, because degree of $N(x) =$ degree of $D(x)$
Additional Points:	

x	-4	-1	0	$\frac{1}{4}$	4
$f(x)$	2.25	3	Undefined	-2	1.75

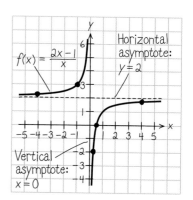

By plotting the intercept, asymptotes, and a few additional points, you can obtain the graph shown in Figure 3.53. Confirm this with a graphing utility.

✓CHECKPOINT   Now try Exercise 13.

Figure 3.53

Example 3   Sketching the Graph of a Rational Function

Sketch the graph of $f(x) = \dfrac{x}{x^2 - x - 2}$.

Solution

Factor the denominator to determine more easily the zeros of the denominator.

$$f(x) = \dfrac{x}{x^2 - x - 2} = \dfrac{x}{(x + 1)(x - 2)}.$$

y-Intercept:	$(0, 0)$, because $f(0) = 0$
x-Intercept:	$(0, 0)$
Vertical Asymptotes:	$x = -1, x = 2$, zeros of denominator
Horizontal Asymptote:	$y = 0$, because degree of $N(x) <$ degree of $D(x)$
Additional Points:	

x	-3	-1	-0.5	1	2	3
$f(x)$	-0.3	Undefined	0.4	-0.5	Undefined	0.75

The graph is shown in Figure 3.54.

✔CHECKPOINT   Now try Exercise 21.

Example 4   Sketching the Graph of a Rational Function

Sketch the graph of $f(x) = \dfrac{x^2 - 9}{x^2 - 2x - 3}$.

Solution

By factoring the numerator and denominator, you have

$$f(x) = \dfrac{x^2 - 9}{x^2 - 2x - 3} = \dfrac{(x - 3)(x + 3)}{(x - 3)(x + 1)} = \dfrac{x + 3}{x + 1}, \quad x \neq 3.$$

y-Intercept:	$(0, 3)$, because $f(0) = 3$
x-Intercept:	$(-3, 0)$
Vertical Asymptote:	$x = -1$, zero of (simplified) denominator
Hole:	$\left(3, \frac{3}{2}\right)$, f is not defined at $x = 3$
Horizontal Asymptote:	$y = 1$, because degree of $N(x) =$ degree of $D(x)$
Additional Points:	

x	-5	-2	-1	-0.5	1	3	4
$f(x)$	0.5	-1	Undefined	5	2	Undefined	1.4

The graph is shown in Figure 3.55.

✔CHECKPOINT   Now try Exercise 23.

Exploration

Use a graphing utility to graph

$$f(x) = 1 + \dfrac{1}{x - \dfrac{1}{x}}.$$

Set the graphing utility to *dot* mode and use a decimal viewing window. Use the *trace* feature to find three "holes" or "breaks" in the graph. Do all three holes represent zeros of the denominator

$$x - \dfrac{1}{x}?$$

Explain.

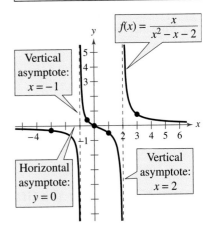

Figure 3.54

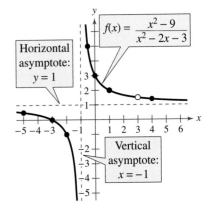

Figure 3.55   *Hole at x = 3*

Slant Asymptotes

Consider a rational function whose denominator is of degree 1 or greater. If the degree of the numerator is exactly *one more* than the degree of the denominator, the graph of the function has a **slant** (or **oblique**) **asymptote.** For example, the graph of

$$f(x) = \frac{x^2 - x}{x + 1}$$

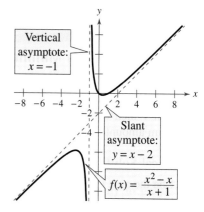

has a slant asymptote, as shown in Figure 3.56. To find the equation of a slant asymptote, use long division. For instance, by dividing $x + 1$ into $x^2 - x$, you have

$$f(x) = \frac{x^2 - x}{x + 1} = \underbrace{x - 2}_{\substack{\text{Slant asymptote} \\ (y = x - 2)}} + \frac{2}{x + 1}.$$

As x increases or decreases without bound, the remainder term $2/(x + 1)$ approaches 0, so the graph of f approaches the line $y = x - 2$, as shown in Figure 3.56.

Figure 3.56

Example 5   A Rational Function with a Slant Asymptote

Sketch the graph of $f(x) = \dfrac{x^2 - x - 2}{x - 1}$.

Solution

First write $f(x)$ in two different ways. Factoring the numerator

$$f(x) = \frac{x^2 - x - 2}{x - 1} = \frac{(x - 2)(x + 1)}{x - 1}$$

enables you to recognize the x-intercepts. Long division

$$f(x) = \frac{x^2 - x - 2}{x - 1} = x - \frac{2}{x - 1}$$

enables you to recognize that the line $y = x$ is a slant asymptote of the graph.

y-Intercept: $(0, 2)$, because $f(0) = 2$
x-Intercepts: $(-1, 0)$ and $(2, 0)$
Vertical Asymptote: $x = 1$, zero of denominator
Horizontal Asymptote: None, because degree of $N(x) >$ degree of $D(x)$
Slant Asymptote: $y = x$
Additional Points:

x	-2	0.5	1	1.5	3
$f(x)$	-1.33	4.5	Undefined	-2.5	2

The graph is shown in Figure 3.57.

✔CHECKPOINT   Now try Exercise 45.

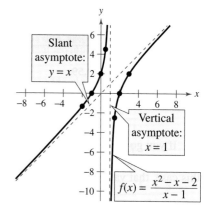

Figure 3.57

Exploration

Do you think it is possible for the graph of a rational function to cross its horizontal asymptote or its slant asymptote? Use the graphs of the following functions to investigate this question. Write a summary of your conclusion. Explain your reasoning.

$$f(x) = \frac{x}{x^2 + 1}$$

$$g(x) = \frac{2x}{3x^2 - 2x + 1}$$

$$h(x) = \frac{x^3}{x^2 + 1}$$

Graphical Reasoning In Exercises 51–54, use the graph to estimate any *x*-intercepts of the rational function. Set $y = 0$ and solve the resulting equation to confirm your result.

51. $y = \dfrac{x + 1}{x - 3}$

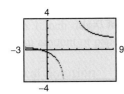

52. $y = \dfrac{2x}{x - 3}$

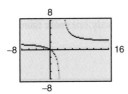

53. $y = \dfrac{1}{x} - x$

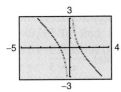

54. $y = x - 3 + \dfrac{2}{x}$

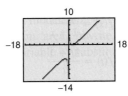

In Exercises 55–58, use a graphing utility to graph the rational function. Determine the domain of the function and identify any asymptotes.

55. $y = \dfrac{2x^2 + x}{x + 1}$

56. $y = \dfrac{x^2 + 5x + 8}{x + 3}$

57. $y = \dfrac{1 + 3x^2 - x^3}{x^2}$

58. $y = \dfrac{12 - 2x - x^2}{2(4 + x)}$

In Exercises 59–64, find all vertical asymptotes, horizontal asymptotes, slant asymptotes, and holes in the graph of the function. Then use a graphing utility to verify your result.

59. $f(x) = \dfrac{x^2 - 5x + 4}{x^2 - 4}$

60. $f(x) = \dfrac{x^2 - 2x - 8}{x^2 - 9}$

61. $f(x) = \dfrac{2x^2 - 5x + 2}{2x^2 - x - 6}$

62. $f(x) = \dfrac{3x^2 - 8x + 4}{2x^2 - 3x - 2}$

63. $f(x) = \dfrac{2x^3 - x^2 - 2x + 1}{x^2 + 3x + 2}$

64. $f(x) = \dfrac{2x^3 + x^2 - 8x - 4}{x^2 - 3x + 2}$

Graphical Reasoning In Exercises 65–76, use a graphing utility to graph the function and determine any *x*-intercepts. Set $y = 0$ and solve the resulting equation to confirm your result.

65. $y = \dfrac{1}{x + 5} + \dfrac{4}{x}$

66. $y = \dfrac{2}{x + 1} - \dfrac{3}{x}$

67. $y = \dfrac{1}{x + 2} + \dfrac{2}{x + 4}$

68. $y = \dfrac{2}{x + 2} - \dfrac{3}{x - 1}$

69. $y = x - \dfrac{6}{x - 1}$

70. $y = x - \dfrac{9}{x}$

71. $y = x + 2 - \dfrac{1}{x + 1}$

72. $y = 2x - 1 + \dfrac{1}{x - 2}$

73. $y = x + 1 + \dfrac{2}{x - 1}$

74. $y = x + 2 + \dfrac{2}{x + 2}$

75. $y = x + 3 - \dfrac{2}{2x - 1}$

76. $y = x - 1 - \dfrac{2}{2x - 3}$

77. *Concentration of a Mixture* A 1000-liter tank contains 50 liters of a 25% brine solution. You add *x* liters of a 75% brine solution to the tank.

(a) Show that the concentration *C*, the proportion of brine to the total solution, of the final mixture is given by

$$C = \dfrac{3x + 50}{4(x + 50)}.$$

(b) Determine the domain of the function based on the physical constraints of the problem.

(c) Use a graphing utility to graph the function. As the tank is filled, what happens to the rate at which the concentration of brine increases? What percent does the concentration of brine appear to approach?

78. *Geometry* A rectangular region of length *x* and width *y* has an area of 500 square meters.

(a) Write the width *y* as a function of *x*.

(b) Determine the domain of the function based on the physical constraints of the problem.

(c) Sketch a graph of the function and determine the width of the rectangle when $x = 30$ meters.

79. **Page Design**   A page that is x inches wide and y inches high contains 30 square inches of print. The margins at the top and bottom are 2 inches deep and the margins on each side are 1 inch wide (see figure).

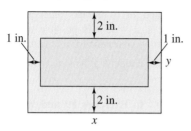

(a) Show that the total area A of the page is given by

$$A = \frac{2x(2x + 11)}{x - 2}.$$

(b) Determine the domain of the function based on the physical constraints of the problem.

(c) Use a graphing utility to graph the area function and approximate the page size such that the minimum amount of paper will be used. Verify your answer numerically using the *table* feature of a graphing utility.

80. **Geometry**   A right triangle is formed in the first quadrant by the x-axis, the y-axis, and a line segment through the point (3, 2) (see figure).

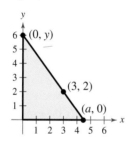

(a) Show that an equation of the line segment is given by

$$y = \frac{2(a - x)}{a - 3}, \quad 0 \le x \le a.$$

(b) Show that the area of the triangle is given by

$$A = \frac{a^2}{a - 3}.$$

(c) Use a graphing utility to graph the area function and estimate the value of a that yields a minimum area. Estimate the minimum area. Verify your answer numerically using the *table* feature of a graphing utility.

81. **Cost**   The ordering and transportation cost C (in thousands of dollars) for the components used in manufacturing a product is given by

$$C = 100\left(\frac{200}{x^2} + \frac{x}{x + 30}\right), \quad x \ge 1$$

where x is the order size (in hundreds). Use a graphing utility to graph the cost function. From the graph, estimate the order size that minimizes cost.

82. **Average Cost**   The cost C of producing x units of a product is given by $C = 0.2x^2 + 10x + 5$, and the average cost per unit is given by

$$\overline{C} = \frac{C}{x} = \frac{0.2x^2 + 10x + 5}{x}, \quad x > 0.$$

Sketch the graph of the average cost function, and estimate the number of units that should be produced to minimize the average cost per unit.

83. **Medicine**   The concentration C of a chemical in the bloodstream t hours after injection into muscle tissue is given by

$$C = \frac{3t^2 + t}{t^3 + 50}, \quad t \ge 0.$$

(a) Determine the horizontal asymptote of the function and interpret its meaning in the context of the problem.

(b) Use a graphing utility to graph the function and approximate the time when the bloodstream concentration is greatest.

(c) Use a graphing utility to determine when the concentration is less than 0.345.

84. **Numerical and Graphical Analysis**   A driver averaged 50 miles per hour on the round trip between Baltimore, Maryland and Philadelphia, Pennsylvania, 100 miles away. The average speeds for going and returning were x and y miles per hour, respectively.

(a) Show that $y = \dfrac{25x}{x - 25}$.

(b) Determine the vertical and horizontal asymptotes of the function.

(c) Use a graphing utility to complete the table. What do you observe?

x	30	35	40	45	50	55	60
y							

(d) Use a graphing utility to graph the function.

(e) Is it possible to average 20 miles per hour in one direction and still average 50 miles per hour on the round trip? Explain.

85. *Comparing Models* The numbers of people A (in thousands) attending women's NCAA Division I college basketball games from 1990 to 2004 are shown in the table. Let t represent the year, with $t = 0$ corresponding to 1990. (Source: NCAA)

Year	Attendance, A (in thousands)
1990	2,777
1991	3,013
1992	3,397
1993	4,193
1994	4,557
1995	4,962
1996	5,234
1997	6,734
1998	7,387
1999	8,010
2000	8,698
2001	8,825
2002	9,533
2003	10,164
2004	10,016

(a) Use the *regression* feature of a graphing utility to find a linear model for the data. Use a graphing utility to plot the data and graph the model in the same viewing window.

(b) Find a rational model for the data. Take the reciprocal of A to generate the points $(t, 1/A)$. Use the *regression* feature of a graphing utility to find a linear model for this data. The resulting line has the form $1/A = at + b$. Solve for A. Use a graphing utility to plot the data and graph the rational model in the same viewing window.

(c) Use the *table* feature of a graphing utility to create a table showing the predicted attendance based on each model for each of the years in the original table. Which model do you prefer? Why?

86. *Elk Population* A herd of elk is released onto state game lands. The expected population P of the herd can be modeled by the equation $P = (10 + 2.7t)/(1 + 0.1t)$, where t is the time in years since the initial number of elk were released.

(a) State the domain of the model. Explain your answer.

(b) Find the initial number of elk in the herd.

(c) Find the populations of elk after 25, 50, and 100 years.

(d) Is there a limit to the size of the herd? If so, what is the expected population?

Use a graphing utility to confirm your results for parts (a) through (d).

Synthesis

True or False? In Exercises 87 and 88, determine whether the statement is true or false. Justify your answer.

87. If the graph of a rational function f has a vertical asymptote at $x = 5$, it is possible to sketch the graph without lifting your pencil from the paper.

88. The graph of a rational function can never cross one of its asymptotes.

Think About It In Exercises 89 and 90, use a graphing utility to graph the function. Explain why there is no vertical asymptote when a superficial examination of the function might indicate that there should be one.

89. $h(x) = \dfrac{6 - 2x}{3 - x}$

90. $g(x) = \dfrac{x^2 + x - 2}{x - 1}$

Think About It In Exercises 91 and 92, write a rational function satisfying the following criteria. (There are many correct answers.)

91. Vertical asymptote: $x = -2$

   Slant asymptote: $y = x + 1$

   Zero of the function: $x = 2$

92. Vertical asymptote: $x = -4$

   Slant asymptote: $y = x - 2$

   Zero of the function: $x = 3$

Skills Review

In Exercises 93–96, simplify the expression.

93. $\left(\dfrac{x}{8}\right)^{-3}$

94. $(4x^2)^{-2}$

95. $\dfrac{3^{7/6}}{3^{1/6}}$

96. $\dfrac{(x^{-2})(x^{1/2})}{(x^{-1})(x^{5/2})}$

In Exercises 97–100, use a graphing utility to graph the function and find its domain and range.

97. $f(x) = \sqrt{6 + x^2}$

98. $f(x) = \sqrt{121 - x^2}$

99. $f(x) = -|x + 9|$

100. $f(x) = -x^2 + 9$

101. ***Make a Decision*** To work an extended application analyzing the total manpower of the Department of Defense, visit this textbook's *Online Study Center*. (Data Source: U.S. Department of Defense)

3.7 Quadratic Models

Classifying Scatter Plots

In real life, many relationships between two variables are parabolic, as in Section 3.1, Example 5. A scatter plot can be used to give you an idea of which type of model will best fit a set of data.

Example 1 Classifying Scatter Plots

Decide whether each set of data could be better modeled by a linear model, $y = ax + b$, or a quadratic model, $y = ax^2 + bx + c$.

a. (0.9, 1.4), (1.3, 1.5), (1.3, 1.9), (1.4, 2.1), (1.6, 2.8), (1.8, 2.9), (2.1, 3.4), (2.1, 3.4), (2.5, 3.6), (2.9, 3.7), (3.2, 4.2), (3.3, 4.3), (3.6, 4.4), (4.0, 4.5), (4.2, 4.8), (4.3, 5.0)

b. (0.9, 2.5), (1.3, 4.03), (1.3, 4.1), (1.4, 4.4), (1.6, 5.1), (1.8, 6.05), (2.1, 7.48), (2.1, 7.6), (2.5, 9.8), (2.9, 12.4), (3.2, 14.3), (3.3, 15.2), (3.6, 18.1), (4.0, 19.9), (4.2, 23.0), (4.3, 23.9)

Solution

Begin by entering the data into a graphing utility, as shown in Figure 3.62.

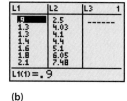

(a)   (b)

Figure 3.62

Then display the scatter plots, as shown in Figure 3.63.

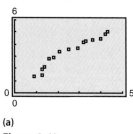   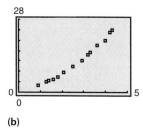

(a)   (b)

Figure 3.63

From the scatter plots, it appears that the data in part (a) follow a linear pattern. So, it can be better modeled by a linear function. The data in part (b) follow a parabolic pattern. So, it can be better modeled by a quadratic function.

✔CHECKPOINT   Now try Exercise 3.

What you should learn

■ Classify scatter plots.
■ Use scatter plots and a graphing utility to find quadratic models for data.
■ Choose a model that best fits a set of data.

Why you should learn it

Many real-life situations can be modeled by quadratic equations. For instance, in Exercise 15 on page 321, a quadratic equation is used to model the monthly precipitation for San Francisco, California.

Justin Sullivan/Getty Images

Fitting a Quadratic Model to Data

In Section 2.7, you created scatter plots of data and used a graphing utility to find the least squares regression lines for the data. You can use a similar procedure to find a model for nonlinear data. Once you have used a scatter plot to determine the type of model that would best fit a set of data, there are several ways that you can actually find the model. Each method is best used with a computer or calculator, rather than with hand calculations.

Example 2   Fitting a Quadratic Model to Data

A study was done to compare the speed x (in miles per hour) with the mileage y (in miles per gallon) of an automobile. The results are shown in the table. (Source: Federal Highway Administration)

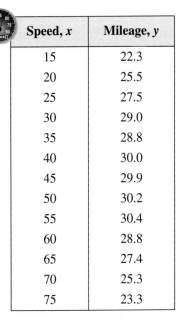

Speed, x	Mileage, y
15	22.3
20	25.5
25	27.5
30	29.0
35	28.8
40	30.0
45	29.9
50	30.2
55	30.4
60	28.8
65	27.4
70	25.3
75	23.3

a. Use a graphing utility to create a scatter plot of the data.

b. Use the *regression* feature of the graphing utility to find a model that best fits the data.

c. Approximate the speed at which the mileage is the greatest.

Solution

a. Begin by entering the data into a graphing utility and displaying the scatter plot, as shown in Figure 3.64. From the scatter plot, you can see that the data appears to follow a parabolic pattern.

b. Using the *regression* feature of a graphing utility, you can find the quadratic model, as shown in Figure 3.65. So, the quadratic equation that best fits the data is given by

$$y = -0.0082x^2 + 0.746x + 13.47. \qquad \text{Quadratic model}$$

c. Graph the data and the model in the same viewing window, as shown in Figure 3.66. Use the *maximum* feature or the *zoom* and *trace* features of the graphing utility to approximate the speed at which the mileage is greatest. You should obtain a maximum of approximately (45, 30), as shown in Figure 3.66. So, the speed at which the mileage is greatest is about 47 miles per hour.

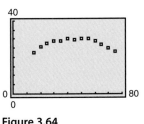

Figure 3.64

Figure 3.65

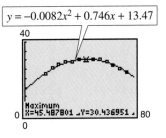

Figure 3.66

✓CHECKPOINT   Now try Exercise 15.

TECHNOLOGY SUPPORT   For instructions on how to use the *regression* feature, see Appendix A; for specific keystrokes, go to this textbook's *Online Study Center*.

Example 3   Fitting a Quadratic Model to Data

A basketball is dropped from a height of about 5.25 feet. The height of the basketball is recorded 23 times at intervals of about 0.02 second.* The results are shown in the table. Use a graphing utility to find a model that best fits the data. Then use the model to predict the time when the basketball will hit the ground.

Time, x	Height, y
0.0	5.23594
0.02	5.20353
0.04	5.16031
0.06	5.09910
0.08	5.02707
0.099996	4.95146
0.119996	4.85062
0.139992	4.74979
0.159988	4.63096
0.179988	4.50132
0.199984	4.35728
0.219984	4.19523
0.23998	4.02958
0.25993	3.84593
0.27998	3.65507
0.299976	3.44981
0.319972	3.23375
0.339961	3.01048
0.359961	2.76921
0.379951	2.52074
0.399941	2.25786
0.419941	1.98058
0.439941	1.63488

Solution

Begin by entering the data into a graphing utility and displaying the scatter plot, as shown in Figure 3.67. From the scatter plot, you can see that the data has a parabolic trend. So, using the *regression* feature of the graphing utility, you can find the quadratic model, as shown in Figure 3.68. The quadratic model that best fits the data is given by

$$y = -15.449x^2 - 1.30x + 5.2.$$ Quadratic model

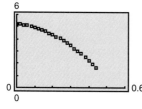

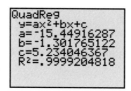

Figure 3.67   **Figure 3.68**

Using this model, you can predict the time when the basketball will hit the ground by substituting 0 for y and solving the resulting equation for x.

$$y = -15.449x^2 - 1.30x + 5.2$$ Write original model.

$$0 = -15.449x^2 - 1.30x + 5.2$$ Substitute 0 for y.

$$x = \frac{-b \pm \sqrt{b^2 - 4ac}}{2a}$$ Quadratic Formula

$$= \frac{-(-1.30) \pm \sqrt{(-1.30)^2 - 4(-15.449)(5.2)}}{2(-15.449)}$$ Substitute for a, b, and c.

$$\approx 0.54$$ Choose positive solution.

So, the solution is about 0.54 second. In other words, the basketball will continue to fall for about $0.54 - 0.44 = 0.1$ second more before hitting the ground.

✓CHECKPOINT   Now try Exercise 17.

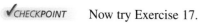

Choosing a Model

Sometimes it is not easy to distinguish from a scatter plot which type of model will best fit the data. You should first find several models for the data, using the *Library of Parent Functions,* and then choose the model that best fits the data by comparing the y-values of each model with the actual y-values.

---

*Data was collected with a Texas Instruments CBL (Calculator-Based Laboratory) System.

Example 4   Choosing a Model

The table shows the amounts y (in billions of dollars) spent on admission to movie theaters in the United States for the years 1997 to 2003. Use the *regression* feature of a graphing utility to find a linear model and a quadratic model for the data. Determine which model better fits the data.   (Source: U.S. Bureau of Economic Analysis)

Year	Amount, y
1997	6.3
1998	6.9
1999	7.9
2000	8.6
2001	9.0
2002	9.6
2003	9.9

Solution

Let x represent the year, with $x = 7$ corresponding to 1997. Begin by entering the data into the graphing utility. Then use the *regression* feature to find a linear model (see Figure 3.69) and a quadratic model (see Figure 3.70) for the data.

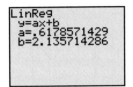

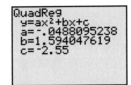

Figure 3.69   *Linear Model*   **Figure 3.70**   *Quadratic Model*

So, a linear model for the data is given by

$$y = 0.62x + 2.1 \qquad \text{Linear model}$$

and a quadratic model for the data is given by

$$y = -0.049x^2 + 1.59x - 2.6. \qquad \text{Quadratic model}$$

Plot the data and the linear model in the same viewing window, as shown in Figure 3.71. Then plot the data and the quadratic model in the same viewing window, as shown in Figure 3.72. To determine which model fits the data better, compare the y-values given by each model with the actual y-values. The model whose y-values are closest to the actual values is the better fit. In this case, the better-fitting model is the quadratic model.

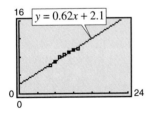

Figure 3.71

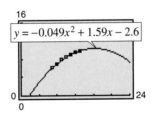

Figure 3.72

✓CHECKPOINT   Now try Exercise 18.

TECHNOLOGY TIP   When you use the regression feature of a graphing utility, the program may output an "r^2-value." This r^2-value is the **coefficient of determination** of the data and gives a measure of how well the model fits the data. The coefficient of determination for the linear model in Example 4 is $r^2 \approx 0.97629$ and the coefficient of determination for the quadratic model is $r^2 \approx 0.99456$. Because the coefficient of determination for the quadratic model is closer to 1, the quadratic model better fits the data.

3.7 Exercises

See www.CalcChat.com for worked-out solutions to odd-numbered exercises.

Vocabulary Check

Fill in the blanks.

1. A scatter plot with either a positive or a negative correlation can be better modeled by a _____ equation.

2. A scatter plot that appears parabolic can be better modeled by a _____ equation.

In Exercises 1–6, determine whether the scatter plot could best be modeled by a linear model, a quadratic model, or neither.

1.
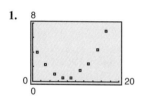

2.
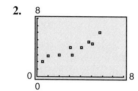

3.
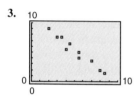

4.
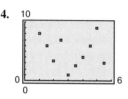

5.
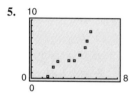

6.
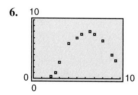

In Exercises 7–10, (a) use a graphing utility to create a scatter plot of the data, (b) determine whether the data could be better modeled by a linear model or a quadratic model, (c) use the *regression* feature of a graphing utility to find a model for the data, (d) use a graphing utility to graph the model with the scatter plot from part (a), and (e) create a table comparing the original data with the data given by the model.

7. $(0, 2.1), (1, 2.4), (2, 2.5), (3, 2.8), (4, 2.9), (5, 3.0),$
   $(6, 3.0), (7, 3.2), (8, 3.4), (9, 3.5), (10, 3.6)$

8. $(-2, 11.0), (-1, 10.7), (0, 10.4), (1, 10.3), (2, 10.1),$
   $(3, 9.9), (4, 9.6), (5, 9.4), (6, 9.4), (7, 9.2), (8, 9.0)$

9. $(0, 3480), (5, 2235), (10, 1250), (15, 565), (20, 150),$
   $(25, 12), (30, 145), (35, 575), (40, 1275), (45, 2225),$
   $(50, 3500), (55, 5010)$

10. $(0, 6140), (2, 6815), (4, 7335), (6, 7710), (8, 7915),$
    $(10, 7590), (12, 7975), (14, 7700), (16, 7325), (18, 6820),$
    $(20, 6125), (22, 5325)$

In Exercises 11–14, (a) use the *regression* feature of a graphing utility to find a linear model and a quadratic model for the data, (b) determine the coefficient of determination for each model, and (c) use the coefficient of determination to determine which model fits the data better.

11. $(1, 4.0), (2, 6.5), (3, 8.8), (4, 10.6), (5, 13.9), (6, 15.0),$
    $(7, 17.5), (8, 20.1), (9, 24.0), (10, 27.1)$

12. $(0, 0.1), (1, 2.0), (2, 4.1), (3, 6.3), (4, 8.3), (5, 10.5),$
    $(6, 12.6), (7, 14.5), (8, 16.8), (9, 19.0)$

13. $(-6, 10.7), (-4, 9.0), (-2, 7.0), (0, 5.4), (2, 3.5),$
    $(4, 1.7), (6, -0.1), (8, -1.8), (10, -3.6), (12, -5.3)$

14. $(-20, 805), (-15, 744), (-10, 704), (-5, 653), (0, 587),$
    $(5, 551), (10, 512), (15, 478), (20, 436), (25, 430)$

15. **Meteorology** The table shows the monthly normal precipitation P (in inches) for San Francisco, California. (Source: U.S. National Oceanic and Atmospheric Administration)

Month	Precipitation, P
January	4.45
February	4.01
March	3.26
April	1.17
May	0.38
June	0.11
July	0.03
August	0.07
September	0.20
October	1.40
November	2.49
December	2.89

(a) Use a graphing utility to create a scatter plot of the data. Let t represent the month, with $t = 1$ corresponding to January.

(b) Use the *regression* feature of a graphing utility to find a quadratic model for the data.

(c) Use a graphing utility to graph the model with the scatter plot from part (a).

(d) Use the graph from part (c) to determine in which month the normal precipitation in San Francisco is the least.

16. Sales   The table shows the sales S (in millions of dollars) for jogging and running shoes from 1998 to 2004. (Source: National Sporting Goods Association)

Year	Sales, S (in millions of dollars)
1998	1469
1999	1502
2000	1638
2001	1670
2002	1733
2003	1802
2004	1838

(a) Use a graphing utility to create a scatter plot of the data. Let t represent the year, with $t = 8$ corresponding to 1998.

(b) Use the *regression* feature of a graphing utility to find a quadratic model for the data.

(c) Use a graphing utility to graph the model with the scatter plot from part (a).

(d) Use the model to find when sales of jogging and running shoes will exceed 2 billion dollars.

(e) Is this a good model for predicting future sales? Explain.

17. Sales   The table shows college textbook sales S (in millions of dollars) in the United States from 2000 to 2005. (Source: Book Industry Study Group, Inc.)

Year	Textbook sales, S (in millions of dollars)
2000	4265.2
2001	4570.7
2002	4899.1
2003	5085.9
2004	5478.6
2005	5703.2

(a) Use a graphing utility to create a scatter plot of the data. Let t represent the year, with $t = 0$ corresponding to 2000.

(b) Use the *regression* feature of a graphing utility to find a quadratic model for the data.

(c) Use a graphing utility to graph the model with the scatter plot from part (a).

(d) Use the model to find when the sales of college textbooks will exceed 10 billion dollars.

(e) Is this a good model for predicting future sales? Explain.

18. Media   The table shows the numbers S of FM radio stations in the United States from 1997 to 2003. (Source: Federal Communications Commission)

Year	FM stations, S
1997	5542
1998	5662
1999	5766
2000	5892
2001	6051
2002	6161
2003	6207

(a) Use a graphing utility to create a scatter plot of the data. Let t represent the year, with $t = 7$ corresponding to 1997.

(b) Use the *regression* feature of a graphing utility to find a linear model for the data and identify the coefficient of determination.

(c) Use a graphing utility to graph the model with the scatter plot from part (a).

(d) Use the *regression* feature of a graphing utility to find a quadratic model for the data and identify the coefficient of determination.

(e) Use a graphing utility to graph the quadratic model with the scatter plot from part (a).

(f) Which model is a better fit for the data?

(g) Use each model to find when the number of FM stations will exceed 7000.

19. Entertainment   The table shows the amounts A (in dollars) spent per person on the Internet in the United States from 2000 to 2005. (Source: Veronis Suhler Stevenson)

Year	Amount, A (in dollars)
2000	49.64
2001	68.94
2002	84.76
2003	96.35
2004	107.02
2005	117.72

(a) Use a graphing utility to create a scatter plot of the data. Let t represent the year, with $t = 0$ corresponding to 2000.

(b) A cubic model for the data is $S = 0.25444t^3 - 3.0440t^2 + 22.485t + 49.55$ which has an r^2-value of 0.99992. Use a graphing utility to graph this model with the scatter plot from part (a). Is the cubic model a good fit for the data? Explain.

(c) Use the *regression* feature of a graphing utility to find a quadratic model for the data and identify the coefficient of determination.

(d) Use a graphing utility to graph the quadratic model with the scatter plot from part (a). Is the quadratic model a good fit for the data? Explain.

(e) Which model is a better fit for the data? Explain.

(f) The projected amounts A^* spent per person on the Internet for the years 2006 to 2008 are shown in the table. Use the models from parts (b) and (c) to predict the amount spent for the same years. Explain why your values may differ from those in the table.

Year	2006	2007	2008
A^*	127.76	140.15	154.29

20. *Entertainment* The table shows the amounts A (in hours) of time per person spent watching television and movies, listening to recorded music, playing video games, and reading books and magazines in the United States from 2000 to 2005. (Source: Veronis Suhler Stevenson)

Year	Amount, A (in hours)
2000	3492
2001	3540
2002	3606
2003	3663
2004	3757
2005	3809

(a) Use a graphing utility to create a scatter plot of the data. Let t represent the year, with $t = 0$ corresponding to 2000.

(b) A cubic model for the data is $A = -1.500t^3 + 13.61t^2 + 33.2t + 3493$ which has an r^2-value of 0.99667. Use a graphing utility to graph this model with the scatter plot from part (a). Is the cubic model a good fit for the data? Explain.

(c) Use the *regression* feature of a graphing utility to find a quadratic model for the data and identify the coefficient of determination.

(d) Use a graphing utility to graph the quadratic model with the scatter plot from part (a). Is the quadratic model a good fit for the data? Explain.

(e) Which model is a better fit for the data? Explain.

(f) The projected amounts A^* of time spent per person for the years 2006 to 2008 are shown in the table. Use the models from parts (b) and (c) to predict the number of hours for the same years. Explain why your values may differ from those in the table.

Year	2006	2007	2008
A^*	3890	3949	4059

Synthesis

True or False? In Exercises 21 and 22, determine whether the statement is true or false. Justify your answer.

21. The graph of a quadratic model with a negative leading coefficient will have a maximum value at its vertex.

22. The graph of a quadratic model with a positive leading coefficient will have a minimum value at its vertex.

23. *Writing* Explain why the parabola shown in the figure is not a good fit for the data.

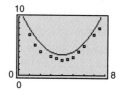

Skills Review

In Exercises 24–27, find (a) $f \circ g$ and (b) $g \circ f$.

24. $f(x) = 2x - 1$, $g(x) = x^2 + 3$

25. $f(x) = 5x + 8$, $g(x) = 2x^2 - 1$

26. $f(x) = x^3 - 1$, $g(x) = \sqrt[3]{x + 1}$

27. $f(x) = \sqrt[3]{x + 5}$, $g(x) = x^3 - 5$

In Exercises 28–31, determine algebraically whether the function is one-to-one. If it is, find its inverse function. Verify your answer graphically.

28. $f(x) = 2x + 5$

29. $f(x) = \dfrac{x - 4}{5}$

30. $f(x) = x^2 + 5, x \geq 0$

31. $f(x) = 2x^2 - 3, x \geq 0$

In Exercises 32–35, plot the complex number in the complex plane.

32. $1 - 3i$

33. $-2 + 4i$

34. $-5i$

35. $8i$

What Did You Learn?

Key Terms

polynomial function, p. 252
linear function, p. 252
quadratic function, p. 252
parabola, p. 252
continuous, p. 263
Leading Coefficient Test, p. 265

repeated zeros, p. 268
multiplicity, p. 268
Intermediate Value Theorem, p. 271
synthetic division, p. 279
Descartes's Rule of Signs, p. 284
upper and lower bounds, p. 285

conjugates, p. 293
rational function, p. 298
vertical asymptote, p. 299
horizontal asymptote, p. 299
slant (oblique) asymptote, p. 311

Key Concepts

3.1 ■ Analyze graphs of quadratic functions

The graph of the quadratic function
$f(x) = a(x - h)^2 + k, a \neq 0$, is a parabola whose axis
is the vertical line $x = h$ and whose vertex is the point
(h, k). If $a > 0$, the parabola opens upward, and if
$a < 0$, the parabola opens downward.

3.2 ■ Analyze graphs of polynomial functions

1. The graph of the polynomial function $f(x) = a_n x^n + a_{n-1}x^{n-1} + \cdots + a_2 x^2 + a_1 x + a_0$ is smooth
   and continuous, and rises or falls as x moves without
   bound to the left or to the right depending on the
   values of n and a_n.

2. If f is a polynomial function and a is a real number,
   $x = a$ is a zero of the function f, $x = a$ is a solution
   of the polynomial equation $f(x) = 0$, $(x - a)$ is
   a factor of the polynomial $f(x)$, and $(a, 0)$ is an
   x-intercept of the graph of f.

3.3 ■ Divide polynomials by other polynomials

1. If $f(x)$ and $d(x)$ are polynomials such that $d(x) \neq 0$,
   and the degree of $d(x)$ is less than or equal to the
   degree of $f(x)$, there exist unique polynomials $q(x)$
   and $r(x)$ such that $f(x) = d(x)q(x) + r(x)$, where
   $r(x) = 0$ or the degree of $r(x)$ is less than the degree
   of $d(x)$. If the remainder $r(x)$ is zero, $d(x)$ divides
   evenly into $f(x)$.

2. If a polynomial $f(x)$ is divided by $x - k$, the
   remainder is $r = f(k)$.

3. A polynomial $f(x)$ has a factor $(x - k)$ if and only if
   $f(k) = 0$.

3.3 ■ Rational zeros of polynomial functions

The Rational Zero Test states: If the polynomial
$f(x) = a_n x^n + a_{n-1}x^{n-1} + \cdots + a_2 x^2 + a_1 x + a_0$
has integer coefficients, every rational zero of f has the
form p/q, where p and q have no common factors other
than 1, p is a factor of the constant term a_0, and q is a
factor of the leading coefficient a_n.

3.4 ■ Real and complex zeros of polynomials

1. The Fundamental Theorem of Algebra states: If $f(x)$
   is a polynomial of degree n, where $n > 0$, then f has
   at least one zero in the complex number system.

2. The Linear Factorization Theorem states: If $f(x)$ is a
   polynomial of degree n, where $n > 0$, f has precisely
   n linear factors $f(x) = a_n(x - c_1)(x - c_2) \cdots$
   $(x - c_n)$, where $c_1, c_2, \ldots, c_n$ are complex numbers.

3. Let $f(x)$ be a polynomial function with real coefficients. If $a + bi$ ($b \neq 0$), is a zero of the function,
   the conjugate $a - bi$ is also a zero of the function.

3.5 ■ Domains and asymptotes of rational functions

1. The domain of a rational function of x includes
   all real numbers except x-values that make the
   denominator 0.

2. Let f be the rational function $f(x) = N(x)/D(x)$,
   where $N(x)$ and $D(x)$ have no common factors. The
   graph of f has vertical asymptotes at the zeros of
   $D(x)$. The graph of f has at most one horizontal
   asymptote determined by comparing the degrees of
   $N(x)$ and $D(x)$.

3.6 ■ Sketch the graphs of rational functions

Find and plot the x- and y-intercepts. Find the zeros
of the denominator, sketch the corresponding vertical
asymptotes, and plot the corresponding holes. Find
and sketch any other asymptotes. Plot at least one point
between and one point beyond each x-intercept and
vertical asymptote. Use smooth curves to complete the
graph between and beyond the vertical asymptotes.

3.7 ■ Find quadratic models for data

1. Use the *regression* feature of a graphing utility to
   find a quadratic function to model a data set.

2. Compare coefficients of determination to determine
   whether a linear model or a quadratic model is a
   better fit for the data set.

Review Exercises

See www.CalcChat.com for worked-out solutions to odd-numbered exercises.

3.1 In Exercises 1 and 2, use a graphing utility to graph each function in the same viewing window. Describe how the graph of each function is related to the graph of $y = x^2$.

1. (a) $y = 2x^2$
   (b) $y = -2x^2$
   (c) $y = x^2 + 2$
   (d) $y = (x + 5)^2$
2. (a) $y = x^2 - 3$
   (b) $y = 3 - x^2$
   (c) $y = (x - 4)^2$
   (d) $y = \frac{1}{2}x^2 + 4$

In Exercises 3–8, sketch the graph of the quadratic function. Identify the vertex and the intercept(s).

3. $f(x) = \left(x + \frac{3}{2}\right)^2 + 1$
4. $f(x) = (x - 4)^2 - 4$
5. $f(x) = \frac{1}{3}(x^2 + 5x - 4)$
6. $f(x) = 3x^2 - 12x + 11$
7. $f(x) = 3 - x^2 - 4x$
8. $f(x) = 30 + 23x + 3x^2$

In Exercises 9–12, write the standard form of the quadratic function that has the indicated vertex and whose graph passes through the given point. Verify your result with a graphing utility.

9. Vertex: $(1, -4)$;   Point: $(2, -3)$
10. Vertex: $(2, 3)$;   Point: $(0, 2)$
11. Vertex: $(-2, -2)$;   Point: $(-1, 0)$
12. Vertex: $\left(-\frac{1}{4}, \frac{3}{2}\right)$;   Point: $(-2, 0)$

13. **Numerical, Graphical, and Analytical Analysis**   A rectangle is inscribed in the region bounded by the x-axis, the y-axis, and the graph of $x + 2y - 8 = 0$, as shown in the figure.

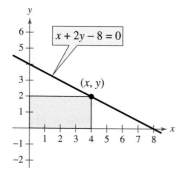

(a) Write the area A as a function of x. Determine the domain of the function in the context of the problem.

(b) Use the *table* feature of a graphing utility to create a table showing possible values of x and the corresponding areas of the rectangle. Use the table to estimate the dimensions that will produce a maximum area.

(c) Use a graphing utility to graph the area function. Use the graph to approximate the dimensions that will produce a maximum area.

(d) Write the area function in standard form to find algebraically the dimensions that will produce a maximum area.

(e) Compare your results from parts (b), (c), and (d).

14. **Cost**   A textile manufacturer has daily production costs of

$$C = 10{,}000 - 110x + 0.45x^2$$

where C is the total cost (in dollars) and x is the number of units produced. Use the *table* feature of a graphing utility to determine how many units should be produced each day to yield a minimum cost.

15. **Gardening**   A gardener has 1500 feet of fencing to enclose three adjacent rectangular gardens, as shown in the figure. Determine the dimensions that will produce a maximum enclosed area.

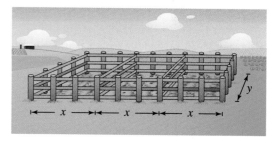

16. **Profit**   An online music company sells songs for $1.75 each. The company's cost C per week is given by the model

$$C = 0.0005x^2 + 500$$

where x is the number of songs sold. Therefore, the company's profit P per week is given by the model

$$P = 1.75x - (0.0005x^2 + 500).$$

(a) Use a graphing utility to graph the profit function.

(b) Use the *maximum* feature of the graphing utility to find the number of songs per week that the company needs to sell to maximize their profit.

(c) Confirm your answer to part (b) algebraically.

(d) Determine the company's maximum profit per week.

3.2 In Exercises 17 and 18, sketch the graph of $y = x^n$ and each specified transformation.

17. $y = x^5$

   (a) $f(x) = (x + 4)^5$ (b) $f(x) = x^5 + 1$

   (c) $f(x) = 3 - \frac{1}{2}x^5$ (d) $f(x) = 2(x + 3)^5$

18. $y = x^6$

   (a) $f(x) = x^6 - 2$ (b) $f(x) = -\frac{1}{4}x^6$

   (c) $f(x) = -\frac{1}{2}x^6 - 5$ (d) $f(x) = -(x + 7)^6 + 2$

Graphical Analysis In Exercises 19 and 20, use a graphing utility to graph the functions f and g in the same viewing window. Zoom out far enough so that the right-hand and left-hand behaviors of f and g appear identical. Show both graphs.

19. $f(x) = \frac{1}{3}x^3 - 2x + 1, \quad g(x) = \frac{1}{3}x^3$

20. $f(x) = -x^4 + 2x^3, \quad g(x) = -x^4$

In Exercises 21–24, use the Leading Coefficient Test to describe the right-hand and left-hand behavior of the graph of the polynomial function.

21. $f(x) = -x^2 + 6x + 9$

22. $f(x) = \frac{1}{3}x^3 + 2x$

23. $g(x) = \frac{3}{4}(x^4 + 3x^2 + 2)$

24. $h(x) = -x^5 - 7x^2 + 10x$

In Exercises 25–30, (a) find the zeros algebraically, (b) use a graphing utility to graph the function, and (c) use the graph to approximate any zeros and compare them with those in part (a).

25. $g(x) = x^4 - x^3 - 2x^2$ **26.** $h(x) = -2x^3 - x^2 + x$

27. $f(t) = t^3 - 3t$ **28.** $f(x) = -(x + 6)^3 - 8$

29. $f(x) = x(x + 3)^2$ **30.** $f(t) = t^4 - 4t^2$

In Exercises 31–34, find a polynomial function that has the given zeros. (There are many correct answers.)

31. $-2, 1, 1, 5$

32. $-3, 0, 1, 4$

33. $3, 2 - \sqrt{3}, 2 + \sqrt{3}$

34. $-7, 4 - \sqrt{6}, 4 + \sqrt{6}$

In Exercises 35 and 36, sketch the graph of the function by (a) applying the Leading Coefficient Test, (b) finding the zeros of the polynomial, (c) plotting sufficient solution points, and (d) drawing a continuous curve through the points.

35. $f(x) = x^4 - 2x^3 - 12x^2 + 18x + 27$

36. $f(x) = 18 + 27x - 2x^2 - 3x^3$

In Exercises 37–40, (a) use the Intermediate Value Theorem and a graphing utility to find graphically any intervals of length 1 in which the polynomial function is guaranteed to have a zero and, (b) use the *zero* or *root* feature of a graphing utility to approximate the real zeros of the function. Verify your results in part (a) by using the *table* feature of a graphing utility.

37. $f(x) = x^3 + 2x^2 - x - 1$

38. $f(x) = 0.24x^3 - 2.6x - 1.4$

39. $f(x) = x^4 - 6x^2 - 4$

40. $f(x) = 2x^4 + \frac{7}{2}x^3 - 2$

3.3 *Graphical Analysis* In Exercises 41–44, use a graphing utility to graph the two equations in the same viewing window. Use the graphs to verify that the expressions are equivalent. Verify the results algebraically.

41. $y_1 = \dfrac{x^2}{x - 2}, \quad y_2 = x + 2 + \dfrac{4}{x - 2}$

42. $y_1 = \dfrac{x^2 + 2x - 1}{x + 3}, \quad y_2 = x - 1 + \dfrac{2}{x + 3}$

43. $y_1 = \dfrac{x^4 + 1}{x^2 + 2}, \quad y_2 = x^2 - 2 + \dfrac{5}{x^2 + 2}$

44. $y_1 = \dfrac{x^4 + x^2 - 1}{x^2 + 1}, \quad y_2 = x^2 - \dfrac{1}{x^2 + 1}$

In Exercises 45–52, use long division to divide.

45. $\dfrac{24x^2 - x - 8}{3x - 2}$ **46.** $\dfrac{4x^2 + 7}{3x - 2}$

47. $\dfrac{x^4 - 3x^2 + 2}{x^2 - 1}$

48. $\dfrac{3x^4 + x^2 - 1}{x^2 - 1}$

49. $(5x^3 - 13x^2 - x + 2) \div (x^2 - 3x + 1)$

50. $(x^4 + x^3 - x^2 + 2x) \div (x^2 + 2x)$

51. $\dfrac{6x^4 + 10x^3 + 13x^2 - 5x + 2}{2x^2 - 1}$

52. $\dfrac{x^4 - 3x^3 + 4x^2 - 6x + 3}{x^2 + 2}$

In Exercises 53–58, use synthetic division to divide.

53. $(0.25x^4 - 4x^3) \div (x + 2)$

54. $(0.1x^3 + 0.3x^2 - 0.5) \div (x - 5)$

55. $(6x^4 - 4x^3 - 27x^2 + 18x) \div \left(x - \frac{2}{3}\right)$

56. $(2x^3 + 2x^2 - x + 2) \div \left(x - \frac{1}{2}\right)$

57. $(3x^3 - 10x^2 + 12x - 22) \div (x - 4)$

58. $(2x^3 + 6x^2 - 14x + 9) \div (x - 1)$

In Exercises 59 and 60, use the Remainder Theorem and synthetic division to evaluate the function at each given value. Use a graphing utility to verify your results.

59. $f(x) = x^4 + 10x^3 - 24x^2 + 20x + 44$

    (a) $f(-3)$ (b) $f(-2)$

60. $g(t) = 2t^5 - 5t^4 - 8t + 20$

    (a) $g(-4)$ (b) $g(\sqrt{2})$

In Exercises 61–64, (a) verify the given factor(s) of the function f, (b) find the remaining factors of f, (c) use your results to write the complete factorization of f, and (d) list all real zeros of f. Confirm your results by using a graphing utility to graph the function.

Function	Factor(s)
61. $f(x) = x^3 + 4x^2 - 25x - 28$	$(x - 4)$
62. $f(x) = 2x^3 + 11x^2 - 21x - 90$	$(x + 6)$
63. $f(x) = x^4 - 4x^3 - 7x^2 + 22x + 24$	$(x + 2),$
	$(x - 3)$
64. $f(x) = x^4 - 11x^3 + 41x^2 - 61x + 30$	$(x - 2),$
	$(x - 5)$

In Exercises 65 and 66, use the Rational Zero Test to list all possible rational zeros of f. Use a graphing utility to verify that the zeros of f are contained in the list.

65. $f(x) = 4x^3 - 11x^2 + 10x - 3$

66. $f(x) = 10x^3 + 21x^2 - x - 6$

In Exercises 67–70, find all the real zeros of the polynomial function.

67. $f(x) = 6x^3 - 5x^2 + 24x - 20$

68. $f(x) = x^3 - 1.3x^2 - 1.7x + 0.6$

69. $f(x) = 6x^4 - 25x^3 + 14x^2 + 27x - 18$

70. $f(x) = 5x^4 + 126x^2 + 25$

In Exercises 71 and 72, use Descartes's Rule of Signs to determine the possible numbers of positive and negative real zeros of the function.

71. $g(x) = 5x^3 - 6x + 9$

72. $f(x) = 2x^5 - 3x^2 + 2x - 1$

In Exercises 73 and 74, use synthetic division to verify the upper and lower bounds of the real zeros of f.

73. $f(x) = 4x^3 - 3x^2 + 4x - 3$

    Upper bound: $x = 1$; Lower bound: $x = -\frac{1}{4}$

74. $f(x) = 2x^3 - 5x^2 - 14x + 8$

    Upper bound: $x = 8$; Lower bound: $x = -4$

3.4 In Exercises 75 and 76, find all the zeros of the function.

75. $f(x) = 3x(x - 2)^2$ **76.** $f(x) = (x - 4)(x + 9)^2$

In Exercises 77–82, find all the zeros of the function and write the polynomial as a product of linear factors. Use a graphing utility to graph the function to verify your results graphically.

77. $f(x) = 2x^4 - 5x^3 + 10x - 12$

78. $g(x) = 3x^4 - 4x^3 + 7x^2 + 10x - 4$

79. $h(x) = x^3 - 7x^2 + 18x - 24$

80. $f(x) = 2x^3 - 5x^2 - 9x + 40$

81. $f(x) = x^5 + x^4 + 5x^3 + 5x^2$

82. $f(x) = x^5 - 5x^3 + 4x$

In Exercises 83–88, (a) find all the zeros of the function, (b) write the polynomial as a product of linear factors, and (c) use your factorization to determine the x-intercepts of the graph of the function. Use a graphing utility to verify that the real zeros are the only x-intercepts.

83. $f(x) = x^3 - 4x^2 + 6x - 4$

84. $f(x) = x^3 - 5x^2 - 7x + 51$

85. $f(x) = -3x^3 - 19x^2 - 4x + 12$

86. $f(x) = 2x^3 - 9x^2 + 22x - 30$

87. $f(x) = x^4 + 34x^2 + 225$

88. $f(x) = x^4 + 10x^3 + 26x^2 + 10x + 25$

In Exercises 89–92, find a polynomial function with real coefficients that has the given zeros. (There are many correct answers.)

89. $4, -2, 5i$ **90.** $2, -2, 2i$

91. $1, -4, -3 + 5i$ **92.** $-4, -4, 1 + \sqrt{3}i$

In Exercises 93 and 94, write the polynomial (a) as the product of factors that are irreducible over the *rationals*, (b) as the product of linear and quadratic factors that are irreducible over the *reals*, and (c) in completely factored form.

93. $f(x) = x^4 - 2x^3 + 8x^2 - 18x - 9$

    (*Hint:* One factor is $x^2 + 9$.)

94. $f(x) = x^4 - 4x^3 + 3x^2 + 8x - 16$

    (*Hint:* One factor is $x^2 - x - 4$.)

In Exercises 95 and 96, use the given zero to find all the zeros of the function.

Function	Zero
95. $f(x) = x^3 + 3x^2 + 4x + 12$	$-2i$
96. $f(x) = 2x^3 - 7x^2 + 14x + 9$	$2 + \sqrt{5}i$

3.5 In Exercises 97–108, (a) find the domain of the function, (b) decide whether the function is continuous, and (c) identify any horizontal and vertical asymptotes.

97. $f(x) = \dfrac{2-x}{x+3}$

98. $f(x) = \dfrac{4x}{x-8}$

99. $f(x) = \dfrac{2}{x^2 - 3x - 18}$

100. $f(x) = \dfrac{2x^2 + 3}{x^2 + x + 3}$

101. $f(x) = \dfrac{7+x}{7-x}$

102. $f(x) = \dfrac{6x}{x^2 - 1}$

103. $f(x) = \dfrac{4x^2}{2x^2 - 3}$

104. $f(x) = \dfrac{3x^2 - 11x - 4}{x^2 + 2}$

105. $f(x) = \dfrac{2x - 10}{x^2 - 2x - 15}$

106. $f(x) = \dfrac{x^3 - 4x^2}{x^2 + 3x + 2}$

107. $f(x) = \dfrac{x-2}{|x|+2}$

108. $f(x) = \dfrac{2x}{|2x-1|}$

109. **Seizure of Illegal Drugs** The cost C (in millions of dollars) for the U.S. government to seize $p\%$ of an illegal drug as it enters the country is given by

$$C = \frac{528p}{100 - p}, \quad 0 \le p < 100.$$

(a) Find the costs of seizing 25%, 50%, and 75% of the illegal drug.

(b) Use a graphing utility to graph the function. Be sure to choose an appropriate viewing window. Explain why you chose the values you used in your viewing window.

(c) According to this model, would it be possible to seize 100% of the drug? Explain.

110. **Wildlife** A biology class performs an experiment comparing the quantity of food consumed by a certain kind of moth with the quantity supplied. The model for the experimental data is given by

$$y = \frac{1.568x - 0.001}{6.360x + 1}, \quad x > 0$$

where x is the quantity (in milligrams) of food supplied and y is the quantity (in milligrams) eaten (see figure). At what level of consumption will the moth become satiated?

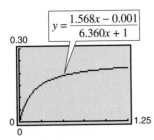

3.6 In Exercises 111–116, find all of the vertical, horizontal, and slant asymptotes, and any holes in the graph of the function. Then use a graphing utility to verify your result.

111. $f(x) = \dfrac{x^2 - 5x + 4}{x^2 - 1}$

112. $f(x) = \dfrac{x^2 - 3x - 8}{x^2 - 4}$

113. $f(x) = \dfrac{2x^2 - 7x + 3}{2x^2 - 3x - 9}$

114. $f(x) = \dfrac{3x^2 + 13x - 10}{2x^2 + 11x + 5}$

115. $f(x) = \dfrac{3x^3 - x^2 - 12x + 4}{x^2 + 3x + 2}$

116. $f(x) = \dfrac{2x^3 + 3x^2 - 2x - 3}{x^2 - 3x + 2}$

In Exercises 117–128, sketch the graph of the rational function by hand. As sketching aids, check for intercepts, vertical asymptotes, horizontal asymptotes, slant asymptotes, and holes.

117. $f(x) = \dfrac{2x - 1}{x - 5}$

118. $f(x) = \dfrac{x - 3}{x - 2}$

119. $f(x) = \dfrac{2x}{x^2 + 4}$

120. $f(x) = \dfrac{2x^2}{x^2 - 4}$

121. $f(x) = \dfrac{x^2}{x^2 + 1}$

122. $f(x) = \dfrac{5x}{x^2 + 1}$

123. $f(x) = \dfrac{2}{(x + 1)^2}$

124. $f(x) = \dfrac{4}{(x - 1)^2}$

125. $f(x) = \dfrac{2x^3}{x^2 + 1}$

126. $f(x) = \dfrac{x^3}{3x^2 - 6}$

127. $f(x) = \dfrac{x^2 - x + 1}{x - 3}$

128. $f(x) = \dfrac{2x^2 + 7x + 3}{x + 1}$

129. **Wildlife** The Parks and Wildlife Commission introduces 80,000 fish into a large human-made lake. The population N of the fish (in thousands) is given by

$$N = \frac{20(4 + 3t)}{1 + 0.05t}, \quad t \ge 0$$

where t is time in years.

(a) Use a graphing utility to graph the function.

(b) Use the graph from part (a) to find the populations when $t = 5$, $t = 10$, and $t = 25$.

(c) What is the maximum number of fish in the lake as time passes? Explain your reasoning.

130. **Page Design** A page that is x inches wide and y inches high contains 30 square inches of print. The top and bottom margins are 2 inches deep and the margins on each side are 2 inches wide.

(a) Draw a diagram that illustrates the problem.

(b) Show that the total area A of the page is given by

$$A = \frac{2x(2x + 7)}{x - 4}.$$

(c) Determine the domain of the function based on the physical constraints of the problem.

(d) Use a graphing utility to graph the area function and approximate the page size such that the minimum amount of paper will be used. Verify your answer numerically using the *table* feature of a graphing utility.

3.7 In Exercises 131–134, determine whether the scatter plot could best be modeled by a linear model, a quadratic model, or neither.

131.   **132.**

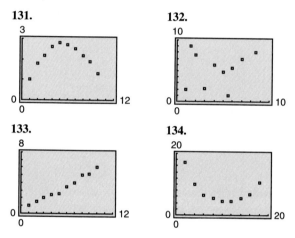

133.   **134.**

135. *Investment*   The table shows the prices P per fine ounce of gold (in dollars) for the years 1996 to 2004.   (Source: U.S. Geological Survey)

Year	Price per fine ounce, P (in dollars)
1996	389
1997	332
1998	295
1999	280
2000	280
2001	272
2002	311
2003	365
2004	410

(a) Use a graphing utility to create a scatter plot of the data. Let t represent the year, with $t = 6$ corresponding to 1996.

(b) Use the *regression* feature of a graphing utility to find a quadratic model for the data and identify the coefficient of determination.

(c) Use a graphing utility to graph the model with the scatter plot from part (a). Is the quadratic model a good fit for the data?

(d) Use the model to find when the price per ounce would have exceeded $500.

(e) Do you think the model can be used to predict the price of gold in the future? Explain.

136. *Broccoli*   The table shows the per capita consumptions, C (in pounds) of broccoli in the United States for the years 1999 to 2003.   (Source: U.S. Department of Agriculture)

Year	Per capita consumption, C (in pounds)
1999	6.2
2000	5.9
2001	5.4
2002	5.3
2003	5.7

(a) Use a graphing utility to create a scatter plot of the data. Let t represent the year, with $t = 9$ corresponding to 1999.

(b) A cubic model for the data is

$$C = 0.0583t^3 - 1.796t^2 + 17.99t - 52.7.$$

Use a graphing utility to graph the cubic model with the scatter plot from part (a). Is the cubic model a good fit for the data? Explain.

(c) Use the *regression* feature of a graphing utility to find a quadratic model for the data.

(d) Use a graphing utility to graph the quadratic model with the scatter plot from part (a). Is the quadratic model a good fit for the data?

(e) Which model is a better fit for the data? Explain.

(f) Which model would be better for predicting the per capita consumption of broccoli in the future? Explain. Use the model you chose to find the per capita consumption of broccoli in 2010.

Synthesis

True or False?   In Exercises 137 and 138, determine whether the statement is true or false. Justify your answer.

137. The graph of $f(x) = \dfrac{2x^3}{x + 1}$ has a slant asymptote.

138. A fourth-degree polynomial with real coefficients can have -5, $-8i$, $4i$, and 5 as its zeros.

139. *Think About It*   What does it mean for a divisor to divide evenly into a dividend?

140. *Writing*   Write a paragraph discussing whether every rational function has a vertical asymptote.

3 Chapter Test   See www.CalcChat.com for worked-out solutions to odd-numbered exercises.

Take this test as you would take a test in class. After you are finished, check your work against the answers given in the back of the book.

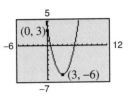

Figure for 2

1. Identify the vertex and intercepts of the graph of $y = x^2 + 4x + 3$.

2. Write an equation of the parabola shown at the right.

3. The path of a ball is given by $y = -\frac{1}{20}x^2 + 3x + 5$, where y is the height (in feet) and x is the horizontal distance (in feet).

   (a) Find the maximum height of the ball.

   (b) Which term determines the height at which the ball was thrown? Does changing this term change the maximum height of the ball? Explain.

4. Find all the real zeros of $f(x) = 4x^3 + 4x^2 + x$. Determine the multiplicity of each zero.

5. Sketch the graph of the function $f(x) = -x^3 + 7x + 6$.

6. Divide using long division: $(3x^3 + 4x - 1) \div (x^2 + 1)$.

7. Divide using synthetic division: $(2x^4 - 5x^2 - 3) \div (x - 2)$.

8. Use synthetic division to evaluate $f(-2)$ for $f(x) = 3x^4 - 6x^2 + 5x - 1$.

In Exercises 9 and 10, list all the possible rational zeros of the function. Use a graphing utility to graph the function and find all the rational zeros.

9. $g(t) = 2t^4 - 3t^3 + 16t - 24$ 10. $h(x) = 3x^5 + 2x^4 - 3x - 2$

11. Find all the zeros of the function $f(x) = x^3 - 7x^2 + 11x + 19$ and write the polynomial as the product of linear factors.

In Exercises 12–14, find a polynomial function with real coefficients that has the given zeros. (There are many correct answers.)

12. $0, 2, 2 + i$ 13. $1 - \sqrt{3}i, 2, 2$ 14. $0, 1 + i$

In Exercises 15–17, sketch the graph of the rational function. As sketching aids, check for intercepts, vertical asymptotes, horizontal asymptotes, and slant asymptotes.

15. $h(x) = \dfrac{4}{x^2} - 1$ 16. $g(x) = \dfrac{x^2 + 2}{x - 1}$ 17. $f(x) = \dfrac{2x^2 + 9}{5x^2 + 2}$

18. The table shows the amounts A (in billions of dollars) budgeted for national defense for the years 1998 to 2004. (Source: U.S. Office of Management and Budget)

   (a) Use a graphing utility to create a scatter plot of the data. Let t represent the year, with $t = 8$ corresponding to 1998.

   (b) Use the *regression* feature of a graphing utility to find a quadratic model for the data.

   (c) Use a graphing utility to graph the quadratic model with the scatter plot from part (a). Is the quadratic model a good fit for the data?

   (d) Use the model to estimate the amounts budgeted for the years 2005 and 2010.

   (e) Do you believe the model is useful for predicting the national defense budgets for years beyond 2004? Explain.

Year	Defense budget, A (in billions of dollars)
1998	271.3
1999	292.3
2000	304.1
2001	335.5
2002	362.1
2003	456.2
2004	490.6

Table for 18

Proofs in Mathematics

These two pages contain proofs of four important theorems about polynomial functions. The first two theorems are from Section 3.3, and the second two theorems are from Section 3.4.

The Remainder Theorem (p. 280)

If a polynomial $f(x)$ is divided by $x - k$, the remainder is

$r = f(k)$.

Proof

From the Division Algorithm, you have

$f(x) = (x - k)q(x) + r(x)$

and because either $r(x) = 0$ or the degree of $r(x)$ is less than the degree of $x - k$, you know that $r(x)$ must be a constant. That is, $r(x) = r$. Now, by evaluating $f(x)$ at $x = k$, you have

$f(k) = (k - k)q(k) + r$

$= (0)q(k) + r = r.$

To be successful in algebra, it is important that you understand the connection among *factors* of a polynomial, *zeros* of a polynomial function, and *solutions* or *roots* of a polynomial equation. The Factor Theorem is the basis for this connection.

The Factor Theorem (p. 280)

A polynomial $f(x)$ has a factor $(x - k)$ if and only if $f(k) = 0$.

Proof

Using the Division Algorithm with the factor $(x - k)$, you have

$f(x) = (x - k)q(x) + r(x).$

By the Remainder Theorem, $r(x) = r = f(k)$, and you have

$f(x) = (x - k)q(x) + f(k)$

where $q(x)$ is a polynomial of lesser degree than $f(x)$. If $f(k) = 0$, then

$f(x) = (x - k)q(x)$

and you see that $(x - k)$ is a factor of $f(x)$. Conversely, if $(x - k)$ is a factor of $f(x)$, division of $f(x)$ by $(x - k)$ yields a remainder of 0. So, by the Remainder Theorem, you have $f(k) = 0$.

Linear Factorization Theorem   (p. 291)

If $f(x)$ is a polynomial of degree n, where $n > 0$, then f has precisely n linear factors

$$f(x) = a_n(x - c_1)(x - c_2) \cdots (x - c_n)$$

where $c_1, c_2, \ldots, c_n$ are complex numbers.

Proof

Using the Fundamental Theorem of Algebra, you know that f must have at least one zero, c_1. Consequently, $(x - c_1)$ is a factor of $f(x)$, and you have

$$f(x) = (x - c_1)f_1(x).$$

If the degree of $f_1(x)$ is greater than zero, you again apply the Fundamental Theorem to conclude that f_1 must have a zero c_2, which implies that

$$f(x) = (x - c_1)(x - c_2)f_2(x).$$

It is clear that the degree of $f_1(x)$ is $n - 1$, that the degree of $f_2(x)$ is $n - 2$, and that you can repeatedly apply the Fundamental Theorem n times until you obtain

$$f(x) = a_n(x - c_1)(x - c_2) \cdots (x - c_n)$$

where a_n is the leading coefficient of the polynomial $f(x)$.

Factors of a Polynomial   (p. 293)

Every polynomial of degree $n > 0$ with real coefficients can be written as the product of linear and quadratic factors with real coefficients, where the quadratic factors have no real zeros.

Proof

To begin, you use the Linear Factorization Theorem to conclude that $f(x)$ can be *completely* factored in the form

$$f(x) = d(x - c_1)(x - c_2)(x - c_3) \cdots (x - c_n).$$

If each c_i is real, there is nothing more to prove. If any c_i is complex ($c_i = a + bi$, $b \neq 0$), then, because the coefficients of $f(x)$ are real, you know that the conjugate $c_j = a - bi$ is also a zero. By multiplying the corresponding factors, you obtain

$$(x - c_i)(x - c_j) = [x - (a + bi)][x - (a - bi)]$$

$$= x^2 - 2ax + (a^2 + b^2)$$

where each coefficient is real.

The Fundamental Theorem of Algebra

The Linear Factorization Theorem is closely related to the Fundamental Theorem of Algebra. The Fundamental Theorem of Algebra has a long and interesting history. In the early work with polynomial equations, The Fundamental Theorem of Algebra was thought to have been not true, because imaginary solutions were not considered. In fact, in the very early work by mathematicians such as Abu al-Khwarizmi (c. 800 A.D.), negative solutions were also not considered.

Once imaginary numbers were accepted, several mathematicians attempted to give a general proof of the Fundamental Theorem of Algebra. These included Gottfried von Leibniz (1702), Jean d'Alembert (1746), Leonhard Euler (1749), Joseph-Louis Lagrange (1772), and Pierre Simon Laplace (1795). The mathematician usually credited with the first correct proof of the Fundamental Theorem of Algebra is Carl Friedrich Gauss, who published the proof in his doctoral thesis in 1799.

Chapter 4

Exponential and Logarithmic Functions

4.1 Exponential Functions and
    Their Graphs

4.2 Logarithmic Functions and
    Their Graphs

4.3 Properties of Logarithms

4.4 Solving Exponential and
    Logarithmic Equations

4.5 Exponential and Logarithmic
    Models

4.6 Nonlinear Models

Selected Applications

Exponential and logarithmic functions have many real life applications. The applications listed below represent a small sample of the applications in this chapter.

- Radioactive Decay,
  Exercises 67 and 68, page 344

- Sound Intensity,
  Exercise 95, page 355

- Home Mortgage,
  Exercise 96, page 355

- Comparing Models,
  Exercise 97, page 362

- Forestry,
  Exercise 138, page 373

- IQ Scores,
  Exercise 37, page 384

- Newton's Law of Cooling,
  Exercises 53 and 54, page 386

- Elections,
  Exercise 27, page 393

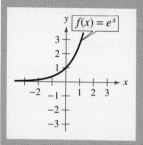 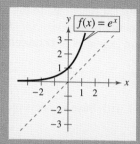 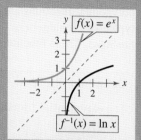

Exponential and logarithmic functions are called transcendental functions because these functions are not algebraic. In Chapter 4, you will learn about the inverse relationship between exponential and logarithmic functions, how to graph these functions, how to solve exponential and logarithmic equations, and how to use these functions in real-life applications.

© Denis O'Regan/Corbis

The relationship between the number of decibels and the intensity of a sound can be modeled by a logarithmic function. A rock concert at a stadium has a decibel rating of 120 decibels. Sounds at this level can cause gradual hearing loss.

4.1 Exponential Functions and Their Graphs

Exponential Functions

So far, this text has dealt mainly with **algebraic functions,** which include polynomial functions and rational functions. In this chapter you will study two types of nonalgebraic functions—*exponential functions* and *logarithmic functions.* These functions are examples of **transcendental functions.**

> **Definition of Exponential Function**
>
> The **exponential function f with base a** is denoted by
>
> $$f(x) = a^x$$
>
> where $a > 0$, $a \neq 1$, and x is any real number.

Note that in the definition of an exponential function, the base $a = 1$ is excluded because it yields $f(x) = 1^x = 1$. This is a constant function, not an exponential function.

You have already evaluated a^x for integer and rational values of x. For example, you know that $4^3 = 64$ and $4^{1/2} = 2$. However, to evaluate 4^x for any real number x, you need to interpret forms with *irrational* exponents. For the purposes of this text, it is sufficient to think of

$$a^{\sqrt{2}} \left(\text{where } \sqrt{2} \approx 1.41421356 \right)$$

as the number that has the successively closer approximations

$$a^{1.4}, a^{1.41}, a^{1.414}, a^{1.4142}, a^{1.41421}, \ldots .$$

Example 1 shows how to use a calculator to evaluate exponential functions.

Example 1 Evaluating Exponential Functions

Use a calculator to evaluate each function at the indicated value of x.

Function	Value
a. $f(x) = 2^x$	$x = -3.1$
b. $f(x) = 2^{-x}$	$x = \pi$
c. $f(x) = 0.6^x$	$x = \frac{3}{2}$

Solution

Function Value	Graphing Calculator Keystrokes	Display
a. $f(-3.1) = 2^{-3.1}$	2 ^ (−) 3.1 ENTER	0.1166291
b. $f(\pi) = 2^{-\pi}$	2 ^ (−) π ENTER	0.1133147
c. $f\left(\frac{3}{2}\right) = (0.6)^{3/2}$	.6 ^ (3 ÷ 2) ENTER	0.4647580

✓CHECKPOINT   Now try Exercise 3.

What you should learn

- Recognize and evaluate exponential functions with base a.
- Graph exponential functions with base a.
- Recognize, evaluate, and graph exponential functions with base e.
- Use exponential functions to model and solve real-life problems.

Why you should learn it

Exponential functions are useful in modeling data that represents quantities that increase or decrease quickly. For instance, Exercise 72 on page 345 shows how an exponential function is used to model the depreciation of a new vehicle.

Sergio Piumatti

TECHNOLOGY TIP

When evaluating exponential functions with a calculator, remember to enclose fractional exponents in parentheses. Because the calculator follows the order of operations, parentheses are crucial in order to obtain the correct result.

Graphs of Exponential Functions

The graphs of all exponential functions have similar characteristics, as shown in Examples 2, 3, and 4.

Example 2   Graphs of $y = a^x$

In the same coordinate plane, sketch the graph of each function by hand.

a. $f(x) = 2^x$ **b.** $g(x) = 4^x$

Solution

The table below lists some values for each function. By plotting these points and connecting them with smooth curves, you obtain the graphs shown in Figure 4.1. Note that both graphs are increasing. Moreover, the graph of $g(x) = 4^x$ is increasing more rapidly than the graph of $f(x) = 2^x$.

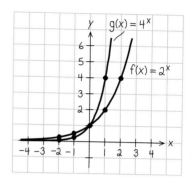

Figure 4.1

x	-2	-1	0	1	2	3
2^x	$\frac{1}{4}$	$\frac{1}{2}$	1	2	4	8
4^x	$\frac{1}{16}$	$\frac{1}{4}$	1	4	16	64

 CHECKPOINT   Now try Exercise 5.

Example 3   Graphs of $y = a^{-x}$

In the same coordinate plane, sketch the graph of each function by hand.

a. $F(x) = 2^{-x}$ **b.** $G(x) = 4^{-x}$

Solution

The table below lists some values for each function. By plotting these points and connecting them with smooth curves, you obtain the graphs shown in Figure 4.2. Note that both graphs are decreasing. Moreover, the graph of $G(x) = 4^{-x}$ is decreasing more rapidly than the graph of $F(x) = 2^{-x}$.

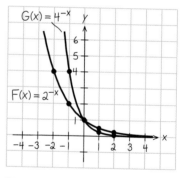

Figure 4.2

x	-3	-2	-1	0	1	2
2^{-x}	8	4	2	1	$\frac{1}{2}$	$\frac{1}{4}$
4^{-x}	64	16	4	1	$\frac{1}{4}$	$\frac{1}{16}$

CHECKPOINT   Now try Exercise 7.

The properties of exponents presented in Section P.2 can also be applied to real-number exponents. For review, these properties are listed below.

1. $a^x a^y = a^{x+y}$ **2.** $\dfrac{a^x}{a^y} = a^{x-y}$ **3.** $a^{-x} = \dfrac{1}{a^x} = \left(\dfrac{1}{a}\right)^x$ **4.** $a^0 = 1$

5. $(ab)^x = a^x b^x$ **6.** $(a^x)^y = a^{xy}$ **7.** $\left(\dfrac{a}{b}\right)^x = \dfrac{a^x}{b^x}$ **8.** $|a^2| = |a|^2 = a^2$

STUDY TIP

In Example 3, note that the functions $F(x) = 2^{-x}$ and $G(x) = 4^{-x}$ can be rewritten with positive exponents.

$$F(x) = 2^{-x} = \left(\frac{1}{2}\right)^x \quad \text{and}$$

$$G(x) = 4^{-x} = \left(\frac{1}{4}\right)^x$$

Comparing the functions in Examples 2 and 3, observe that

$$F(x) = 2^{-x} = f(-x) \quad \text{and} \quad G(x) = 4^{-x} = g(-x).$$

Consequently, the graph of F is a reflection (in the y-axis) of the graph of f, as shown in Figure 4.3. The graphs of G and g have the same relationship, as shown in Figure 4.4.

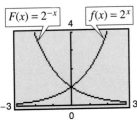

Figure 4.3

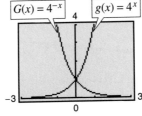

Figure 4.4

The graphs in Figures 4.3 and 4.4 are typical of the graphs of the exponential functions $f(x) = a^x$ and $f(x) = a^{-x}$. They have one y-intercept and one horizontal asymptote (the x-axis), and they are continuous.

Library of Parent Functions: Exponential Function

The *exponential function*

$$f(x) = a^x, \quad a > 0, \quad a \neq 1$$

is different from all the functions you have studied so far because the variable x is an *exponent*. A distinguishing characteristic of an exponential function is its rapid increase as x increases (for $a > 1$). Many real-life phenomena with patterns of rapid growth (or decline) can be modeled by exponential functions. The basic characteristics of the exponential function are summarized below. A review of exponential functions can be found in the *Study Capsules*.

Graph of $f(x) = a^x$, $a > 1$

Domain: $(-\infty, \infty)$

Range: $(0, \infty)$

Intercept: $(0, 1)$

Increasing on $(-\infty, \infty)$

x-axis is a horizontal asymptote

$(a^x \to 0$ as $x \to -\infty)$

Continuous

Graph of $f(x) = a^{-x}$, $a > 1$

Domain: $(-\infty, \infty)$

Range: $(0, \infty)$

Intercept: $(0, 1)$

Decreasing on $(-\infty, \infty)$

x-axis is a horizontal asymptote

$(a^{-x} \to 0$ as $x \to \infty)$

Continuous

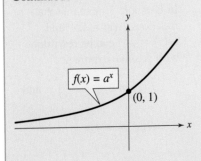

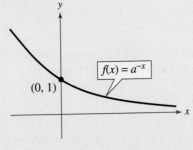

In the following example, the graph of $y = a^x$ is used to graph functions of the form $f(x) = b \pm a^{x+c}$, where b and c are any real numbers.

Example 4 Transformations of Graphs of Exponential Functions

Each of the following graphs is a transformation of the graph of $f(x) = 3^x$.

a. Because $g(x) = 3^{x+1} = f(x + 1)$, the graph of g can be obtained by shifting the graph of f one unit to the *left*, as shown in Figure 4.5.

b. Because $h(x) = 3^x - 2 = f(x) - 2$, the graph of h can be obtained by shifting the graph of f *downward* two units, as shown in Figure 4.6.

c. Because $k(x) = -3^x = -f(x)$, the graph of k can be obtained by *reflecting* the graph of f in the x-axis, as shown in Figure 4.7.

d. Because $j(x) = 3^{-x} = f(-x)$, the graph of j can be obtained by *reflecting* the graph of f in the y-axis, as shown in Figure 4.8.

> **Prerequisite Skills**
>
> If you have difficulty with this example, review shifting and reflecting of graphs in Section 1.5.

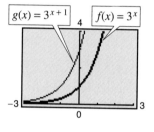

Figure 4.5

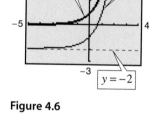

Figure 4.6

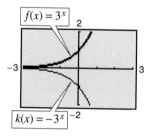

Figure 4.7

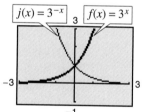

Figure 4.8

> ### Exploration
>
> The following table shows some points on the graphs in Figure 4.5. The functions $f(x)$ and $g(x)$ are represented by Y_1 and Y_2, respectively. Explain how you can use the table to describe the transformation.
>
> | X | Y₁ | Y₂ |
> |---|---|---|
> | -3 | .03704 | .11111 |
> | -2 | .11111 | .33333 |
> | -1 | .33333 | 1 |
> | 0 | 1 | 3 |
> | 1 | 3 | 9 |
> | 2 | 9 | 27 |
> | 3 | 27 | 81 |
> | X= -3 | | |

✓CHECKPOINT   Now try Exercise 17.

Notice that the transformations in Figures 4.5, 4.7, and 4.8 keep the x-axis ($y = 0$) as a horizontal asymptote, but the transformation in Figure 4.6 yields a new horizontal asymptote of $y = -2$. Also, be sure to note how the y-intercept is affected by each transformation.

The Natural Base e

For many applications, the convenient choice for a base is the irrational number

$$e = 2.718281828\ldots.$$

This number is called the **natural base.** The function $f(x) = e^x$ is called the **natural exponential function** and its graph is shown in Figure 4.9. The graph of the exponential function has the same basic characteristics as the graph of the function $f(x) = a^x$ (see page 336). Be sure you see that for the exponential function $f(x) = e^x$, e is the constant 2.718281828 . . . ., whereas x is the variable.

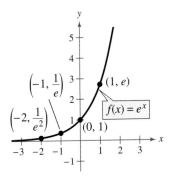

Figure 4.9   The Natural Exponential Function

In Example 5, you will see that the number e can be approximated by the expression

$$\left(1 + \frac{1}{x}\right)^x \text{ for large values of } x.$$

Example 5   Approximation of the Number e

Evaluate the expression $[1 + (1/x)]^x$ for several large values of x to see that the values approach $e \approx 2.718281828$ as x increases without bound.

Graphical Solution

Use a graphing utility to graph

$$y_1 = [1 + (1/x)]^x \qquad \text{and} \qquad y_2 = e$$

in the same viewing window, as shown in Figure 4.10. Use the *trace* feature of the graphing utility to verify that as x increases, the graph of y_1 gets closer and closer to the line $y_2 = e$.

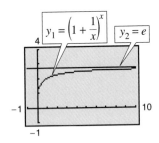

Figure 4.10

✓CHECKPOINT   Now try Exercise 77.

Numerical Solution

Use the *table* feature (in *ask* mode) of a graphing utility to create a table of values for the function $y = [1 + (1/x)]^x$, beginning at $x = 10$ and increasing the x-values as shown in Figure 4.11.

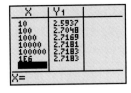

Figure 4.11

From the table, it seems reasonable to conclude that

$$\left(1 + \frac{1}{x}\right)^x \to e \text{ as } x \to \infty.$$

Exploration

Use your graphing utility to graph the functions

$$y_1 = 2^x$$

$$y_2 = e^x$$

$$y_3 = 3^x$$

in the same viewing window. From the relative positions of these graphs, make a guess as to the value of the real number e. Then try to find a number a such that the graphs of $y_2 = e^x$ and $y_4 = a^x$ are as close as possible.

TECHNOLOGY SUPPORT

For instructions on how to use the *trace* feature and the *table* feature, see Appendix A; for specific keystrokes, go to this textbook's *Online Study Center.*

Example 6   Evaluating the Natural Exponential Function

Use a calculator to evaluate the function $f(x) = e^x$ at each indicated value of x.

a. $x = -2$ **b.** $x = 0.25$ **c.** $x = -0.4$

Solution

Function Value	Graphing Calculator Keystrokes	Display
a. $f(-2) = e^{-2}$	$\boxed{e^x}$ $\boxed{(-)}$ 2 $\boxed{\text{ENTER}}$	0.1353353
b. $f(0.25) = e^{0.25}$	$\boxed{e^x}$ .25 $\boxed{\text{ENTER}}$	1.2840254
c. $f(-0.4) = e^{-0.4}$	$\boxed{e^x}$ $\boxed{(-)}$ .4 $\boxed{\text{ENTER}}$	0.6703200

✓**CHECKPOINT**   Now try Exercise 23.

> **Exploration**
>
> Use a graphing utility to graph $y = (1 + x)^{1/x}$. Describe the behavior of the graph near $x = 0$. Is there a y-intercept? How does the behavior of the graph near $x = 0$ relate to the result of Example 5? Use the *table* feature of a graphing utility to create a table that shows values of y for values of x near $x = 0$, to help you describe the behavior of the graph near this point.

Example 7   Graphing Natural Exponential Functions

Sketch the graph of each natural exponential function.

a. $f(x) = 2e^{0.24x}$ **b.** $g(x) = \frac{1}{2}e^{-0.58x}$

Solution

To sketch these two graphs, you can use a calculator to construct a table of values, as shown below.

x	-3	-2	-1	0	1	2	3
$f(x)$	0.974	1.238	1.573	2.000	2.542	3.232	4.109
$g(x)$	2.849	1.595	0.893	0.500	0.280	0.157	0.088

After constructing the table, plot the points and connect them with smooth curves. Note that the graph in Figure 4.12 is increasing, whereas the graph in Figure 4.13 is decreasing. Use a graphing calculator to verify these graphs.

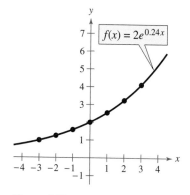

Figure 4.12

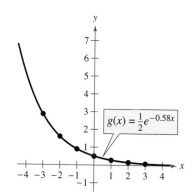

Figure 4.13

✓**CHECKPOINT**   Now try Exercise 43.

Applications

One of the most familiar examples of exponential growth is that of an investment earning *continuously compounded interest*. Suppose a principal P is invested at an annual interest rate r, compounded once a year. If the interest is added to the principal at the end of the year, the new balance P_1 is $P_1 = P + Pr = P(1 + r)$. This pattern of multiplying the previous principal by $1 + r$ is then repeated each successive year, as shown in the table.

Time in years	Balance after each compounding
0	$P = P$
1	$P_1 = P(1 + r)$
2	$P_2 = P_1(1 + r) = P(1 + r)(1 + r) = P(1 + r)^2$
$\vdots$	$\vdots$
t	$P_t = P(1 + r)^t$

To accommodate more frequent (quarterly, monthly, or daily) compounding of interest, let n be the number of compoundings per year and let t be the number of years. (The product nt represents the total number of times the interest will be compounded.) Then the interest rate per compounding period is r/n, and the account balance after t years is

$$A = P\left(1 + \frac{r}{n}\right)^{nt}. \qquad \text{Amount (balance) with } n \text{ compoundings per year}$$

If you let the number of compoundings n increase without bound, the process approaches what is called **continuous compounding.** In the formula for n compoundings per year, let $m = n/r$. This produces

$$A = P\left(1 + \frac{r}{n}\right)^{nt} = P\left(1 + \frac{1}{m}\right)^{mrt} = P\left[\left(1 + \frac{1}{m}\right)^{m}\right]^{rt}.$$

As m increases without bound, you know from Example 5 that $[1 + (1/m)]^m$ approaches e. So, for continuous compounding, it follows that

$$P\left[\left(1 + \frac{1}{m}\right)^{m}\right]^{rt} \rightarrow P[e]^{rt}$$

and you can write $A = Pe^{rt}$. This result is part of the reason that e is the "natural" choice for a base of an exponential function.

> ### Formulas for Compound Interest
>
> After t years, the balance A in an account with principal P and annual interest rate r (in decimal form) is given by the following formulas.
>
> 1. For n compoundings per year: $A = P\left(1 + \dfrac{r}{n}\right)^{nt}$
>
> 2. For continuous compounding: $A = Pe^{rt}$

Example 8 Finding the Balance for Compound Interest

A total of $9000 is invested at an annual interest rate of 2.5%, compounded annually. Find the balance in the account after 5 years.

Algebraic Solution

In this case,

$$P = 9000, r = 2.5\% = 0.025, n = 1, t = 5.$$

Using the formula for compound interest with n compoundings per year, you have

$$A = P\left(1 + \frac{r}{n}\right)^{nt} \qquad \text{Formula for compound interest}$$

$$= 9000\left(1 + \frac{0.025}{1}\right)^{1(5)} \qquad \text{Substitute for } P, r, n, \text{ and } t.$$

$$= 9000(1.025)^5 \qquad \text{Simplify.}$$

$$\approx \$10,182.67. \qquad \text{Use a calculator.}$$

So, the balance in the account after 5 years will be about $10,182.67.

Graphical Solution

Substitute the values for P, r, and n into the formula for compound interest with n compoundings per year as follows.

$$A = P\left(1 + \frac{r}{n}\right)^{nt} \qquad \text{Formula for compound interest}$$

$$= 9000\left(1 + \frac{0.025}{1}\right)^{(1)t} \qquad \text{Substitute for } P, r, \text{ and } n.$$

$$= 9000(1.025)^t \qquad \text{Simplify.}$$

Use a graphing utility to graph $y = 9000(1.025)^x$. Using the *value* feature or the *zoom* and *trace* features, you can approximate the value of y when $x = 5$ to be about 10,182.67, as shown in Figure 4.14. So, the balance in the account after 5 years will be about $10,182.67.

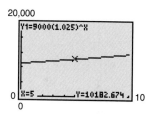

Figure 4.14

✓CHECKPOINT   Now try Exercise 53.

Example 9 Finding Compound Interest

A total of $12,000 is invested at an annual interest rate of 3%. Find the balance after 4 years if the interest is compounded (a) quarterly and (b) continuously.

Solution

a. For quarterly compoundings, $n = 4$. So, after 4 years at 3%, the balance is

$$A = P\left(1 + \frac{r}{n}\right)^{nt} = 12,000\left(1 + \frac{0.03}{4}\right)^{4(4)}$$

$$\approx \$13,523.91.$$

b. For continuous compounding, the balance is

$$A = Pe^{rt} = 12,000e^{0.03(4)}$$

$$\approx \$13,529.96.$$

Note that a continuous-compounding account yields more than a quarterly-compounding account.

✓CHECKPOINT   Now try Exercise 55.

Example 10   Radioactive Decay

Let y represent a mass, in grams, of radioactive strontium (^{90}Sr), whose half-life is 29 years. The quantity of strontium present after t years is $y = 10\left(\frac{1}{2}\right)^{t/29}$.

a. What is the initial mass (when $t = 0$)?

b. How much of the initial mass is present after 80 years?

Algebraic Solution

a. $y = 10\left(\dfrac{1}{2}\right)^{t/29}$ Write original equation.

$\quad = 10\left(\dfrac{1}{2}\right)^{0/29}$ Substitute 0 for t.

$\quad = 10$ Simplify.

So, the initial mass is 10 grams.

b. $y = 10\left(\dfrac{1}{2}\right)^{t/29}$ Write original equation.

$\quad = 10\left(\dfrac{1}{2}\right)^{80/29}$ Substitute 80 for t.

$\quad \approx 10\left(\dfrac{1}{2}\right)^{2.759}$ Simplify.

$\quad \approx 1.48$ Use a calculator.

So, about 1.48 grams is present after 80 years.

CHECKPOINT   Now try Exercise 67.

Graphical Solution

Use a graphing utility to graph $y = 10\left(\frac{1}{2}\right)^{x/29}$.

a. Use the *value* feature or the *zoom* and *trace* features of the graphing utility to determine that the value of y when $x = 0$ is 10, as shown in Figure 4.15. So, the initial mass is 10 grams.

b. Use the *value* feature or the *zoom* and *trace* features of the graphing utility to determine that the value of y when $x = 80$ is about 1.48, as shown in Figure 4.16. So, about 1.48 grams is present after 80 years.

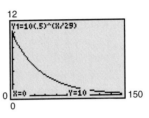

Figure 4.15

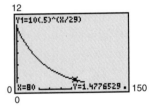

Figure 4.16

Example 11   Population Growth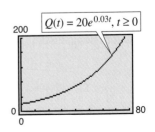

The approximate number of fruit flies in an experimental population after t hours is given by $Q(t) = 20e^{0.03t}$, where $t \geq 0$.

a. Find the initial number of fruit flies in the population.

b. How large is the population of fruit flies after 72 hours?

c. Graph Q.

Solution

a. To find the initial population, evaluate $Q(t)$ when $t = 0$.

$$Q(0) = 20e^{0.03(0)} = 20e^0 = 20(1) = 20 \text{ flies}$$

b. After 72 hours, the population size is

$$Q(72) = 20e^{0.03(72)} = 20e^{2.16} \approx 173 \text{ flies}.$$

c. The graph of Q is shown in Figure 4.17.

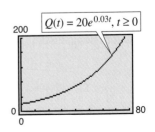

$Q(t) = 20e^{0.03t}, t \geq 0$

Figure 4.17

CHECKPOINT   Now try Exercise 69.

4.1 Exercises

See www.CalcChat.com for worked-out solutions to odd-numbered exercises.

Vocabulary Check

Fill in the blanks.

1. Polynomial and rational functions are examples of _____ functions.

2. Exponential and logarithmic functions are examples of nonalgebraic functions, also called _____ functions.

3. The exponential function $f(x) = e^x$ is called the _____ function, and the base e is called the _____ base.

4. To find the amount A in an account after t years with principal P and annual interest rate r compounded n times per year, you can use the formula _____ .

5. To find the amount A in an account after t years with principal P and annual interest rate r compounded continuously, you can use the formula _____ .

In Exercises 1–4, use a calculator to evaluate the function at the indicated value of x. Round your result to three decimal places.

Function	Value
1. $f(x) = 3.4^x$	$x = 6.8$
2. $f(x) = 1.2^x$	$x = \frac{1}{3}$
3. $g(x) = 5^x$	$x = -\pi$
4. $h(x) = 8.6^{-3x}$	$x = -\sqrt{2}$

In Exercises 5–12, graph the exponential function by hand. Identify any asymptotes and intercepts and determine whether the graph of the function is increasing or decreasing.

5. $g(x) = 5^x$ **6.** $f(x) = \left(\frac{3}{2}\right)^x$

7. $f(x) = 5^{-x}$ **8.** $h(x) = \left(\frac{3}{2}\right)^{-x}$

9. $h(x) = 5^{x-2}$ **10.** $g(x) = \left(\frac{3}{2}\right)^{x+2}$

11. $g(x) = 5^{-x} - 3$ **12.** $f(x) = \left(\frac{3}{2}\right)^{-x} + 2$

Library of Parent Functions   In Exercises 13–16, use the graph of $y = 2^x$ to match the function with its graph. [The graphs are labeled (a), (b), (c), and (d).]

(a)
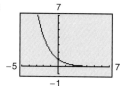

(b)
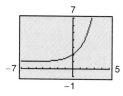

(c)
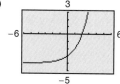

(d)
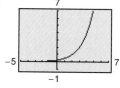

13. $f(x) = 2^{x-2}$

14. $f(x) = 2^{-x}$

15. $f(x) = 2^x - 4$

16. $f(x) = 2^x + 1$

In Exercises 17–22, use the graph of f to describe the transformation that yields the graph of g.

17. $f(x) = 3^x$, $g(x) = 3^{x-5}$

18. $f(x) = -2^x$, $g(x) = 5 - 2^x$

19. $f(x) = \left(\frac{3}{5}\right)^x$, $g(x) = -\left(\frac{3}{5}\right)^{x+4}$

20. $f(x) = 0.3^x$, $g(x) = -0.3^x + 5$

21. $f(x) = 4^x$, $g(x) = 4^{x-2} - 3$

22. $f(x) = \left(\frac{1}{2}\right)^x$, $g(x) = \left(\frac{1}{2}\right)^{-(x+4)}$

In Exercises 23–26, use a calculator to evaluate the function at the indicated value of x. Round your result to the nearest thousandth.

Function	Value
23. $f(x) = e^x$	$x = 9.2$
24. $f(x) = e^{-x}$	$x = -\frac{3}{4}$
25. $g(x) = 50e^{4x}$	$x = 0.02$
26. $h(x) = -5.5e^{-x}$	$x = 200$

In Exercises 27–44, use a graphing utility to construct a table of values for the function. Then sketch the graph of the function. Identify any asymptotes of the graph.

27. $f(x) = \left(\frac{5}{2}\right)^x$ **28.** $f(x) = \left(\frac{5}{2}\right)^{-x}$

29. $f(x) = 6^x$ **30.** $f(x) = 2^{x-1}$

31. $f(x) = 3^{x+2}$ **32.** $f(x) = 4^{x-3} + 3$

33. $y = 2^{-x^2}$ **34.** $y = 3^{-|x|}$

35. $y = 3^{x-2} + 1$ **36.** $y = 4^{x+1} - 2$

37. $f(x) = e^{-x}$

38. $s(t) = 3e^{-0.2t}$

39. $f(x) = 3e^{x+4}$

40. $f(x) = 2e^{-0.5x}$

41. $f(x) = 2 + e^{x-5}$

42. $g(x) = 2 - e^{-x}$

43. $s(t) = 2e^{0.12t}$

44. $g(x) = 1 + e^{-x}$

In Exercises 45–48, use a graphing utility to (a) graph the function and (b) find any asymptotes numerically by creating a table of values for the function.

45. $f(x) = \dfrac{8}{1 + e^{-0.5x}}$

46. $g(x) = \dfrac{8}{1 + e^{-0.5/x}}$

47. $f(x) = -\dfrac{6}{2 - e^{0.2x}}$

48. $f(x) = \dfrac{6}{2 - e^{0.2/x}}$

In Exercises 49 and 50, use a graphing utility to find the point(s) of intersection, if any, of the graphs of the functions. Round your result to three decimal places.

49. $y = 20e^{0.05x}$

$y = 1500$

50. $y = 100e^{0.01x}$

$y = 12,500$

In Exercises 51 and 52, (a) use a graphing utility to graph the function, (b) use the graph to find the open intervals on which the function is increasing and decreasing, and (c) approximate any relative maximum or minimum values.

51. $f(x) = x^2 e^{-x}$

52. $f(x) = 2x^2 e^{x+1}$

Compound Interest **In Exercises 53–56, complete the table to determine the balance A for P dollars invested at rate r for t years and compounded n times per year.**

n	1	2	4	12	365	Continuous
A						

53. $P = \$2500$, $r = 2.5\%$, $t = 10$ years

54. $P = \$1000$, $r = 6\%$, $t = 10$ years

55. $P = \$2500$, $r = 4\%$, $t = 20$ years

56. $P = \$1000$, $r = 3\%$, $t = 40$ years

Compound Interest **In Exercises 57–60, complete the table to determine the balance A for \$12,000 invested at a rate r for t years, compounded continuously.**

t	1	10	20	30	40	50
A						

57. $r = 4\%$

58. $r = 6\%$

59. $r = 3.5\%$

60. $r = 2.5\%$

Annuity **In Exercises 61–64, find the total amount A of an annuity after n months using the annuity formula**

$$A = P\left[\frac{(1 + r/12)^n - 1}{r/12}\right]$$

where P is the amount deposited every month earning $r\%$ interest, compounded monthly.

61. $P = \$25$, $r = 12\%$, $n = 48$ months

62. $P = \$100$, $r = 9\%$, $n = 60$ months

63. $P = \$200$, $r = 6\%$, $n = 72$ months

64. $P = \$75$, $r = 3\%$, $n = 24$ months

65. *Demand* The demand function for a product is given by

$$p = 5000\left[1 - \frac{4}{4 + e^{-0.002x}}\right]$$

where p is the price and x is the number of units.

(a) Use a graphing utility to graph the demand function for $x > 0$ and $p > 0$.

(b) Find the price p for a demand of $x = 500$ units.

(c) Use the graph in part (a) to approximate the highest price that will still yield a demand of at least 600 units.

Verify your answers to parts (b) and (c) numerically by creating a table of values for the function.

66. *Compound Interest* There are three options for investing \$500. The first earns 7% compounded annually, the second earns 7% compounded quarterly, and the third earns 7% compounded continuously.

(a) Find equations that model each investment growth and use a graphing utility to graph each model in the same viewing window over a 20-year period.

(b) Use the graph from part (a) to determine which investment yields the highest return after 20 years. What is the difference in earnings between each investment?

67. *Radioactive Decay* Let Q represent a mass, in grams, of radioactive radium (^{226}Ra), whose half-life is 1599 years. The quantity of radium present after t years is given by $Q = 25\left(\frac{1}{2}\right)^{t/1599}$.

(a) Determine the initial quantity (when $t = 0$).

(b) Determine the quantity present after 1000 years.

(c) Use a graphing utility to graph the function over the interval $t = 0$ to $t = 5000$.

(d) When will the quantity of radium be 0 grams? Explain.

68. *Radioactive Decay* Let Q represent a mass, in grams, of carbon 14 (^{14}C), whose half-life is 5715 years. The quantity present after t years is given by $Q = 10\left(\frac{1}{2}\right)^{t/5715}$.

(a) Determine the initial quantity (when $t = 0$).

(b) Determine the quantity present after 2000 years.

(c) Sketch the graph of the function over the interval $t = 0$ to $t = 10,000$.

69. *Bacteria Growth* A certain type of bacteria increases according to the model $P(t) = 100e^{0.2197t}$, where t is the time in hours.

(a) Use a graphing utility to graph the model.

(b) Use a graphing utility to approximate $P(0)$, $P(5)$, and $P(10)$.

(c) Verify your answers in part (b) algebraically.

70. *Population Growth* The projected populations of California for the years 2015 to 2030 can be modeled by

$$P = 34.706e^{0.0097t}$$

where P is the population (in millions) and t is the time (in years), with $t = 15$ corresponding to 2015.   (Source: U.S. Census Bureau)

(a) Use a graphing utility to graph the function for the years 2015 through 2030.

(b) Use the *table* feature of a graphing utility to create a table of values for the same time period as in part (a).

(c) According to the model, when will the population of California exceed 50 million?

71. *Inflation* If the annual rate of inflation averages 4% over the next 10 years, the approximate cost C of goods or services during any year in that decade will be modeled by $C(t) = P(1.04)^t$, where t is the time (in years) and P is the present cost. The price of an oil change for your car is presently $23.95.

(a) Use a graphing utility to graph the function.

(b) Use the graph in part (a) to approximate the price of an oil change 10 years from now.

(c) Verify your answer in part (b) algebraically.

72. *Depreciation* In early 2006, a new Jeep Wrangler Sport Edition had a manufacturer's suggested retail price of $23,970. After t years the Jeep's value is given by

$$V(t) = 23,970\left(\tfrac{3}{4}\right)^t.$$

(Source: DaimlerChrysler Corporation)

(a) Use a graphing utility to graph the function.

(b) Use a graphing utility to create a table of values that shows the value V for $t = 1$ to $t = 10$ years.

(c) According to the model, when will the Jeep have no value?

Synthesis

True or False? In Exercises 73 and 74, determine whether the statement is true or false. Justify your answer.

73. $f(x) = 1^x$ is not an exponential function.

74. $e = \dfrac{271,801}{99,990}$

75. *Library of Parent Functions* Determine which equation(s) may be represented by the graph shown. (There may be more than one correct answer.)

(a) $y = e^x + 1$

(b) $y = -e^{-x} + 1$

(c) $y = e^{-x} - 1$

(d) $y = e^{-x} + 1$

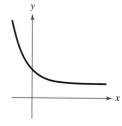

76. *Exploration* Use a graphing utility to graph $y_1 = e^x$ and each of the functions $y_2 = x^2$, $y_3 = x^3$, $y_4 = \sqrt{x}$, and $y_5 = |x|$ in the same viewing window.

(a) Which function increases at the fastest rate for "large" values of x?

(b) Use the result of part (a) to make a conjecture about the rates of growth of $y_1 = e^x$ and $y = x^n$, where n is a natural number and x is "large."

(c) Use the results of parts (a) and (b) to describe what is implied when it is stated that a quantity is growing exponentially.

77. *Graphical Analysis* Use a graphing utility to graph $f(x) = (1 + 0.5/x)^x$ and $g(x) = e^{0.5}$ in the same viewing window. What is the relationship between f and g as x increases without bound?

78. *Think About It* Which functions are exponential? Explain.

(a) $3x$ (b) $3x^2$ (c) 3^x (d) 2^{-x}

Think About It In Exercises 79–82, place the correct symbol ($<$ or $>$) between the pair of numbers.

79. e^π ___ π^e

80. 2^{10} ___ 10^2

81. 5^{-3} ___ 3^{-5}

82. $4^{1/2}$ ___ $\left(\tfrac{1}{2}\right)^4$

Skills Review

In Exercises 83–86, determine whether the function has an inverse function. If it does, find f^{-1}.

83. $f(x) = 5x - 7$

84. $f(x) = -\tfrac{2}{3}x + \tfrac{5}{2}$

85. $f(x) = \sqrt[3]{x + 8}$

86. $f(x) = \sqrt{x^2 + 6}$

In Exercises 87 and 88, sketch the graph of the rational function.

87. $f(x) = \dfrac{2x}{x - 7}$

88. $f(x) = \dfrac{x^2 + 3}{x + 1}$

89. *Make a Decision* To work an extended application analyzing the population per square mile in the United States, visit this textbook's *Online Study Center*. (Data Source: U.S. Census Bureau)

4.2   Logarithmic Functions and Their Graphs

Logarithmic Functions

In Section 1.7, you studied the concept of an inverse function. There, you learned that if a function is one-to-one—that is, if the function has the property that no horizontal line intersects its graph more than once—the function must have an inverse function. By looking back at the graphs of the exponential functions introduced in Section 4.1, you will see that every function of the form

$$f(x) = a^x, \quad a > 0, a \neq 1$$

passes the Horizontal Line Test and therefore must have an inverse function. This inverse function is called the **logarithmic function with base a.**

Definition of Logarithmic Function

For $x > 0$, $a > 0$, and $a \neq 1$,

$$y = \log_a x \quad \text{if and only if} \quad x = a^y.$$

The function given by

$$f(x) = \log_a x \qquad \text{Read as "log base } a \text{ of } x.\text{"}$$

is called the **logarithmic function with base a.**

From the definition above, you can see that every logarithmic equation can be written in an equivalent exponential form and every exponential equation can be written in logarithmic form. The equations $y = \log_a x$ and $x = a^y$ are equivalent.

When evaluating logarithms, remember that *a logarithm is an exponent.* This means that $\log_a x$ is the exponent to which a must be raised to obtain x. For instance, $\log_2 8 = 3$ because 2 must be raised to the third power to get 8.

Example 1   Evaluating Logarithms

Use the definition of logarithmic function to evaluate each logarithm at the indicated value of x.

a. $f(x) = \log_2 x$, $x = 32$ **b.** $f(x) = \log_3 x$, $x = 1$

c. $f(x) = \log_4 x$, $x = 2$ **d.** $f(x) = \log_{10} x$, $x = \frac{1}{100}$

Solution

a. $f(32) = \log_2 32 = 5$ because $2^5 = 32$.

b. $f(1) = \log_3 1 = 0$ because $3^0 = 1$.

c. $f(2) = \log_4 2 = \frac{1}{2}$ because $4^{1/2} = \sqrt{4} = 2$.

d. $f\left(\frac{1}{100}\right) = \log_{10} \frac{1}{100} = -2$ because $10^{-2} = \frac{1}{10^2} = \frac{1}{100}$.

✓**CHECKPOINT**   Now try Exercise 25.

What you should learn

- Recognize and evaluate logarithmic functions with base a.
- Graph logarithmic functions with base a.
- Recognize, evaluate, and graph natural logarithmic functions.
- Use logarithmic functions to model and solve real-life problems.

Why you should learn it

Logarithmic functions are useful in modeling data that represents quantities that increase or decrease slowly. For instance, Exercises 97 and 98 on page 355 show how to use a logarithmic function to model the minimum required ventilation rates in public school classrooms.

Mark Richards/PhotoEdit

The logarithmic function with base 10 is called the **common logarithmic function.** On most calculators, this function is denoted by (LOG). Example 2 shows how to use a calculator to evaluate common logarithmic functions. You will learn how to use a calculator to calculate logarithms to any base in the next section.

Example 2   Evaluating Common Logarithms on a Calculator

Use a calculator to evaluate the function $f(x) = \log_{10} x$ at each value of x.

a. $x = 10$ **b.** $x = 2.5$ **c.** $x = -2$ **d.** $x = \frac{1}{4}$

Solution

Function Value	Graphing Calculator Keystrokes	Display
a. $f(10) = \log_{10} 10$	(LOG) 10 (ENTER)	1
b. $f(2.5) = \log_{10} 2.5$	(LOG) 2.5 (ENTER)	0.3979400
c. $f(-2) = \log_{10}(-2)$	(LOG) (−) 2 (ENTER)	ERROR
d. $f\left(\frac{1}{4}\right) = \log_{10} \frac{1}{4}$	(LOG) ( ) 1 (÷) 4 ( ) (ENTER)	−0.6020600

Note that the calculator displays an error message when you try to evaluate $\log_{10}(-2)$. In this case, there is no *real* power to which 10 can be raised to obtain -2.

 Now try Exercise 29.

TECHNOLOGY TIP

Some graphing utilities do not give an error message for $\log_{10}(-2)$. Instead, the graphing utility will display a complex number. For the purpose of this text, however, it will be said that the domain of a logarithmic function is the set of positive *real* numbers.

The following properties follow directly from the definition of the logarithmic function with base a.

Properties of Logarithms

1. $\log_a 1 = 0$ because $a^0 = 1$.

2. $\log_a a = 1$ because $a^1 = a$.

3. $\log_a a^x = x$ and $a^{\log_a x} = x$.   Inverse Properties

4. If $\log_a x = \log_a y$, then $x = y$.   One-to-One Property

---

Example 3   Using Properties of Logarithms

a. Solve for x: $\log_2 x = \log_2 3$ **b.** Solve for x: $\log_4 4 = x$
c. Simplify: $\log_5 5^x$ **d.** Simplify: $7^{\log_7 14}$

Solution

a. Using the One-to-One Property (Property 4), you can conclude that $x = 3$.

b. Using Property 2, you can conclude that $x = 1$.

c. Using the Inverse Property (Property 3), it follows that $\log_5 5^x = x$.

d. Using the Inverse Property (Property 3), it follows that $7^{\log_7 14} = 14$.

 Now try Exercise 33.

Graphs of Logarithmic Functions

To sketch the graph of $y = \log_a x$, you can use the fact that the graphs of inverse functions are reflections of each other in the line $y = x$.

Example 4 Graphs of Exponential and Logarithmic Functions

In the same coordinate plane, sketch the graph of each function by hand.

a. $f(x) = 2^x$ **b.** $g(x) = \log_2 x$

Solution

a. For $f(x) = 2^x$, construct a table of values. By plotting these points and connecting them with a smooth curve, you obtain the graph of f shown in Figure 4.18.

x	-2	-1	0	1	2	3
$f(x) = 2^x$	$\frac{1}{4}$	$\frac{1}{2}$	1	2	4	8

b. Because $g(x) = \log_2 x$ is the inverse function of $f(x) = 2^x$, the graph of g is obtained by plotting the points $(f(x), x)$ and connecting them with a smooth curve. The graph of g is a reflection of the graph of f in the line $y = x$, as shown in Figure 4.18.

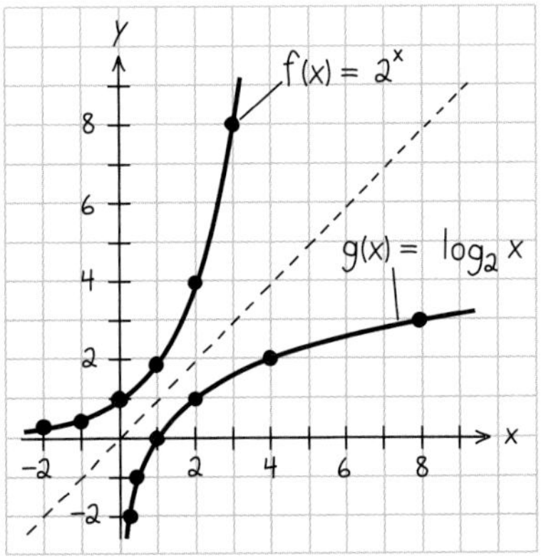

✓**CHECKPOINT**   Now try Exercise 43.

Figure 4.18

Before you can confirm the result of Example 4 using a graphing utility, you need to know how to enter $\log_2 x$. You will learn how to do this using the *change-of-base formula* discussed in Section 4.3.

Example 5 Sketching the Graph of a Logarithmic Function

Sketch the graph of the common logarithmic function $f(x) = \log_{10} x$ by hand.

Solution

Begin by constructing a table of values. Note that some of the values can be obtained without a calculator by using the Inverse Property of Logarithms. Others require a calculator. Next, plot the points and connect them with a smooth curve, as shown in Figure 4.19.

Figure 4.19

x	Without calculator				With calculator		
	$\frac{1}{100}$	$\frac{1}{10}$	1	10	2	5	8
$f(x) = \log_{10} x$	-2	-1	0	1	0.301	0.699	0.903

✓**CHECKPOINT**   Now try Exercise 47.

The nature of the graph in Figure 4.19 is typical of functions of the form $f(x) = \log_a x$, $a > 1$. They have one x-intercept and one vertical asymptote. Notice how slowly the graph rises for $x > 1$.

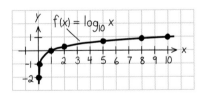

STUDY TIP

In Example 5, you can also sketch the graph of $f(x) = \log_{10} x$ by evaluating the inverse function of f, $g(x) = 10^x$, for several values of x. Plot the points, sketch the graph of g, and then reflect the graph in the line $y = x$ to obtain the graph of f.

Library of Parent Functions: Logarithmic Function

The *logarithmic function*

$$f(x) = \log_a x, \quad a > 0, \ a \neq 1$$

is the inverse function of the exponential function. Its domain is the set of positive real numbers and its range is the set of all real numbers. This is the opposite of the exponential function. Moreover, the logarithmic function has the y-axis as a vertical asymptote, whereas the exponential function has the x-axis as a horizontal asymptote. Many real-life phenomena with a slow rate of growth can be modeled by logarithmic functions. The basic characteristics of the logarithmic function are summarized below. A review of logarithmic functions can be found in the *Study Capsules*.

Graph of $f(x) = \log_a x, \ a > 1$

Domain: $(0, \infty)$

Range: $(-\infty, \infty)$

Intercept: $(1, 0)$

Increasing on $(0, \infty)$

y-axis is a vertical asymptote
$(\log_a x \to -\infty \text{ as } x \to 0^+)$

Continuous

Reflection of graph of $f(x) = a^x$
in the line $y = x$

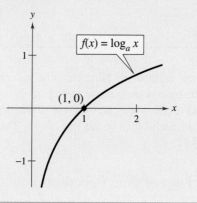

Exploration

Use a graphing utility to graph $y = \log_{10} x$ and $y = 8$ in the same viewing window. Find a viewing window that shows the point of intersection. What is the point of intersection? Use the point of intersection to complete the equation below.

$$\log_{10} \boxed{} = 8$$

Example 6   Transformations of Graphs of Logarithmic Functions

Each of the following functions is a transformation of the graph of $f(x) = \log_{10} x$.

a. Because $g(x) = \log_{10}(x - 1) = f(x - 1)$, the graph of g can be obtained by shifting the graph of f one unit to the *right*, as shown in Figure 4.20.

b. Because $h(x) = 2 + \log_{10} x = 2 + f(x)$, the graph of h can be obtained by shifting the graph of f two units *upward*, as shown in Figure 4.21.

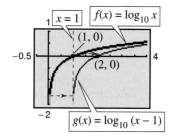

Figure 4.20

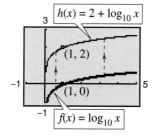

Figure 4.21

Notice that the transformation in Figure 4.21 keeps the y-axis as a vertical asymptote, but the transformation in Figure 4.20 yields the new vertical asymptote $x = 1$.

✔CHECKPOINT   Now try Exercise 57.

TECHNOLOGY TIP

When a graphing utility graphs a logarithmic function, it may appear that the graph has an endpoint. Recall from Section 1.1 that this occurs because some graphing utilities have a limited resolution. So, in this text a blue or light red curve is placed behind the graphing utility's display to indicate where the graph should appear.

The Natural Logarithmic Function

By looking back at the graph of the natural exponential function introduced in Section 4.1, you will see that $f(x) = e^x$ is one-to-one and so has an inverse function. This inverse function is called the **natural logarithmic function** and is denoted by the special symbol ln x, read as "the natural log of x" or "el en of x."

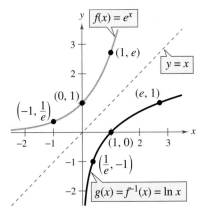

The Natural Logarithmic Function

For $x > 0$,

$\quad y = \ln x$ if and only if $x = e^y$.

The function given by

$\quad f(x) = \log_e x = \ln x$

is called the **natural logarithmic function.**

Reflection of graph of $f(x) = e^x$ in the line $y = x$

Figure 4.22

The equations $y = \ln x$ and $x = e^y$ are equivalent. Note that the natural logarithm ln x is written without a base. The base is understood to be e.

Because the functions $f(x) = e^x$ and $g(x) = \ln x$ are inverse functions of each other, their graphs are reflections of each other in the line $y = x$. This reflective property is illustrated in Figure 4.22.

Example 7   Evaluating the Natural Logarithmic Function

Use a calculator to evaluate the function $f(x) = \ln x$ at each indicated value of x.

a. $x = 2$ **b.** $x = 0.3$ **c.** $x = -1$

Solution

Function Value	Graphing Calculator Keystrokes	Display
a. $f(2) = \ln 2$	(LN) 2 (ENTER)	0.6931472
b. $f(0.3) = \ln 0.3$	(LN) .3 (ENTER)	−1.2039728
c. $f(-1) = \ln(-1)$	(LN) (−) 1 (ENTER)	ERROR

✓**CHECKPOINT**   Now try Exercise 63.

The four properties of logarithms listed on page 347 are also valid for natural logarithms.

Properties of Natural Logarithms

1. $\ln 1 = 0$ because $e^0 = 1$.

2. $\ln e = 1$ because $e^1 = e$.

3. $\ln e^x = x$ and $e^{\ln x} = x$.   Inverse Properties

4. If $\ln x = \ln y$, then $x = y$.   One-to-One Property

TECHNOLOGY TIP

On most calculators, the natural logarithm is denoted by (LN), as illustrated in Example 7.

STUDY TIP

In Example 7(c), be sure you see that $\ln(-1)$ gives an error message on most calculators. This occurs because the domain of ln x is the set of *positive* real numbers (see Figure 4.22). So, $\ln(-1)$ is undefined.

Example 8   Using Properties of Natural Logarithms

Use the properties of natural logarithms to rewrite each expression.

a. $\ln \dfrac{1}{e}$ **b.** $e^{\ln 5}$ **c.** $4 \ln 1$ **d.** $2 \ln e$

Solution

a. $\ln \dfrac{1}{e} = \ln e^{-1} = -1$ Inverse Property   **b.** $e^{\ln 5} = 5$ Inverse Property

c. $4 \ln 1 = 4(0) = 0$ Property 1   **d.** $2 \ln e = 2(1) = 2$ Property 2

CHECKPOINT   Now try Exercise 67.

Example 9   Finding the Domains of Logarithmic Functions

Find the domain of each function.

a. $f(x) = \ln(x - 2)$ **b.** $g(x) = \ln(2 - x)$ **c.** $h(x) = \ln x^2$

Algebraic Solution

a. Because $\ln(x - 2)$ is defined only if

$$x - 2 > 0$$

it follows that the domain of f is $(2, \infty)$.

b. Because $\ln(2 - x)$ is defined only if

$$2 - x > 0$$

it follows that the domain of g is $(-\infty, 2)$.

c. Because $\ln x^2$ is defined only if

$$x^2 > 0$$

it follows that the domain of h is all real numbers except $x = 0$.

CHECKPOINT   Now try Exercise 71.

Graphical Solution

Use a graphing utility to graph each function using an appropriate viewing window. Then use the *trace* feature to determine the domain of each function.

a. From Figure 4.23, you can see that the x-coordinates of the points on the graph appear to extend from the right of 2 to $+\infty$. So, you can estimate the domain to be $(2, \infty)$.

b. From Figure 4.24, you can see that the x-coordinates of the points on the graph appear to extend from $-\infty$ to the left of 2. So, you can estimate the domain to be $(-\infty, 2)$.

c. From Figure 4.25, you can see that the x-coordinates of the points on the graph appear to include all real numbers except $x = 0$. So, you can estimate the domain to be all real numbers except $x = 0$.

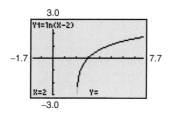

Figure 4.23

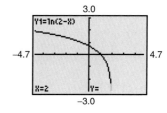

Figure 4.24

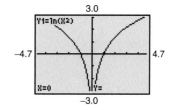

Figure 4.25

In Example 9, suppose you had been asked to analyze the function $h(x) = \ln|x - 2|$. How would the domain of this function compare with the domains of the functions given in parts (a) and (b) of the example?

Application

Logarithmic functions are used to model many situations in real life, as shown in the next example.

Example 10   Human Memory Model

Students participating in a psychology experiment attended several lectures on a subject and were given an exam. Every month for a year after the exam, the students were retested to see how much of the material they remembered. The average scores for the group are given by the *human memory model*

$$f(t) = 75 - 6 \ln(t + 1), \qquad 0 \le t \le 12$$

where t is the time in months.

a. What was the average score on the original exam $(t = 0)$?

b. What was the average score at the end of $t = 2$ months?

c. What was the average score at the end of $t = 6$ months?

TECHNOLOGY SUPPORT

For instructions on how to use the *value* feature and the *zoom* and *trace* features, see Appendix A; for specific keystrokes, go to this textbook's *Online Study Center*.

Algebraic Solution

a. The original average score was

$$f(0) = 75 - 6 \ln(0 + 1)$$
$$= 75 - 6 \ln 1$$
$$= 75 - 6(0)$$
$$= 75.$$

b. After 2 months, the average score was

$$f(2) = 75 - 6 \ln(2 + 1)$$
$$= 75 - 6 \ln 3$$
$$\approx 75 - 6(1.0986)$$
$$\approx 68.41.$$

c. After 6 months, the average score was

$$f(6) = 75 - 6 \ln(6 + 1)$$
$$= 75 - 6 \ln 7$$
$$\approx 75 - 6(1.9459)$$
$$\approx 63.32.$$

Graphical Solution

Use a graphing utility to graph the model $y = 75 - 6 \ln(x + 1)$. Then use the *value* or *trace* feature to approximate the following.

a. When $x = 0$, $y = 75$ (see Figure 4.26). So, the original average score was 75.

b. When $x = 2$, $y \approx 68.41$ (see Figure 4.27). So, the average score after 2 months was about 68.41.

c. When $x = 6$, $y \approx 63.32$ (see Figure 4.28). So, the average score after 6 months was about 63.32.

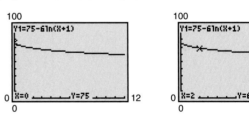

Figure 4.26   Figure 4.27

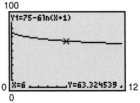

Figure 4.28

✓CHECKPOINT   Now try Exercise 91.

4.2 Exercises

See www.CalcChat.com for worked-out solutions to odd-numbered exercises.

Vocabulary Check

Fill in the blanks.

1. The inverse function of the exponential function $f(x) = a^x$ is called the _____ with base a.
2. The common logarithmic function has base _____ .
3. The logarithmic function $f(x) = \ln x$ is called the _____ function.
4. The inverse property of logarithms states that $\log_a a^x = x$ and _____ .
5. The one-to-one property of natural logarithms states that if $\ln x = \ln y$, then _____ .

In Exercises 1–6, write the logarithmic equation in exponential form. For example, the exponential form of $\log_5 25 = 2$ is $5^2 = 25$.

1. $\log_4 64 = 3$
2. $\log_3 81 = 4$
3. $\log_7 \frac{1}{49} = -2$
4. $\log_{10} \frac{1}{1000} = -3$
5. $\log_{32} 4 = \frac{2}{5}$
6. $\log_{16} 8 = \frac{3}{4}$

In Exercises 7–12, write the logarithmic equation in exponential form. For example, the exponential form of $\ln 5 = 1.6094\ldots$ is $e^{1.6094\cdots} = 5$.

7. $\ln 1 = 0$
8. $\ln 4 = 1.3862\ldots$
9. $\ln e = 1$
10. $\ln e^3 = 3$
11. $\ln \sqrt{e} = \dfrac{1}{2}$
12. $\ln \dfrac{1}{e^2} = -2$

In Exercises 13–18, write the exponential equation in logarithmic form. For example, the logarithmic form of $2^3 = 8$ is $\log_2 8 = 3$.

13. $5^3 = 125$
14. $8^2 = 64$
15. $81^{1/4} = 3$
16. $9^{3/2} = 27$
17. $6^{-2} = \frac{1}{36}$
18. $10^{-3} = 0.001$

In Exercises 19–24, write the exponential equation in logarithmic form. For example, the logarithmic form of $e^2 = 7.3890\ldots$ is $\ln 7.3890\ldots = 2$.

19. $e^3 = 20.0855\ldots$
20. $e^4 = 54.5981\ldots$
21. $e^{1.3} = 3.6692\ldots$
22. $e^{2.5} = 12.1824\ldots$
23. $\sqrt[3]{e} = 1.3956\ldots$
24. $\dfrac{1}{e^4} = 0.0183\ldots$

In Exercises 25–28, evaluate the function at the indicated value of x without using a calculator.

Function	Value
25. $f(x) = \log_2 x$	$x = 16$
26. $f(x) = \log_{16} x$	$x = \frac{1}{4}$
27. $g(x) = \log_{10} x$	$x = \frac{1}{1000}$
28. $g(x) = \log_{10} x$	$x = 10,000$

In Exercises 29–32, use a calculator to evaluate the function at the indicated value of x. Round your result to three decimal places.

Function	Value
29. $f(x) = \log_{10} x$	$x = 345$
30. $f(x) = \log_{10} x$	$x = \frac{4}{5}$
31. $h(x) = 6 \log_{10} x$	$x = 14.8$
32. $h(x) = 1.9 \log_{10} x$	$x = 4.3$

In Exercises 33–38, solve the equation for x.

33. $\log_7 x = \log_7 9$
34. $\log_5 5 = x$
35. $\log_6 6^2 = x$
36. $\log_2 2^{-1} = x$
37. $\log_8 x = \log_8 10^{-1}$
38. $\log_4 4^3 = x$

In Exercises 39–42, use the properties of logarithms to rewrite the expression.

39. $\log_4 4^{3x}$
40. $6^{\log_6 36}$
41. $3 \log_2 \frac{1}{2}$
42. $\frac{1}{4} \log_4 16$

In Exercises 43–46, sketch the graph of f. Then use the graph of f to sketch the graph of g.

43. $f(x) = 3^x$
    $g(x) = \log_3 x$
44. $f(x) = 5^x$
    $g(x) = \log_5 x$

45. $f(x) = e^{2x}$

$g(x) = \frac{1}{2} \ln x$

46. $f(x) = 4^x$

$g(x) = \log_4 x$

In Exercises 47–52, find the domain, vertical asymptote, and x-intercept of the logarithmic function, and sketch its graph by hand.

47. $y = \log_2(x + 2)$

48. $y = \log_2(x - 1)$

49. $y = 1 + \log_2 x$

50. $y = 2 - \log_2 x$

51. $y = 1 + \log_2(x - 2)$

52. $y = 2 + \log_2(x + 1)$

Library of Parent Functions In Exercises 53–56, use the graph of $y = \log_3 x$ to match the function with its graph. [The graphs are labeled (a), (b), (c), and (d).]

(a)

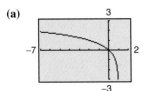

(b)

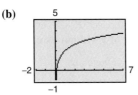

(c)

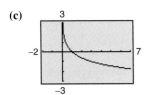

(d)

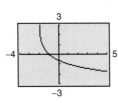

53. $f(x) = \log_3 x + 2$

54. $f(x) = -\log_3 x$

55. $f(x) = -\log_3(x + 2)$

56. $f(x) = \log_3(1 - x)$

In Exercises 57–62, use the graph of f to describe the transformation that yields the graph of g.

57. $f(x) = \log_{10} x$, $g(x) = -\log_{10} x$

58. $f(x) = \log_{10} x$, $g(x) = \log_{10}(x + 7)$

59. $f(x) = \log_2 x$, $g(x) = 4 - \log_2 x$

60. $f(x) = \log_2 x$, $g(x) = 3 + \log_2 x$

61. $f(x) = \log_8 x$, $g(x) = -2 + \log_8(x + 3)$

62. $f(x) = \log_8 x$, $g(x) = 4 + \log_8(x - 1)$

In Exercises 63–66, use a calculator to evaluate the function at the indicated value of x. Round your result to three decimal places.

Function	Value
63. $f(x) = \ln x$	$x = \sqrt{42}$
64. $f(x) = \ln x$	$x = 18.31$
65. $f(x) = -\ln x$	$x = \frac{1}{2}$
66. $f(x) = 3 \ln x$	$x = 0.75$

In Exercises 67–70, use the properties of natural logarithms to rewrite the expression.

67. $\ln e^2$

68. $-\ln e$

69. $e^{\ln 1.8}$

70. $7 \ln e^0$

In Exercises 71–74, find the domain, vertical asymptote, and x-intercept of the logarithmic function, and sketch its graph by hand. Verify using a graphing utility.

71. $f(x) = \ln(x - 1)$

72. $h(x) = \ln(x + 1)$

73. $g(x) = \ln(-x)$

74. $f(x) = \ln(3 - x)$

In Exercises 75–80, use the graph of $f(x) = \ln x$ to describe the transformation that yields the graph of g.

75. $g(x) = \ln(x + 3)$

76. $g(x) = \ln(x - 4)$

77. $g(x) = \ln x - 5$

78. $g(x) = \ln x + 4$

79. $g(x) = \ln(x - 1) + 2$

80. $g(x) = \ln(x + 2) - 5$

In Exercises 81–90, (a) use a graphing utility to graph the function, (b) find the domain, (c) use the graph to find the open intervals on which the function is increasing and decreasing, and (d) approximate any relative maximum or minimum values of the function. Round your result to three decimal places.

81. $f(x) = \dfrac{x}{2} - \ln \dfrac{x}{4}$

82. $g(x) = \dfrac{12 \ln x}{x}$

83. $h(x) = 4x \ln x$

84. $f(x) = \dfrac{x}{\ln x}$

85. $f(x) = \ln\left(\dfrac{x + 2}{x - 1}\right)$

86. $f(x) = \ln\left(\dfrac{2x}{x + 2}\right)$

87. $f(x) = \ln\left(\dfrac{x^2}{10}\right)$

88. $f(x) = \ln\left(\dfrac{x}{x^2 + 1}\right)$

89. $f(x) = \sqrt{\ln x}$

90. $f(x) = (\ln x)^2$

91. *Human Memory Model* Students in a mathematics class were given an exam and then tested monthly with an equivalent exam. The average scores for the class are given by the human memory model

$$f(t) = 80 - 17 \log_{10}(t + 1), \quad 0 \le t \le 12$$

where t is the time in months.

(a) What was the average score on the original exam ($t = 0$)?

(b) What was the average score after 4 months?

(c) What was the average score after 10 months?

Verify your answers in parts (a), (b), and (c) using a graphing utility.

92. Data Analysis   The table shows the temperatures T (in °F) at which water boils at selected pressures p (in pounds per square inch). (Source: Standard Handbook of Mechanical Engineers)

Pressure, p	Temperature, T
5	162.24°
10	193.21°
14.696 (1 atm)	212.00°
20	227.96°
30	250.33°
40	267.25°
60	292.71°
80	312.03°
100	327.81°

A model that approximates the data is given by

$$T = 87.97 + 34.96 \ln p + 7.91 \sqrt{p}.$$

(a) Use a graphing utility to plot the data and graph the model in the same viewing window. How well does the model fit the data?

(b) Use the graph to estimate the pressure required for the boiling point of water to exceed 300°F.

(c) Calculate T when the pressure is 74 pounds per square inch. Verify your answer graphically.

93. Compound Interest   A principal P, invested at $5\frac{1}{2}\%$ and compounded continuously, increases to an amount K times the original principal after t years, where

$$t = (\ln K)/0.055.$$

(a) Complete the table and interpret your results.

K	1	2	4	6	8	10	12
t							

(b) Use a graphing utility to graph the function.

94. Population   The time t in years for the world population to double if it is increasing at a continuous rate of r is given by

$$t = \frac{\ln 2}{r}.$$

(a) Complete the table and interpret your results.

r	0.005	0.010	0.015	0.020	0.025	0.030
t						

(b) Use a graphing utility to graph the function.

95. Sound Intensity   The relationship between the number of decibels β and the intensity of a sound I in watts per square meter is given by

$$\beta = 10 \log_{10}\left(\frac{I}{10^{-12}}\right).$$

(a) Determine the number of decibels of a sound with an intensity of 1 watt per square meter.

(b) Determine the number of decibels of a sound with an intensity of 10^{-2} watt per square meter.

(c) The intensity of the sound in part (a) is 100 times as great as that in part (b). Is the number of decibels 100 times as great? Explain.

96. Home Mortgage   The model

$$t = 16.625 \ln\left(\frac{x}{x - 750}\right), \quad x > 750$$

approximates the length of a home mortgage of $150,000 at 6% in terms of the monthly payment. In the model, t is the length of the mortgage in years and x is the monthly payment in dollars.

(a) Use the model to approximate the lengths of a $150,000 mortgage at 6% when the monthly payment is $897.72 and when the monthly payment is $1659.24.

(b) Approximate the total amounts paid over the term of the mortgage with a monthly payment of $897.72 and with a monthly payment of $1659.24. What amount of the total is interest costs for each payment?

Ventilation Rates   **In Exercises 97 and 98, use the model**

$$y = 80.4 - 11 \ln x, \quad 100 \le x \le 1500$$

which approximates the minimum required ventilation rate in terms of the air space per child in a public school classroom. In the model, x is the air space per child (in cubic feet) and y is the ventilation rate per child (in cubic feet per minute).

97. Use a graphing utility to graph the function and approximate the required ventilation rate when there is 300 cubic feet of air space per child.

98. A classroom is designed for 30 students. The air-conditioning system in the room has the capacity to move 450 cubic feet of air per minute.

(a) Determine the ventilation rate per child, assuming that the room is filled to capacity.

(b) Use the graph in Exercise 97 to estimate the air space required per child.

(c) Determine the minimum number of square feet of floor space required for the room if the ceiling height is 30 feet.

Synthesis

True or False? **In Exercises 99 and 100, determine whether the statement is true or false. Justify your answer.**

99. You can determine the graph of $f(x) = \log_6 x$ by graphing $g(x) = 6^x$ and reflecting it about the x-axis.

100. The graph of $f(x) = \log_3 x$ contains the point $(27, 3)$.

Think About It **In Exercises 101–104, find the value of the base b so that the graph of $f(x) = \log_b x$ contains the given point.**

101. $(32, 5)$ **102.** $(81, 4)$

103. $\left(\frac{1}{16}, 2\right)$ **104.** $\left(\frac{1}{27}, 3\right)$

Library of Parent Functions **In Exercises 105 and 106, determine which equation(s) may be represented by the graph shown. (There may be more than one correct answer.)**

105.

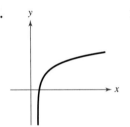

106.

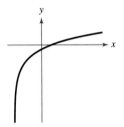

(a) $y = \log_2(x + 1) + 2$ (a) $y = \ln(x - 1) + 2$

(b) $y = \log_2(x - 1) + 2$ (b) $y = \ln(x + 2) - 1$

(c) $y = 2 - \log_2(x - 1)$ (c) $y = 2 - \ln(x - 1)$

(d) $y = \log_2(x + 2) + 1$ (d) $y = \ln(x - 2) + 1$

107. *Writing* Explain why $\log_a x$ is defined only for $0 < a < 1$ and $a > 1$.

108. *Graphical Analysis* Use a graphing utility to graph $f(x) = \ln x$ and $g(x)$ in the same viewing window and determine which is increasing at the greater rate as x approaches $+\infty$. What can you conclude about the rate of growth of the natural logarithmic function?

(a) $g(x) = \sqrt{x}$ (b) $g(x) = \sqrt[4]{x}$

109. *Exploration* The following table of values was obtained by evaluating a function. Determine which of the statements may be true and which must be false.

x	1	2	8
y	0	1	3

(a) y is an exponential function of x.

(b) y is a logarithmic function of x.

(c) x is an exponential function of y.

(d) y is a linear function of x.

110. *Pattern Recognition*

(a) Use a graphing utility to compare the graph of the function $y = \ln x$ with the graph of each function.

$$y_1 = x - 1, \; y_2 = (x - 1) - \tfrac{1}{2}(x - 1)^2,$$

$$y_3 = (x - 1) - \tfrac{1}{2}(x - 1)^2 + \tfrac{1}{3}(x - 1)^3$$

(b) Identify the pattern of successive polynomials given in part (a). Extend the pattern one more term and compare the graph of the resulting polynomial function with the graph of $y = \ln x$. What do you think the pattern implies?

111. *Numerical and Graphical Analysis*

(a) Use a graphing utility to complete the table for the function

$$f(x) = \frac{\ln x}{x}.$$

x	1	5	10	10^2	10^4	10^6
$f(x)$						

(b) Use the table in part (a) to determine what value $f(x)$ approaches as x increases without bound. Use a graphing utility to confirm the result of part (b).

112. *Writing* Use a graphing utility to determine how many months it would take for the average score in Example 10 to decrease to 60. Explain your method of solving the problem. Describe another way that you can use a graphing utility to determine the answer. Also, make a statement about the general shape of the model. Would a student forget more quickly soon after the test or after some time had passed? Explain your reasoning.

Skills Review

In Exercises 113–120, factor the polynomial.

113. $x^2 + 2x - 3$ **114.** $2x^2 + 3x - 5$

115. $12x^2 + 5x - 3$ **116.** $16x^2 + 16x + 7$

117. $16x^2 - 25$ **118.** $36x^2 - 49$

119. $2x^3 + x^2 - 45x$ **120.** $3x^3 - 5x^2 - 12x$

In Exercises 121–124, evaluate the function for $f(x) = 3x + 2$ and $g(x) = x^3 - 1$.

121. $(f + g)(2)$ **122.** $(f - g)(-1)$

123. $(fg)(6)$ **124.** $\left(\dfrac{f}{g}\right)(0)$

In Exercises 125–128, solve the equation graphically.

125. $5x - 7 = x + 4$ **126.** $-2x + 3 = 8x$

127. $\sqrt{3x - 2} = 9$ **128.** $\sqrt{x - 11} = x + 2$

4.3   Properties of Logarithms

Change of Base

Most calculators have only two types of log keys, one for common logarithms (base 10) and one for natural logarithms (base e). Although common logs and natural logs are the most frequently used, you may occasionally need to evaluate logarithms to other bases. To do this, you can use the following **change-of-base formula.**

> **Change-of-Base Formula**
>
> Let a, b, and x be positive real numbers such that $a \neq 1$ and $b \neq 1$. Then $\log_a x$ can be converted to a different base using any of the following formulas.
>
> | Base b | Base 10 | Base e |
> |---|---|---|
> | $\log_a x = \dfrac{\log_b x}{\log_b a}$ | $\log_a x = \dfrac{\log_{10} x}{\log_{10} a}$ | $\log_a x = \dfrac{\ln x}{\ln a}$ |

One way to look at the change-of-base formula is that logarithms to base a are simply *constant multiples* of logarithms to base b. The constant multiplier is $1/(\log_b a)$.

Example 1   Changing Bases Using Common Logarithms

a. $\log_4 25 = \dfrac{\log_{10} 25}{\log_{10} 4}$ $\log_a x = \dfrac{\log_{10} x}{\log_{10} a}$

$\approx \dfrac{1.39794}{0.60206} \approx 2.32$ Use a calculator.

b. $\log_2 12 = \dfrac{\log_{10} 12}{\log_{10} 2} \approx \dfrac{1.07918}{0.30103} \approx 3.58$

✓CHECKPOINT   Now try Exercise 9.

Example 2   Changing Bases Using Natural Logarithms

a. $\log_4 25 = \dfrac{\ln 25}{\ln 4}$ $\log_a x = \dfrac{\ln x}{\ln a}$

$\approx \dfrac{3.21888}{1.38629} \approx 2.32$ Use a calculator.

b. $\log_2 12 = \dfrac{\ln 12}{\ln 2} \approx \dfrac{2.48491}{0.69315} \approx 3.58$

✓CHECKPOINT   Now try Exercise 15.

What you should learn

- Rewrite logarithms with different bases.
- Use properties of logarithms to evaluate or rewrite logarithmic expressions.
- Use properties of logarithms to expand or condense logarithmic expressions.
- Use logarithmic functions to model and solve real-life problems.

Why you should learn it

Logarithmic functions can be used to model and solve real-life problems, such as the human memory model in Exercise 96 on page 362.

Gary Conner/PhotoEdit

STUDY TIP

Notice in Examples 1 and 2 that the result is the same whether common logarithms or natural logarithms are used in the change-of-base formula.

Properties of Logarithms

You know from the previous section that the logarithmic function with base a is the *inverse function* of the exponential function with base a. So, it makes sense that the properties of exponents (see Section 4.1) should have corresponding properties involving logarithms. For instance, the exponential property $a^0 = 1$ has the corresponding logarithmic property $\log_a 1 = 0$.

Properties of Logarithms (See the proof on page 403.)

Let a be a positive number such that $a \neq 1$, and let n be a real number. If u and v are positive real numbers, the following properties are true.

	Logarithm with Base a	*Natural Logarithm*
1. Product Property:	$\log_a(uv) = \log_a u + \log_a v$	$\ln(uv) = \ln u + \ln v$
2. Quotient Property:	$\log_a \dfrac{u}{v} = \log_a u - \log_a v$	$\ln \dfrac{u}{v} = \ln u - \ln v$
3. Power Property:	$\log_a u^n = n \log_a u$	$\ln u^n = n \ln u$

STUDY TIP

There is no general property that can be used to rewrite $\log_a(u \pm v)$. Specifically, $\log_a(x + y)$ is *not* equal to $\log_a x + \log_a y$.

Example 3 Using Properties of Logarithms

Write each logarithm in terms of $\ln 2$ and $\ln 3$.

a. $\ln 6$ **b.** $\ln \dfrac{2}{27}$

Solution

a. $\ln 6 = \ln(2 \cdot 3)$ Rewrite 6 as $2 \cdot 3$.

    $= \ln 2 + \ln 3$ Product Property

b. $\ln \dfrac{2}{27} = \ln 2 - \ln 27$ Quotient Property

     $= \ln 2 - \ln 3^3$ Rewrite 27 as 3^3.

     $= \ln 2 - 3 \ln 3$ Power Property

 Now try Exercise 17.

Example 4 Using Properties of Logarithms

Use the properties of logarithms to verify that $-\log_{10} \frac{1}{100} = \log_{10} 100$.

Solution

$-\log_{10} \frac{1}{100} = -\log_{10}(100^{-1})$ Rewrite $\frac{1}{100}$ as 100^{-1}.

     $= -(-1) \log_{10} 100$ Power Property

     $= \log_{10} 100$ Simplify.

 Now try Exercise 35.

Rewriting Logarithmic Expressions

The properties of logarithms are useful for rewriting logarithmic expressions in forms that simplify the operations of algebra. This is true because they convert complicated products, quotients, and exponential forms into simpler sums, differences, and products, respectively.

Example 5   Expanding Logarithmic Expressions

Use the properties of logarithms to expand each expression.

a. $\log_4 5x^3 y$ **b.** $\ln \dfrac{\sqrt{3x-5}}{7}$

Solution

a. $\log_4 5x^3 y = \log_4 5 + \log_4 x^3 + \log_4 y$ Product Property

$\qquad\qquad\quad = \log_4 5 + 3\log_4 x + \log_4 y$ Power Property

b. $\ln \dfrac{\sqrt{3x-5}}{7} = \ln\left[\dfrac{(3x-5)^{1/2}}{7}\right]$ Rewrite radical using rational exponent.

$\qquad\qquad\quad = \ln(3x-5)^{1/2} - \ln 7$ Quotient Property

$\qquad\qquad\quad = \tfrac{1}{2}\ln(3x-5) - \ln 7$ Power Property

✓CHECKPOINT   Now try Exercise 55.

> ### Exploration
> Use a graphing utility to graph the functions
> $$y = \ln x - \ln(x-3)$$
> and
> $$y = \ln \dfrac{x}{x-3}$$
> in the same viewing window. Does the graphing utility show the functions with the same domain? If so, should it? Explain your reasoning.

In Example 5, the properties of logarithms were used to *expand* logarithmic expressions. In Example 6, this procedure is reversed and the properties of logarithms are used to *condense* logarithmic expressions.

Example 6   Condensing Logarithmic Expressions

Use the properties of logarithms to condense each logarithmic expression.

a. $\tfrac{1}{2}\log_{10} x + 3\log_{10}(x+1)$ **b.** $2\ln(x+2) - \ln x$

c. $\tfrac{1}{3}[\log_2 x + \log_2(x-4)]$

Solution

a. $\tfrac{1}{2}\log_{10} x + 3\log_{10}(x+1) = \log_{10} x^{1/2} + \log_{10}(x+1)^3$ Power Property

$\qquad\qquad\qquad\qquad\qquad = \log_{10}\left[\sqrt{x}(x+1)^3\right]$ Product Property

b. $2\ln(x+2) - \ln x = \ln(x+2)^2 - \ln x$ Power Property

$\qquad\qquad\qquad\quad = \ln \dfrac{(x+2)^2}{x}$ Quotient Property

c. $\tfrac{1}{3}[\log_2 x + \log_2(x-4)] = \tfrac{1}{3}\{\log_2[x(x-4)]\}$ Product Property

$\qquad\qquad\qquad\qquad\quad = \log_2[x(x-4)]^{1/3}$ Power Property

$\qquad\qquad\qquad\qquad\quad = \log_2 \sqrt[3]{x(x-4)}$ Rewrite with a radical.

✓CHECKPOINT   Now try Exercise 71.

Graphical Analysis In Exercises 57 and 58, (a) use a graphing utility to graph the two equations in the same viewing window and (b) use the *table* feature of the graphing utility to create a table of values for each equation. (c) What do the graphs and tables suggest? Explain your reasoning.

57. $y_1 = \ln[x^3(x+4)]$, $y_2 = 3\ln x + \ln(x+4)$

58. $y_1 = \ln\left(\dfrac{\sqrt{x}}{x-2}\right)$, $y_2 = \frac{1}{2}\ln x - \ln(x-2)$

In Exercises 59–76, condense the expression to the logarithm of a single quantity.

59. $\ln x + \ln 4$
60. $\ln y + \ln z$
61. $\log_4 z - \log_4 y$
62. $\log_5 8 - \log_5 t$
63. $2\log_2(x+3)$
64. $\frac{5}{2}\log_7(z-4)$
65. $\frac{1}{2}\ln(x^2+4)$
66. $2\ln x + \ln(x+1)$
67. $\ln x - 3\ln(x+1)$
68. $\ln x - 2\ln(x+2)$
69. $\ln(x-2) - \ln(x+2)$
70. $3\ln x + 2\ln y - 4\ln z$
71. $\ln x - 2[\ln(x+2) + \ln(x-2)]$
72. $4[\ln z + \ln(z+5)] - 2\ln(z-5)$
73. $\frac{1}{3}[2\ln(x+3) + \ln x - \ln(x^2-1)]$
74. $2[\ln x - \ln(x+1) - \ln(x-1)]$
75. $\frac{1}{3}[\ln y + 2\ln(y+4)] - \ln(y-1)$
76. $\frac{1}{2}[\ln(x+1) + 2\ln(x-1)] + 3\ln x$

Graphical Analysis In Exercises 77 and 78, (a) use a graphing utility to graph the two equations in the same viewing window and (b) use the *table* feature of the graphing utility to create a table of values for each equation. (c) What do the graphs and tables suggest? Verify your conclusion algebraically.

77. $y_1 = 2[\ln 8 - \ln(x^2+1)]$, $y_2 = \ln\left[\dfrac{64}{(x^2+1)^2}\right]$

78. $y_1 = \ln x + \frac{1}{2}\ln(x+1)$, $y_2 = \ln(x\sqrt{x+1})$

Think About It In Exercises 79 and 80, (a) use a graphing utility to graph the two equations in the same viewing window and (b) use the *table* feature of the graphing utility to create a table of values for each equation. (c) Are the expressions equivalent? Explain.

79. $y_1 = \ln x^2$, $y_2 = 2\ln x$
80. $y_1 = \frac{1}{4}\ln[x^4(x^2+1)]$, $y_2 = \ln x + \frac{1}{4}\ln(x^2+1)$

In Exercises 81–94, find the exact value of the logarithm without using a calculator. If this is not possible, state the reason.

81. $\log_3 9$
82. $\log_6 \sqrt[3]{6}$
83. $\log_4 16^{3.4}$
84. $\log_5\left(\frac{1}{125}\right)$
85. $\log_2(-4)$
86. $\log_4(-16)$
87. $\log_5 75 - \log_5 3$
88. $\log_4 2 + \log_4 32$
89. $\ln e^3 - \ln e^7$
90. $\ln e^6 - 2\ln e^5$
91. $2\ln e^4$
92. $\ln e^{4.5}$
93. $\ln \dfrac{1}{\sqrt{e}}$
94. $\ln \sqrt[5]{e^3}$

95. *Sound Intensity* The relationship between the number of decibels β and the intensity of a sound I in watts per square meter is given by

$$\beta = 10\log_{10}\left(\dfrac{I}{10^{-12}}\right).$$

(a) Use the properties of logarithms to write the formula in a simpler form.

(b) Use a graphing utility to complete the table.

I	10^{-4}	10^{-6}	10^{-8}	10^{-10}	10^{-12}	10^{-14}
β						

(c) Verify your answers in part (b) algebraically.

96. *Human Memory Model* Students participating in a psychology experiment attended several lectures and were given an exam. Every month for the next year, the students were retested to see how much of the material they remembered. The average scores for the group are given by the human memory model

$$f(t) = 90 - 15\log_{10}(t+1), \quad 0 \le t \le 12$$

where t is the time (in months).

(a) Use a graphing utility to graph the function over the specified domain.

(b) What was the average score on the original exam $(t=0)$?

(c) What was the average score after 6 months?

(d) What was the average score after 12 months?

(e) When did the average score decrease to 75?

97. *Comparing Models* A cup of water at an initial temperature of 78°C is placed in a room at a constant temperature of 21°C. The temperature of the water is measured every 5 minutes during a half-hour period. The results are recorded as ordered pairs of the form (t, T), where t is the time (in minutes) and T is the temperature (in degrees Celsius).

(0, 78.0°), (5, 66.0°), (10, 57.5°), (15, 51.2°), (20, 46.3°), (25, 42.5°), (30, 39.6°)

(a) The graph of the model for the data should be asymptotic with the graph of the temperature of the room. Subtract the room temperature from each of the temperatures in the ordered pairs. Use a graphing utility to plot the data points (t, T) and $(t, T - 21)$.

(b) An exponential model for the data $(t, T - 21)$ is given by

$$T - 21 = 54.4(0.964)^t.$$

Solve for T and graph the model. Compare the result with the plot of the original data.

(c) Take the natural logarithms of the revised temperatures. Use a graphing utility to plot the points $(t, \ln(T - 21))$ and observe that the points appear linear. Use the *regression* feature of a graphing utility to fit a line to the data. The resulting line has the form

$$\ln(T - 21) = at + b.$$

Use the properties of logarithms to solve for T. Verify that the result is equivalent to the model in part (b).

(d) Fit a rational model to the data. Take the reciprocals of the y-coordinates of the revised data points to generate the points

$$\left(t, \frac{1}{T - 21}\right).$$

Use a graphing utility to plot these points and observe that they appear linear. Use the *regression* feature of a graphing utility to fit a line to the data. The resulting line has the form

$$\frac{1}{T - 21} = at + b.$$

Solve for T, and use a graphing utility to graph the rational function and the original data points.

98. Writing   Write a short paragraph explaining why the transformations of the data in Exercise 97 were necessary to obtain the models. Why did taking the logarithms of the temperatures lead to a linear scatter plot? Why did taking the reciprocals of the temperatures lead to a linear scatter plot?

Synthesis

True or False?   **In Exercises 99–106, determine whether the statement is true or false given that $f(x) = \ln x$, where $x > 0$. Justify your answer.**

99. $f(ax) = f(a) + f(x), \ a > 0$

100. $f(x - a) = f(x) - f(a), \ x > a$

101. $f\left(\dfrac{x}{a}\right) = \dfrac{f(x)}{f(a)}, \ f(a) \neq 0$

102. $f(x + a) = f(x)f(a), \ a > 0$

103. $\sqrt{f(x)} = \frac{1}{2}f(x)$

104. $[f(x)]^n = nf(x)$

105. If $f(x) < 0$, then $0 < x < e$.

106. If $f(x) > 0$, then $x > e$.

107. *Proof* Prove that $\dfrac{\log_a x}{\log_{a/b} x} = 1 + \log_a \dfrac{1}{b}$.

108. *Think About It* Use a graphing utility to graph

$$f(x) = \ln \frac{x}{2}, \quad g(x) = \frac{\ln x}{\ln 2}, \quad h(x) = \ln x - \ln 2$$

in the same viewing window. Which two functions have identical graphs? Explain why.

In Exercises 109–114, use the change-of-base formula to rewrite the logarithm as a ratio of logarithms. Then use a graphing utility to graph the ratio.

109. $f(x) = \log_2 x$

110. $f(x) = \log_4 x$

111. $f(x) = \log_3 \sqrt{x}$

112. $f(x) = \log_2 \sqrt[3]{x}$

113. $f(x) = \log_5 \dfrac{x}{3}$

114. $f(x) = \log_3 \dfrac{x}{5}$

115. *Exploration* For how many integers between 1 and 20 can the natural logarithms be approximated given that $\ln 2 \approx 0.6931$, $\ln 3 \approx 1.0986$, and $\ln 5 \approx 1.6094$? Approximate these logarithms. (Do not use a calculator.)

Skills Review

In Exercises 116–119, simplify the expression.

116. $\dfrac{24xy^{-2}}{16x^{-3}y}$

117. $\left(\dfrac{2x^2}{3y}\right)^{-3}$

118. $(18x^3y^4)^{-3}(18x^3y^4)^3$

119. $xy(x^{-1} + y^{-1})^{-1}$

In Exercises 120–125, find all solutions of the equation. Be sure to check all your solutions.

120. $x^2 - 6x + 2 = 0$

121. $2x^3 + 20x^2 + 50x = 0$

122. $x^4 - 19x^2 + 48 = 0$

123. $9x^4 - 37x^2 + 4 = 0$

124. $x^3 - 6x^2 - 4x + 24 = 0$

125. $9x^4 - 226x^2 + 25 = 0$

4.4 Solving Exponential and Logarithmic Equations

Introduction

So far in this chapter, you have studied the definitions, graphs, and properties of exponential and logarithmic functions. In this section, you will study procedures for *solving equations* involving exponential and logarithmic functions.

There are two basic strategies for solving exponential or logarithmic equations. The first is based on the One-to-One Properties and the second is based on the Inverse Properties. For $a > 0$ and $a \neq 1$, the following properties are true for all x and y for which $\log_a x$ and $\log_a y$ are defined.

One-to-One Properties

$a^x = a^y$ if and only if $x = y$.

$\log_a x = \log_a y$ if and only if $x = y$.

Inverse Properties

$a^{\log_a x} = x$

$\log_a a^x = x$

Example 1   Solving Simple Exponential and Logarithmic Equations

Original Equation	Rewritten Equation	Solution	Property
a. $2^x = 32$	$2^x = 2^5$	$x = 5$	One-to-One
b. $\ln x - \ln 3 = 0$	$\ln x = \ln 3$	$x = 3$	One-to-One
c. $\left(\frac{1}{3}\right)^x = 9$	$3^{-x} = 3^2$	$x = -2$	One-to-One
d. $e^x = 7$	$\ln e^x = \ln 7$	$x = \ln 7$	Inverse
e. $\ln x = -3$	$e^{\ln x} = e^{-3}$	$x = e^{-3}$	Inverse
f. $\log_{10} x = -1$	$10^{\log_{10} x} = 10^{-1}$	$x = 10^{-1} = \frac{1}{10}$	Inverse

✓**CHECKPOINT**   Now try Exercise 21.

The strategies used in Example 1 are summarized as follows.

Strategies for Solving Exponential and Logarithmic Equations

1. Rewrite the original equation in a form that allows the use of the One-to-One Properties of exponential or logarithmic functions.

2. Rewrite an *exponential* equation in logarithmic form and apply the Inverse Property of logarithmic functions.

3. Rewrite a *logarithmic* equation in exponential form and apply the Inverse Property of exponential functions.

Solving Exponential Equations

Example 2   Solving Exponential Equations

Solve each equation.   **a.** $e^x = 72$ **b.** $3(2^x) = 42$

Algebraic Solution

a.

$e^x = 72$	Write original equation.
$\ln e^x = \ln 72$	Take natural log of each side.
$x = \ln 72 \approx 4.28$	Inverse Property

The solution is $x = \ln 72 \approx 4.28$. Check this in the original equation.

b.

$3(2^x) = 42$	Write original equation.
$2^x = 14$	Divide each side by 3.
$\log_2 2^x = \log_2 14$	Take log (base 2) of each side.
$x = \log_2 14$	Inverse Property
$x = \dfrac{\ln 14}{\ln 2} \approx 3.81$	Change-of-base formula

The solution is $x = \log_2 14 \approx 3.81$. Check this in the original equation.

 CHECKPOINT   Now try Exercise 55.

Graphical Solution

a. Use a graphing utility to graph the left- and right-hand sides of the equation as $y_1 = e^x$ and $y_2 = 72$ in the same viewing window. Use the *intersect* feature or the *zoom* and *trace* features of the graphing utility to approximate the intersection point, as shown in Figure 4.32. So, the approximate solution is $x \approx 4.28$.

b. Use a graphing utility to graph $y_1 = 3(2^x)$ and $y_2 = 42$ in the same viewing window. Use the *intersect* feature or the *zoom* and *trace* features to approximate the intersection point, as shown in Figure 4.33. So, the approximate solution is $x \approx 3.81$.

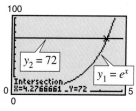

Figure 4.32

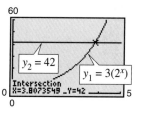

Figure 4.33

Example 3   Solving an Exponential Equation

Solve $4e^{2x} - 3 = 2$.

Algebraic Solution

$4e^{2x} - 3 = 2$	Write original equation.
$4e^{2x} = 5$	Add 3 to each side.
$e^{2x} = \frac{5}{4}$	Divide each side by 4.
$\ln e^{2x} = \ln \frac{5}{4}$	Take natural log of each side.
$2x = \ln \frac{5}{4}$	Inverse Property
$x = \frac{1}{2} \ln \frac{5}{4} \approx 0.11$	Divide each side by 2.

The solution is $x = \frac{1}{2} \ln \frac{5}{4} \approx 0.11$. Check this in the original equation.

Graphical Solution

Rather than using the procedure in Example 2, another way to solve the equation graphically is first to rewrite the equation as $4e^{2x} - 5 = 0$, then use a graphing utility to graph $y = 4e^{2x} - 5$. Use the *zero* or *root* feature or the *zoom* and *trace* features of the graphing utility to approximate the value of x for which $y = 0$. From Figure 4.34, you can see that the zero occurs at $x \approx 0.11$. So, the solution is $x \approx 0.11$.

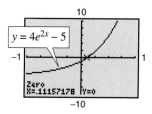

Figure 4.34

 CHECKPOINT   Now try Exercise 59.

Example 4 Solving an Exponential Equation

Solve $2(3^{2t-5}) - 4 = 11$.

Solution

$$2(3^{2t-5}) - 4 = 11$$ Write original equation.

$$2(3^{2t-5}) = 15$$ Add 4 to each side.

$$3^{2t-5} = \frac{15}{2}$$ Divide each side by 2.

$$\log_3 3^{2t-5} = \log_3 \frac{15}{2}$$ Take log (base 3) of each side.

$$2t - 5 = \log_3 \frac{15}{2}$$ Inverse Property

$$2t = 5 + \log_3 7.5$$ Add 5 to each side.

$$t = \frac{5}{2} + \frac{1}{2}\log_3 7.5$$ Divide each side by 2.

$$t \approx 3.42$$ Use a calculator.

The solution is $t = \frac{5}{2} + \frac{1}{2}\log_3 7.5 \approx 3.42$. Check this in the original equation.

✓**CHECKPOINT**   Now try Exercise 49.

> **STUDY TIP**
>
> Remember that to evaluate a logarithm such as $\log_3 7.5$, you need to use the change-of-base formula.
>
> $$\log_3 7.5 = \frac{\ln 7.5}{\ln 3} \approx 1.834$$

When an equation involves two or more exponential expressions, you can still use a procedure similar to that demonstrated in the previous three examples. However, the algebra is a bit more complicated.

Example 5 Solving an Exponential Equation in Quadratic Form

Solve $e^{2x} - 3e^x + 2 = 0$.

Algebraic Solution

$$e^{2x} - 3e^x + 2 = 0$$ Write original equation.

$$(e^x)^2 - 3e^x + 2 = 0$$ Write in quadratic form.

$$(e^x - 2)(e^x - 1) = 0$$ Factor.

$$e^x - 2 = 0$$ Set 1st factor equal to 0.

$$e^x = 2$$ Add 2 to each side.

$$x = \ln 2$$ Solution

$$e^x - 1 = 0$$ Set 2nd factor equal to 0.

$$e^x = 1$$ Add 1 to each side.

$$x = \ln 1$$ Inverse Property

$$x = 0$$ Solution

The solutions are $x = \ln 2 \approx 0.69$ and $x = 0$. Check these in the original equation.

✓**CHECKPOINT**   Now try Exercise 61.

Graphical Solution

Use a graphing utility to graph $y = e^{2x} - 3e^x + 2$. Use the *zero* or *root* feature or the *zoom* and *trace* features of the graphing utility to approximate the values of x for which $y = 0$. In Figure 4.35, you can see that the zeros occur at $x = 0$ and at $x \approx 0.69$. So, the solutions are $x = 0$ and $x \approx 0.69$.

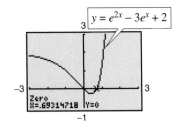

Figure 4.35

Solving Logarithmic Equations

To solve a logarithmic equation, you can write it in exponential form.

$\ln x = 3$ Logarithmic form

$e^{\ln x} = e^3$ Exponentiate each side.

$x = e^3$ Exponential form

This procedure is called *exponentiating* each side of an equation. It is applied after the logarithmic expression has been isolated.

Example 6   Solving Logarithmic Equations

Solve each logarithmic equation.

a. $\ln 3x = 2$ **b.** $\log_3(5x - 1) = \log_3(x + 7)$

Solution

a. $\ln 3x = 2$ Write original equation.

$e^{\ln 3x} = e^2$ Exponentiate each side.

$3x = e^2$ Inverse Property

$x = \frac{1}{3}e^2 \approx 2.46$ Multiply each side by $\frac{1}{3}$.

The solution is $x = \frac{1}{3}e^2 \approx 2.46$. Check this in the original equation.

b. $\log_3(5x - 1) = \log_3(x + 7)$ Write original equation.

$5x - 1 = x + 7$ One-to-One Property

$x = 2$ Solve for x.

The solution is $x = 2$. Check this in the original equation.

 CHECKPOINT   Now try Exercise 87.

> **TECHNOLOGY SUPPORT**
>
> For instructions on how to use the *intersect* feature, the *zoom* and *trace* features, and the *zero* or *root* feature, see Appendix A; for specific keystrokes, go to this textbook's *Online Study Center*.

Example 7   Solving a Logarithmic Equation

Solve $5 + 2 \ln x = 4$.

Algebraic Solution

$5 + 2 \ln x = 4$ Write original equation.

$2 \ln x = -1$ Subtract 5 from each side.

$\ln x = -\frac{1}{2}$ Divide each side by 2.

$e^{\ln x} = e^{-1/2}$ Exponentiate each side.

$x = e^{-1/2}$ Inverse Property

$x \approx 0.61$ Use a calculator.

The solution is $x = e^{-1/2} \approx 0.61$. Check this in the original equation.

 CHECKPOINT   Now try Exercise 89.

Graphical Solution

Use a graphing utility to graph $y_1 = 5 + 2 \ln x$ and $y_2 = 4$ in the same viewing window. Use the *intersect* feature or the *zoom* and *trace* features to approximate the intersection point, as shown in Figure 4.36. So, the solution is $x \approx 0.61$.

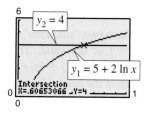

Figure 4.36

141. *Data Analysis*   An object at a temperature of 160°C was removed from a furnace and placed in a room at 20°C. The temperature T of the object was measured after each hour h and recorded in the table. A model for the data is given by

$$T = 20[1 + 7(2^{-h})].$$

Hour, h	Temperature
0	160°
1	90°
2	56°
3	38°
4	29°
5	24°

(a) Use a graphing utility to plot the data and graph the model in the same viewing window.

(b) Identify the horizontal asymptote of the graph of the model and interpret the asymptote in the context of the problem.

(c) Approximate the time when the temperature of the object is 100°C.

142. *Finance*   The table shows the numbers N of commercial banks in the United States from 1996 to 2005. The data can be modeled by the logarithmic function

$$N = 13,387 - 2190.5 \ln t$$

where t represents the year, with $t = 6$ corresponding to 1996. (Source: Federal Deposit Insurance Corp.)

Year	Number, N
1996	9527
1997	9143
1998	8774
1999	8580
2000	8315
2001	8079
2002	7888
2003	7770
2004	7630
2005	7540

(a) Use the model to determine during which year the number of banks dropped to 7250.

(b) Use a graphing utility to graph the model, and use the graph to verify your answer in part (a).

Synthesis

True or False?   In Exercises 143 and 144, determine whether the statement is true or false. Justify your answer.

143. An exponential equation must have at least one solution.

144. A logarithmic equation can have at most one extraneous solution.

145. *Writing*   Write two or three sentences stating the general guidelines that you follow when (a) solving exponential equations and (b) solving logarithmic equations.

146. *Graphical Analysis*   Let $f(x) = \log_a x$ and $g(x) = a^x$, where $a > 1$.

(a) Let $a = 1.2$ and use a graphing utility to graph the two functions in the same viewing window. What do you observe? Approximate any points of intersection of the two graphs.

(b) Determine the value(s) of a for which the two graphs have one point of intersection.

(c) Determine the value(s) of a for which the two graphs have two points of intersection.

147. *Think About It*   Is the time required for a continuously compounded investment to quadruple twice as long as the time required for it to double? Give a reason for your answer and verify your answer algebraically.

148. *Writing*   Write a paragraph explaining whether or not the time required for a continuously compounded investment to double is dependent on the size of the investment.

Skills Review

In Exercises 149–154, sketch the graph of the function.

149. $f(x) = 3x^3 - 4$

150. $f(x) = -(x + 1)^3 + 2$

151. $f(x) = |x| + 9$

152. $f(x) = |x + 2| - 8$

153. $f(x) = \begin{cases} 2x, & x < 0 \\ -x^2 + 4, & x \geq 0 \end{cases}$

154. $f(x) = \begin{cases} x - 9, & x \leq -1 \\ x^2 + 1, & x > -1 \end{cases}$

4.5 Exponential and Logarithmic Models

Introduction

The five most common types of mathematical models involving exponential functions and logarithmic functions are as follows.

1. **Exponential growth model:** $y = ae^{bx}$, $b > 0$
2. **Exponential decay model:** $y = ae^{-bx}$, $b > 0$
3. **Gaussian model:** $y = ae^{-(x-b)^2/c}$
4. **Logistic growth model:** $y = \dfrac{a}{1 + be^{-rx}}$
5. **Logarithmic models:** $y = a + b \ln x$, $y = a + b \log_{10} x$

The basic shapes of these graphs are shown in Figure 4.42.

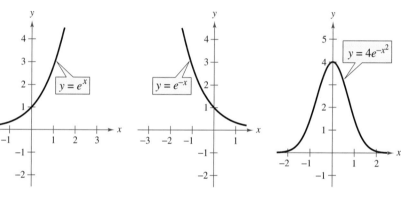

Exponential Growth Model   Exponential Decay Model   Gaussian Model

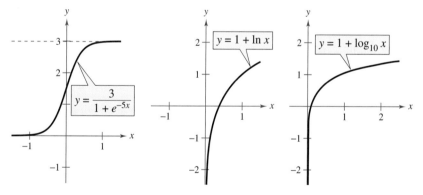

Logistic Growth Model   Natural Logarithmic Model   Common Logarithmic Model

Figure 4.42

What you should learn

- Recognize the five most common types of models involving exponential or logarithmic functions.
- Use exponential growth and decay functions to model and solve real-life problems.
- Use Gaussian functions to model and solve real-life problems.
- Use logistic growth functions to model and solve real-life problems.
- Use logarithmic functions to model and solve real-life problems

Why you should learn it

Exponential growth and decay models are often used to model the population of a country. In Exercise 27 on page 383, you will use such models to predict the population of five countries in 2030.

Kevin Schafer/Peter Arnold, Inc.

You can often gain quite a bit of insight into a situation modeled by an exponential or logarithmic function by identifying and interpreting the function's asymptotes. Use the graphs in Figure 4.42 to identify the asymptotes of each function.

Exponential Growth and Decay

Example 1   Population Growth

Estimates of the world population (in millions) from 1998 through 2007 are shown in the table. A scatter plot of the data is shown in Figure 4.43.   (Source: U.S. Bureau of the Census)

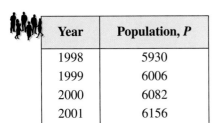

Year	Population, P
1998	5930
1999	6006
2000	6082
2001	6156
2002	6230

Year	Population, P
2003	6303
2004	6377
2005	6451
2006	6525
2007	6600

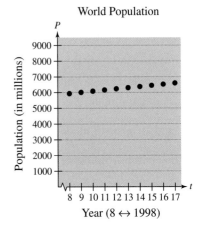

World Population

Figure 4.43

An exponential growth model that approximates this data is given by

$$P = 5400e^{0.011852t}, \qquad 8 \le t \le 17$$

where P is the population (in millions) and $t = 8$ represents 1998. Compare the values given by the model with the estimates shown in the table. According to this model, when will the world population reach 6.8 billion?

Algebraic Solution

The following table compares the two sets of population figures.

Year	1998	1999	2000	2001	2002	2003	2004	2005	2006	2007
Population	5930	6006	6082	6156	6230	6303	6377	6451	6525	6600
Model	5937	6008	6079	6152	6225	6300	6375	6451	6528	6605

To find when the world population will reach 6.8 billion, let $P = 6800$ in the model and solve for t.

$5400e^{0.011852t} = P$	Write original model.
$5400e^{0.011852t} = 6800$	Substitute 6800 for P.
$e^{0.011852t} \approx 1.25926$	Divide each side by 5400.
$\ln e^{0.011852t} \approx \ln 1.25926$	Take natural log of each side.
$0.011852t \approx 0.23052$	Inverse Property
$t \approx 19.4$	Divide each side by 0.011852.

According to the model, the world population will reach 6.8 billion in 2009.

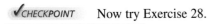

✓CHECKPOINT   Now try Exercise 28.

Graphical Solution

Use a graphing utility to graph the model $y = 5400e^{0.011852x}$ and the data in the same viewing window. You can see in Figure 4.44 that the model appears to closely fit the data.

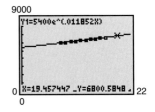

Figure 4.44

Use the *zoom* and *trace* features of the graphing utility to find that the approximate value of x for $y = 6800$ is $x \approx 19.4$. So, according to the model, the world population will reach 6.8 billion in 2009.

An exponential model increases (or decreases) by the same percent each year. What is the annual percent increase for the model in Example 1?

Gaussian

As mentioned

$$y = ae^{-(x}$$

This type of n
populations tha
model takes th

$$y = \frac{1}{\sqrt{2\pi}}$$

The graph of a
normal distribu
bell-shaped cu

The averag
by observing v
corresponding
value of the inc

Example 4 S.

In 2005, the
college-bound

$$y = 0.003$$

where x is the
function and es

Solution

The graph of th
maximum valu
feature or the z
average mathen

✔CHECKPOINT

In Example
lower than 520.

In Example 1, you were given the exponential growth model. Sometimes you must find such a model. One technique for doing this is shown in Example 2.

Example 2 Modeling Population Growth

In a research experiment, a population of fruit flies is increasing according to the law of exponential growth. After 2 days there are 100 flies, and after 4 days there are 300 flies. How many flies will there be after 5 days?

Solution

Let y be the number of flies at time t (in days). From the given information, you know that $y = 100$ when $t = 2$ and $y = 300$ when $t = 4$. Substituting this information into the model $y = ae^{bt}$ produces

$$100 = ae^{2b} \quad \text{and} \quad 300 = ae^{4b}.$$

To solve for b, solve for a in the first equation.

$$100 = ae^{2b} \quad \Longrightarrow \quad a = \frac{100}{e^{2b}} \qquad \text{Solve for } a \text{ in the first equation.}$$

Then substitute the result into the second equation.

$$300 = ae^{4b} \qquad \text{Write second equation.}$$

$$300 = \left(\frac{100}{e^{2b}}\right)e^{4b} \qquad \text{Substitute } \frac{100}{e^{2b}} \text{ for } a.$$

$$3 = e^{2b} \qquad \text{Divide each side by 100.}$$

$$\ln 3 = \ln e^{2b} \qquad \text{Take natural log of each side.}$$

$$\ln 3 = 2b \qquad \text{Inverse Property}$$

$$\frac{1}{2}\ln 3 = b \qquad \text{Solve for } b.$$

Using $b = \frac{1}{2}\ln 3$ and the equation you found for a, you can determine that

$$a = \frac{100}{e^{2[(1/2)\ln 3]}} \qquad \text{Substitute } \frac{1}{2}\ln 3 \text{ for } b.$$

$$= \frac{100}{e^{\ln 3}} \qquad \text{Simplify.}$$

$$= \frac{100}{3} \approx 33.33. \qquad \text{Inverse Property}$$

So, with $a \approx 33.33$ and $b = \frac{1}{2}\ln 3 \approx 0.5493$, the exponential growth model is

$$y = 33.33e^{0.5493t},$$

as shown in Figure 4.45. This implies that after 5 days, the population will be

$$y = 33.33e^{0.5493(5)} \approx 520 \text{ flies.}$$

✔CHECKPOINT   Now try Exercise 29.

Prerequisite Skills

If you have difficulty with this example, review the properties of exponents in Section P.2.

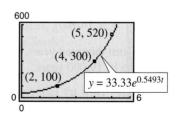

Figure 4.45

In living
isotopes (carb
is about 1 to
fixed, wherea
years. To esti
formula, whic
(in years).

$$R = \frac{1}{10^{12}}$$

The graph of

Example 3

The ratio of c

$$R = \frac{1}{10^{13}}$$

Estimate the a

Algebraic Sc

In the carbon
to obtain the

$$\frac{1}{10^{12}}e^{-t/8}$$

$$\frac{e^{-t/8}}{10^1}$$

$$e^{-t/8}$$

$$\ln e^{-t/8}$$

$$-\frac{}{82}$$

So, to the nea
of the fossil to

✓CHECKPOINT

The carbo
12 ratio was
occurred and
age correspon
Try checking

4.5 Exercises

See www.CalcChat.com for worked-out solutions to odd-numbered exercises.

Vocabulary Check

1. Match the equation with its model.

(a) Exponential growth model

(b) Exponential decay model

(c) Logistic growth model

(d) Logistic decay model

(e) Gaussian model

(f) Natural logarithmic model

(g) Common logarithmic model

(i) $y = ae^{-bx}, \; b > 0$

(ii) $y = a + b \ln x$

(iii) $y = \dfrac{a}{1 + be^{-rx}}, \; r < 0$

(iv) $y = ae^{bx}, \; b > 0$

(v) $y = a + b \log_{10} x$

(vi) $y = \dfrac{1}{1 + be^{-rx}}, \; r > 0$

(vii) $y = ae^{-(x-b)^2/c}$

In Exercises 2–4, fill in the blanks.

2. Gaussian models are commonly used in probability and statistics to represent populations that are _____ distributed.

3. Logistic growth curves are also called _____ curves.

4. The graph of a Gaussian model is called a _____-_____ curve, where the average value or _____ is the x-value corresponding to the maximum y-value of the graph.

Library of Functions **In Exercises 1–6, match the function with its graph. [The graphs are labeled (a), (b), (c), (d), (e), and (f).]**

(a)

(b)

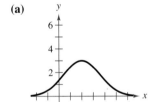

(c)

(d)

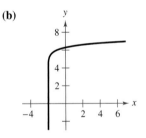

(e)

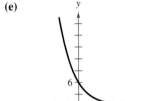

(f)

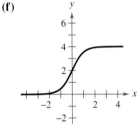

1. $y = 2e^{x/4}$

2. $y = 6e^{-x/4}$

3. $y = 6 + \log_{10}(x + 2)$

4. $y = 3e^{-(x-2)^2/5}$

5. $y = \ln(x + 1)$

6. $y = \dfrac{4}{1 + e^{-2x}}$

Compound Interest **In Exercises 7–14, complete the table for a savings account in which interest is compounded continuously.**

Initial Investment	Annual % Rate	Time to Double	Amount After 10 Years
7. $10,000	3.5%		
8. $2000	1.5%		
9. $7500		21 years	

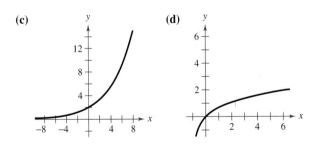

Initial Investment	Annual % Rate	Time to Double	Amount After 10 Years
10. $1000		12 years	
11. $5000			$5665.74
12. $300			$385.21
13.	4.5%		$100,000.00
14.	2%		$2500.00

15. **Compound Interest** Complete the table for the time t necessary for P dollars to triple if interest is compounded continuously at rate r. Create a scatter plot of the data.

r	2%	4%	6%	8%	10%	12%
t						

16. **Compound Interest** Complete the table for the time t necessary for P dollars to triple if interest is compounded annually at rate r. Create a scatter plot of the data.

r	2%	4%	6%	8%	10%	12%
t						

17. **Comparing Investments** If $1 is invested in an account over a 10-year period, the amount A in the account, where t represents the time in years, is given by $A = 1 + 0.075 [\![t]\!]$ or $A = e^{0.07t}$ depending on whether the account pays simple interest at $7\frac{1}{2}\%$ or continuous compound interest at 7%. Use a graphing utility to graph each function in the same viewing window. Which grows at a greater rate? (Remember that $[\![t]\!]$ is the greatest integer function discussed in Section 1.4.)

18. **Comparing Investments** If $1 is invested in an account over a 10-year period, the amount A in the account, where t represents the time in years, is given by

$$A = 1 + 0.06 [\![t]\!] \quad \text{or} \quad A = \left(1 + \frac{0.055}{365}\right)^{[\![365t]\!]}$$

depending on whether the account pays simple interest at 6% or compound interest at $5\frac{1}{2}\%$ compounded daily. Use a graphing utility to graph each function in the same viewing window. Which grows at a greater rate?

Radioactive Decay **In Exercises 19–22, complete the table for the radioactive isotope.**

Isotope	Half-Life (years)	Initial Quantity	Amount After 1000 Years
19. ^{226}Ra	1599	10 g	
20. ^{226}Ra	1599		1.5 g
21. ^{14}C	5715	3 g	
22. ^{239}Pu	24,100		0.4 g

In Exercises 23–26, find the exponential model $y = ae^{bx}$ that fits the points shown in the graph or table.

23.

24.

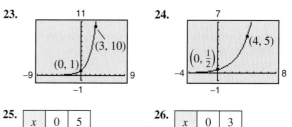

25.

x	0	5
y	4	1

26.

x	0	3
y	1	$\frac{1}{4}$

27. **Population** The table shows the populations (in millions) of five countries in 2000 and the projected populations (in millions) for the year 2010. (Source: U.S. Census Bureau)

Country	2000	2010
Australia	19.2	20.9
Canada	31.3	34.3
Philippines	79.7	95.9
South Africa	44.1	43.3
Turkey	65.7	73.3

(a) Find the exponential growth or decay model, $y = ae^{bt}$ or $y = ae^{-bt}$, for the population of each country by letting $t = 0$ correspond to 2000. Use the model to predict the population of each country in 2030.

(b) You can see that the populations of Australia and Turkey are growing at different rates. What constant in the equation $y = ae^{bt}$ is determined by these different growth rates? Discuss the relationship between the different growth rates and the magnitude of the constant.

(c) You can see that the population of Canada is increasing while the population of South Africa is decreasing. What constant in the equation $y = ae^{bt}$ reflects this difference? Explain.

28. **Population** The populations P (in thousands) of Pittsburgh, Pennsylvania from 1990 to 2004 can be modeled by $P = 372.55e^{-0.01052t}$, where t is the year, with $t = 0$ corresponding to 1990. (Source: U.S. Census Bureau)

(a) According to the model, was the population of Pittsburgh increasing or decreasing from 1990 to 2004? Explain your reasoning.

(b) What were the populations of Pittsburgh in 1990, 2000, and 2004?

(c) According to the model, when will the population be approximately 300,000?

29. *Population* The population P (in thousands) of Reno, Nevada can be modeled by

$$P = 134.0e^{kt}$$

where t is the year, with $t = 0$ corresponding to 1990. In 2000, the population was 180,000. (Source: U.S. Census Bureau)

(a) Find the value of k for the model. Round your result to four decimal places.

(b) Use your model to predict the population in 2010.

30. *Population* The population P (in thousands) of Las Vegas, Nevada can be modeled by

$$P = 258.0e^{kt}$$

where t is the year, with $t = 0$ corresponding to 1990. In 2000, the population was 478,000. (Source: U.S. Census Bureau)

(a) Find the value of k for the model. Round your result to four decimal places.

(b) Use your model to predict the population in 2010.

31. *Radioactive Decay* The half-life of radioactive radium (^{226}Ra) is 1599 years. What percent of a present amount of radioactive radium will remain after 100 years?

32. *Carbon Dating* Carbon 14 (^{14}C) dating assumes that the carbon dioxide on Earth today has the same radioactive content as it did centuries ago. If this is true, the amount of ^{14}C absorbed by a tree that grew several centuries ago should be the same as the amount of ^{14}C absorbed by a tree growing today. A piece of ancient charcoal contains only 15% as much radioactive carbon as a piece of modern charcoal. How long ago was the tree burned to make the ancient charcoal if the half-life of ^{14}C is 5715 years?

33. *Depreciation* A new 2006 SUV that sold for $30,788 has a book value V of $24,000 after 2 years.

(a) Find a linear depreciation model for the SUV.

(b) Find an exponential depreciation model for the SUV. Round the numbers in the model to four decimal places.

(c) Use a graphing utility to graph the two models in the same viewing window.

(d) Which model represents at a greater depreciation rate in the first 2 years?

(e) Explain the advantages and disadvantages of each model to both a buyer and a seller.

34. *Depreciation* A new laptop computer that sold for $1150 in 2005 has a book value V of $550 after 2 years.

(a) Find a linear depreciation model for the laptop.

(b) Find an exponential depreciation model for the laptop. Round the numbers in the model to four decimal places.

(c) Use a graphing utility to graph the two models in the same viewing window.

(d) Which model represents at a greater depreciation rate in the first 2 years?

(e) Explain the advantages and disadvantages of each model to both a buyer and a seller.

35. *Sales* The sales S (in thousands of units) of a new CD burner after it has been on the market t years are given by $S = 100(1 - e^{kt})$. Fifteen thousand units of the new product were sold the first year.

(a) Complete the model by solving for k.

(b) Use a graphing utility to graph the model.

(c) Use the graph in part (b) to estimate the number of units sold after 5 years.

36. *Sales* The sales S (in thousands of units) of a cleaning solution after x hundred dollars is spent on advertising are given by $S = 10(1 - e^{kx})$. When $500 is spent on advertising, 2500 units are sold.

(a) Complete the model by solving for k.

(b) Estimate the number of units that will be sold if advertising expenditures are raised to $700.

37. *IQ Scores* The IQ scores for adults roughly follow the normal distribution

$$y = 0.0266e^{-(x-100)^2/450}, \quad 70 \le x \le 115$$

where x is the IQ score.

(a) Use a graphing utility to graph the function.

(b) From the graph in part (a), estimate the average IQ score.

38. *Education* The time (in hours per week) a student uses a math lab roughly follows the normal distribution

$$y = 0.7979e^{-(x-5.4)^2/0.5}, \quad 4 \le x \le 7$$

where x is the time spent in the lab.

(a) Use a graphing utility to graph the function.

(b) From the graph in part (a), estimate the average time a student spends per week in the math lab.

39. *Wildlife* A conservation organization releases 100 animals of an endangered species into a game preserve. The organization believes that the preserve has a carrying capacity of 1000 animals and that the growth of the herd will follow the logistic curve

$$p(t) = \frac{1000}{1 + 9e^{-0.1656t}}$$

where t is measured in months.

(a) What is the population after 5 months?

(b) After how many months will the population reach 500?

(c) Use a graphing utility to graph the function. Use the graph to determine the values of p at which the horizontal asymptotes occur. Interpret the meaning of the larger asymptote in the context of the problem.

40. Yeast Growth   The amount Y of yeast in a culture is given by the model

$$Y = \frac{663}{1 + 72e^{-0.547t}}, \quad 0 \le t \le 18$$

where t represents the time (in hours).

(a) Use a graphing utility to graph the model.

(b) Use the model to predict the populations for the 19th hour and the 30th hour.

(c) According to this model, what is the limiting value of the population?

(d) Why do you think the population of yeast follows a logistic growth model instead of an exponential growth model?

Geology   In Exercises 41 and 42, use the Richter scale (see page 381) for measuring the magnitudes of earthquakes.

41. Find the intensities I of the following earthquakes measuring R on the Richter scale (let $I_0 = 1$).   (Source: U.S. Geological Survey)

(a) Santa Cruz Islands in 2006, $R = 6.1$

(b) Pakistan in 2005, $R = 7.6$

(c) Northern Sumatra in 2004, $R = 9.0$

42. Find the magnitudes R of the following earthquakes of intensity I (let $I_0 = 1$).

(a) $I = 39,811,000$

(b) $I = 12,589,000$

(c) $I = 251,200$

Sound Intensity   In Exercises 43–46, use the following information for determining sound intensity. The level of sound β (in decibels) with an intensity I is $\beta = 10 \log_{10}(I/I_0)$, where I_0 is an intensity of 10^{-12} watt per square meter, corresponding roughly to the faintest sound that can be heard by the human ear. In Exercises 43 and 44, find the level of each sound β.

43. (a) $I = 10^{-10}$ watt per m² (quiet room)

(b) $I = 10^{-5}$ watt per m² (busy street corner)

(c) $I \approx 10^0$ watt per m² (threshold of pain)

44. (a) $I = 10^{-4}$ watt per m² (door slamming)

(b) $I = 10^{-3}$ watt per m² (loud car horn)

(c) $I = 10^{-2}$ watt per m² (siren at 30 meters)

45. As a result of the installation of a muffler, the noise level of an engine was reduced from 88 to 72 decibels. Find the percent decrease in the intensity level of the noise due to the installation of the muffler.

46. As a result of the installation of noise suppression materials, the noise level in an auditorium was reduced from 93 to 80 decibels. Find the percent decrease in the intensity level of the noise due to the installation of these materials.

pH Levels   In Exercises 47–50, use the acidity model given by pH $= -\log_{10}[H^+]$, where acidity (pH) is a measure of the hydrogen ion concentration $[H^+]$ (measured in moles of hydrogen per liter) of a solution.

47. Find the pH if $[H^+] = 2.3 \times 10^{-5}$.

48. Compute $[H^+]$ for a solution for which pH $= 5.8$.

49. A grape has a pH of 3.5, and milk of magnesia has a pH of 10.5. The hydrogen ion concentration of the grape is how many times that of the milk of magnesia?

50. The pH of a solution is decreased by one unit. The hydrogen ion concentration is increased by what factor?

51. Home Mortgage   A \$120,000 home mortgage for 30 years at $7\frac{1}{2}\%$ has a monthly payment of \$839.06. Part of the monthly payment goes toward the interest charge on the unpaid balance, and the remainder of the payment is used to reduce the principal. The amount that goes toward the interest is given by

$$u = M - \left(M - \frac{Pr}{12}\right)\left(1 + \frac{r}{12}\right)^{12t}$$

and the amount that goes toward reduction of the principal is given by

$$v = \left(M - \frac{Pr}{12}\right)\left(1 + \frac{r}{12}\right)^{12t}.$$

In these formulas, P is the size of the mortgage, r is the interest rate, M is the monthly payment, and t is the time (in years).

(a) Use a graphing utility to graph each function in the same viewing window. (The viewing window should show all 30 years of mortgage payments.)

(b) In the early years of the mortgage, the larger part of the monthly payment goes for what purpose? Approximate the time when the monthly payment is evenly divided between interest and principal reduction.

(c) Repeat parts (a) and (b) for a repayment period of 20 years ($M = \$966.71$). What can you conclude?

52. *Home Mortgage* The total interest u paid on a home mortgage of P dollars at interest rate r for t years is given by

$$u = P\left[\frac{rt}{1 - \left(\dfrac{1}{1 + r/12}\right)^{12t}} - 1\right].$$

Consider a \$120,000 home mortgage at $7\frac{1}{2}\%$.

(a) Use a graphing utility to graph the total interest function.

(b) Approximate the length of the mortgage when the total interest paid is the same as the size of the mortgage. Is it possible that a person could pay twice as much in interest charges as the size of his or her mortgage?

53. *Newton's Law of Cooling* At 8:30 A.M., a coroner was called to the home of a person who had died during the night. In order to estimate the time of death, the coroner took the person's temperature twice. At 9:00 A.M. the temperature was 85.7°F, and at 11:00 A.M. the temperature was 82.8°F. From these two temperatures the coroner was able to determine that the time elapsed since death and the body temperature were related by the formula

$$t = -10 \ln \frac{T - 70}{98.6 - 70}$$

where t is the time (in hours elapsed since the person died) and T is the temperature (in degrees Fahrenheit) of the person's body. Assume that the person had a normal body temperature of 98.6°F at death and that the room temperature was a constant 70°F. Use the formula to estimate the time of death of the person. (This formula is derived from a general cooling principle called Newton's Law of Cooling.)

54. *Newton's Law of Cooling* You take a five-pound package of steaks out of a freezer at 11 A.M. and place it in the refrigerator. Will the steaks be thawed in time to be grilled at 6 P.M.? Assume that the refrigerator temperature is 40°F and the freezer temperature is 0°F. Use the formula for Newton's Law of Cooling

$$t = -5.05 \ln \frac{T - 40}{0 - 40}$$

where t is the time in hours (with $t = 0$ corresponding to 11 A.M.) and T is the temperature of the package of steaks (in degrees Fahrenheit).

Synthesis

True or False? **In Exercises 55–58, determine whether the statement is true or false. Justify your answer.**

55. The domain of a logistic growth function cannot be the set of real numbers.

56. The graph of a logistic growth function will always have an x-intercept.

57. The graph of a Gaussian model will never have an x-intercept.

58. The graph of a Gaussian model will always have a maximum point.

Skills Review

Library of Parent Functions **In Exercises 59–62, match the equation with its graph, and identify any intercepts. [The graphs are labeled (a), (b), (c), and (d).]**

(a)
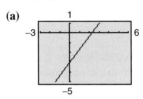

(b)
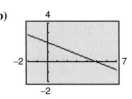

(c)
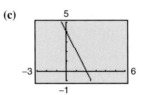

(d)
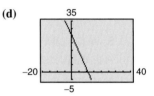

59. $4x - 3y - 9 = 0$

60. $2x + 5y - 10 = 0$

61. $y = 25 - 2.25x$

62. $\dfrac{x}{2} + \dfrac{y}{4} = 1$

In Exercises 63–66, use the Leading Coefficient Test to determine the right-hand and left-hand behavior of the graph of the polynomial function.

63. $f(x) = 2x^3 - 3x^2 + x - 1$

64. $f(x) = 5 - x^2 - 4x^4$

65. $g(x) = -1.6x^5 + 4x^2 - 2$

66. $g(x) = 7x^6 + 9.1x^5 - 3.2x^4 + 25x^3$

In Exercises 67 and 68, divide using synthetic division.

67. $(2x^3 - 8x^2 + 3x - 9) \div (x - 4)$

68. $(x^4 - 3x + 1) \div (x + 5)$

69. *Make a Decision* To work an extended application analyzing the net sales for Kohl's Corporation from 1992 to 2005, visit this textbook's *Online Study Center*. (Data Source: Kohl's Illinois, Inc.)

4.6   Nonlinear Models

Classifying Scatter Plots

In Section 2.7, you saw how to fit linear models to data, and in Section 3.7, you saw how to fit quadratic models to data. In real life, many relationships between two variables are represented by different types of growth patterns. A scatter plot can be used to give you an idea of which type of model will best fit a set of data.

Example 1   Classifying Scatter Plots

Decide whether each set of data could best be modeled by an exponential model

$$y = ab^x$$

or a logarithmic model

$$y = a + b \ln x.$$

a. (2, 1), (2.5, 1.2), (3, 1.3), (3.5, 1.5), (4, 1.8), (4.5, 2), (5, 2.4), (5.5, 2.5), (6, 3.1), (6.5, 3.8), (7, 4.5), (7.5, 5), (8, 6.5), (8.5, 7.8), (9, 9), (9.5, 10)

b. (2, 2), (2.5, 3.1), (3, 3.8), (3.5, 4.3), (4, 4.6), (4.5, 5.3), (5, 5.6), (5.5, 5.9), (6, 6.2), (6.5, 6.4), (7, 6.9), (7.5, 7.2), (8, 7.6), (8.5, 7.9), (9, 8), (9.5, 8.2)

Solution

Begin by entering the data into a graphing utility. You should obtain the scatter plots shown in Figure 4.51.

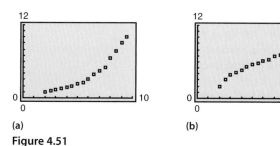

(a)   **(b)**

Figure 4.51

From the scatter plots, it appears that the data in part (a) can be modeled by an exponential function and the data in part (b) can be modeled by a logarithmic function.

✓CHECKPOINT   Now try Exercise 9.

Fitting Nonlinear Models to Data

Once you have used a scatter plot to determine the type of model that would best fit a set of data, there are several ways that you can actually find the model. Each method is best used with a computer or calculator, rather than with hand calculations.

What you should learn

- Classify scatter plots.
- Use scatter plots and a graphing utility to find models for data and choose a model that best fits a set of data.
- Use a graphing utility to find exponential and logistic models for data.

Why you should learn it

Many real-life applications can be modeled by nonlinear equations. For instance, in Exercise 28 on page 393, you are asked to find three different nonlinear models for the price of a half-gallon of ice cream in the United States.

Creatas/PhotoLibrary

TECHNOLOGY SUPPORT

Remember to use the *list editor* of your graphing utility to enter the data in Example 1, as shown below. For instructions on how to use the *list editor*, see Appendix A; for specific keystrokes, go to this textbook's *Online Study Center.*

L1	L2	L3	1
2	1	------	
2.5	1.2		
3	1.3		
3.5	1.5		
4	1.8		
4.5	2		
5	2.4		

L1(1)=2

From Example 1(a), you already know that the data can be modeled by an exponential function. In the next example you will determine whether an exponential model best fits the data.

Example 2   Fitting a Model to Data

Fit the following data from Example 1(a) to a quadratic model, an exponential model, and a power model. Identify the coefficient of determination and determine which model best fits the data.

$$(2, 1), (2.5, 1.2), (3, 1.3), (3.5, 1.5), (4, 1.8), (4.5, 2), (5, 2.4), (5.5, 2.5),$$
$$(6, 3.1), (6.5, 3.8), (7, 4.5), (7.5, 5), (8, 6.5), (8.5, 7.8), (9, 9), (9.5, 10)$$

Solution

Begin by entering the data into a graphing utility. Then use the *regression* feature of the graphing utility to find quadratic, exponential, and power models for the data, as shown in Figure 4.52.

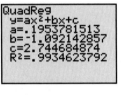
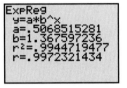
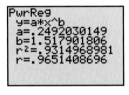

Quadratic Model   *Exponential Model*   *Power Model*

Figure 4.52

TECHNOLOGY SUPPORT

For instructions on how to use the *regression* feature, see Appendix A; for specific keystrokes, go to this textbook's *Online Study Center.*

So, a quadratic model for the data is $y = 0.195x^2 - 1.09x + 2.7$; an exponential model for the data is $y = 0.507(1.368)^x$; and a power model for the data is $y = 0.249x^{1.518}$. Plot the data and each model in the same viewing window, as shown in Figure 4.53. To determine which model best fits the data, compare the coefficients of determination for each model. The model whose r^2-value is closest to 1 is the model that best fits the data. In this case, the best-fitting model is the exponential model.

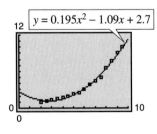
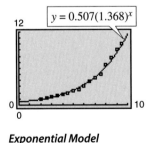
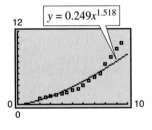

Quadratic Model   *Exponential Model*   *Power Model*

Figure 4.53

✓CHECKPOINT   Now try Exercise 27.

Deciding which model best fits a set of data is a question that is studied in detail in statistics. Recall from Section 2.7 that the model that best fits a set of data is the one whose *sum of squared differences* is the least. In Example 2, the sums of squared differences are 0.89 for the quadratic model, 0.85 for the exponential model, and 14.39 for the power model.

Example 3   Fitting a Model to Data

The table shows the yield y (in milligrams) of a chemical reaction after x minutes. Use a graphing utility to find a logarithmic model and a linear model for the data and identify the coefficient of determination for each model. Determine which model fits the data better.

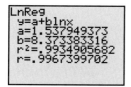

Minutes, x	Yield, y
1	1.5
2	7.4
3	10.2
4	13.4
5	15.8
6	16.3
7	18.2
8	18.3

Solution

Begin by entering the data into a graphing utility. Then use the *regression* feature of the graphing utility to find logarithmic and linear models for the data, as shown in Figure 4.54.

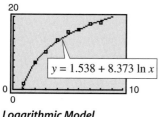

```
LnReg
y=a+blnx
a=1.537949373
b=8.373383316
r²=.9934905682
r=.9967399702
```
Logarithmic Model
Figure 4.54

```
LinReg
y=ax+b
a=2.289285714
b=2.335714286
r²=.9005643856
r=.9489807088
```
Linear Model

So, a logarithmic model for the data is $y = 1.538 + 8.373 \ln x$ and a linear model for the data is $y = 2.29x + 2.3$. Plot the data and each model in the same viewing window, as shown in Figure 4.55. To determine which model fits the data better, compare the coefficients of determination for each model. The model whose coefficient of determination that is closer to 1 is the model that better fits the data. In this case, the better-fitting model is the logarithmic model.

20

$y = 1.538 + 8.373 \ln x$

0
0   10

Logarithmic Model
Figure 4.55

20

$y = 2.29x + 2.3$

0
0   10

Linear Model

✓CHECKPOINT   Now try Exercise 29.

Exploration

Use a graphing utility to find a quadratic model for the data in Example 3. Do you think this model fits the data better than the logarithmic model in Example 3? Explain your reasoning.

In Example 3, the sum of the squared differences for the logarithmic model is 1.55 and the sum of the squared differences for the linear model is 23.86.

Modeling With Exponential and Logistic Functions

Example 4 Fitting an Exponential Model to Data

The table at the right shows the amounts of revenue R (in billions of dollars) collected by the Internal Revenue Service (IRS) for selected years from 1960 to 2005. Use a graphing utility to find a model for the data. Then use the model to estimate the revenue collected in 2010. (Source: IRS Data Book)

Year	Revenue, R
1960	91.8
1965	114.4
1970	195.7
1975	293.8
1980	519.4
1985	742.9
1990	1056.4
1995	1375.7
2000	2096.9
2005	2268.9

Solution

Let x represent the year, with $x = 0$ corresponding to 1960. Begin by entering the data into a graphing utility and displaying the scatter plot, as shown in Figure 4.56.

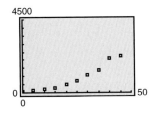

Figure 4.56

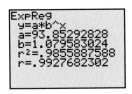

Figure 4.57

From the scatter plot, it appears that an exponential model is a good fit. Use the *regression* feature of the graphing utility to find the exponential model, as shown in Figure 4.57. Change the model to a natural exponential model, as follows.

$R = 93.85(1.080)^x$ Write original model.

$\approx 93.85e^{(\ln 1.080)x}$ $b = e^{\ln b}$

$\approx 93.85e^{0.077x}$ Simplify.

Graph the data and the model in the same viewing window, as shown in Figure 4.58. From the model, you can see that the revenue collected by the IRS from 1960 to 2005 had an average annual increase of about 8%. From this model, you can estimate the 2010 revenue to be

$R = 93.85e^{0.077x}$ Write original model.

$= 93.85e^{0.077(50)} \approx 4410.3$ billion Substitute 50 for x.

which is more than twice the amount collected in 2000. You can also use the *value* feature or the *zoom* and *trace* features of a graphing utility to approximate the revenue in 2010 to be $4410.3 billion, as shown in Figure 4.58.

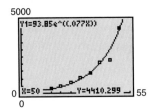

Figure 4.58

✓CHECKPOINT   Now try Exercise 33.

The next example demonstrates how to use a graphing utility to fit a logistic model to data.

Example 5   Fitting a Logistic Model to Data

To estimate the amount of defoliation caused by the gypsy moth during a given year, a forester counts the number x of egg masses on $\frac{1}{40}$ of an acre (circle of radius 18.6 feet) in the fall. The percent of defoliation y the next spring is shown in the table.   (Source: USDA, Forest Service)

Egg masses, x	Percent of defoliation, y
0	12
25	44
50	81
75	96
100	99

a. Use the *regression* feature of a graphing utility to find a logistic model for the data.

b. How closely does the model represent the data?

Graphical Solution

a. Enter the data into the graphing utility. Using the *regression* feature of the graphing utility, you can find the logistic model, as shown in Figure 4.59. You can approximate this model to be

$$y = \frac{100}{1 + 7e^{-0.069x}}.$$

b. You can use a graphing utility to graph the actual data and the model in the same viewing window. In Figure 4.60, it appears that the model is a good fit for the actual data.

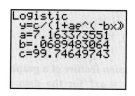

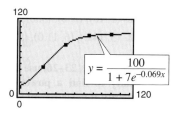

Figure 4.59   **Figure 4.60**

✔CHECKPOINT   Now try Exercise 34.

Numerical Solution

a. Enter the data into the graphing utility. Using the *regression* feature of the graphing utility, you can approximate the logistic model to be

$$y = \frac{100}{1 + 7e^{-0.069x}}.$$

b. You can see how well the model fits the data by comparing the actual values of y with the values of y given by the model, which are labeled y^* in the table below.

x	0	25	50	75	100
y	12	44	81	96	99
y^*	12.5	44.5	81.8	96.2	99.3

In the table, you can see that the model appears to be a good fit for the actual data.

What Did You Learn?

Key Terms

transcendental function, *p.* 334

exponential function, base *a*, *p.* 334

natural base, *p.* 338

natural exponential function, *p.* 338

continuous compounding, *p.* 340

logarithmic function, base *a*, *p.* 346

common logarithmic function, *p.* 347

natural logarithmic function, *p.* 350

change-of-base formula, *p.* 357

exponential growth model, *p.* 375

exponential decay model, *p.* 375

Gaussian model, *p.* 375

logistic growth model, *p.* 375

logarithmic models, *p.* 375

normally distributed, *p.* 379

bell-shaped curve, *p.* 379

logistic curve, *p.* 380

Key Concepts

4.1 ■ Evaluate and graph exponential functions

1. The exponential function f with base a is denoted by $f(x) = a^x$, where $a > 0$, $a \neq 1$, and x is any real number.

2. The graphs of the exponential functions $f(x) = a^x$ and $f(x) = a^{-x}$ have one *y*-intercept, one horizontal asymptote (the *x*-axis), and are continuous.

3. The natural exponential function is $f(x) = e^x$, where e is the constant 2.718281828 . . . . Its graph has the same basic characteristics as the graph of $f(x) = a^x$.

4.2 ■ Evaluate and graph logarithmic functions

1. For $x > 0$, $a > 0$, and $a \neq 1$, $y = \log_a x$ if and only if $x = a^y$. The function given by $f(x) = \log_a x$ is called the logarithmic function with base a.

2. The graph of the logarithmic function $f(x) = \log_a x$, where $a > 1$, is the inverse of the graph of $f(x) = a^x$, has one *x*-intercept, one vertical asymptote (the *y*-axis), and is continuous.

3. For $x > 0$, $y = \ln x$ if and only if $x = e^y$. The function given by $f(x) = \log_e x = \ln x$ is called the natural logarithmic function. Its graph has the same basic characteristics as the graph of $f(x) = \log_a x$.

4.2 ■ Properties of logarithms

1. $\log_a 1 = 0$ and $\ln 1 = 0$

2. $\log_a a = 1$ and $\ln e = 1$

3. $\log_a a^x = x$, $a^{\log_a x} = x$; $\ln e^x = x$, and $e^{\ln x} = x$

4. If $\log_a x = \log_a y$, then $x = y$. If $\ln x = \ln y$, then $x = y$.

4.3 ■ Change-of-base formulas and properties of logarithms

1. Let a, b, and x be positive real numbers such that $a \neq 1$ and $b \neq 1$. Then $\log_a x$ can be converted to a different base using any of the following formulas.

$$\log_a x = \frac{\log_b x}{\log_b a}, \quad \log_a x = \frac{\log_{10} x}{\log_{10} a}, \quad \log_a x = \frac{\ln x}{\ln a}$$

2. Let a be a positive number such that $a \neq 1$, and let n be a real number. If u and v are positive real numbers, the following properties are true.

Product Property

$\log_a(uv) = \log_a u + \log_a v \qquad \ln(uv) = \ln u + \ln v$

Quotient Property

$\log_a \dfrac{u}{v} = \log_a u - \log_a v \qquad \ln \dfrac{u}{v} = \ln u - \ln v$

Power Property

$\log_a u^n = n \log_a u \qquad \ln u^n = n \ln u$

4.4 ■ Solve exponential and logarithmic equations

1. Rewrite the original equation to allow the use of the One-to-One Properties or logarithmic functions.

2. Rewrite an exponential equation in logarithmic form and apply the Inverse Property of logarithmic functions.

3. Rewrite a logarithmic equation in exponential form and apply the Inverse Property of exponential functions.

4.5 ■ Use nonalgebraic models to solve real-life problems

1. Exponential growth model: $y = ae^{bx}$, $b > 0$.

2. Exponential decay model: $y = ae^{-bx}$, $b > 0$.

3. Gaussian model: $y = ae^{-(x-b)^2/c}$.

4. Logistic growth model: $y = a/(1 + be^{-rx})$.

5. Logarithmic models: $y = a + b \ln x$, $y = a + b \log_{10} x$.

4.6 ■ Fit nonlinear models to data

1. Create a scatter plot of the data to determine the type of model (quadratic, exponential, logarithmic, power, or logistic) that would best fit the data.

2. Use a calculator or computer to find the model.

3. The model whose *y*-values are closest to the actual *y*-values is the one that fits best.

Review Exercises

See www.CalcChat.com for worked-out solutions to odd-numbered exercises.

4.1 In Exercises 1–8, use a calculator to evaluate the function at the indicated value of x. Round your result to four decimal places.

Function	Value
1. $f(x) = 1.45^x$	$x = 2\pi$
2. $f(x) = 7^x$	$x = -\sqrt{11}$
3. $g(x) = 60^{2x}$	$x = -1.1$
4. $g(x) = 25^{-3x}$	$x = \frac{3}{2}$
5. $f(x) = e^x$	$x = 8$
6. $f(x) = 5e^x$	$x = \sqrt{5}$
7. $f(x) = e^{-x}$	$x = -2.1$
8. $f(x) = -4e^x$	$x = -\frac{3}{5}$

Library of Parent Functions In Exercises 9–12, match the function with its graph. [The graphs are labeled (a), (b), (c), and (d).]

(a)
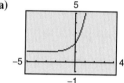

(b)
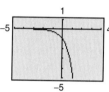

(c)
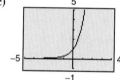

(d)
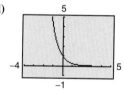

9. $f(x) = 4^x$

10. $f(x) = 4^{-x}$

11. $f(x) = -4^x$

12. $f(x) = 4^x + 1$

In Exercises 13–16, graph the exponential function by hand. Identify any asymptotes and intercepts and determine whether the graph of the function is increasing or decreasing.

13. $f(x) = 6^x$ **14.** $f(x) = 0.3^{x+1}$

15. $g(x) = 1 + 6^{-x}$ **16.** $g(x) = 0.3^{-x}$

In Exercises 17–22, use a graphing utility to construct a table of values for the function. Then sketch the graph of the function. Identify any asymptotes of the graph.

17. $h(x) = e^{x-1}$ **18.** $f(x) = e^{x+2}$

19. $h(x) = -e^x$ **20.** $f(x) = 3 - e^{-x}$

21. $f(x) = 4e^{-0.5x}$ **22.** $f(x) = 2 + e^{x+3}$

In Exercises 23 and 24, use a graphing utility to (a) graph the exponential function and (b) find any asymptotes numerically by creating a table of values for the function.

23. $f(x) = \dfrac{10}{1 + 2^{-0.05x}}$

24. $f(x) = -\dfrac{12}{1 + 4^{-x}}$

Compound Interest In Exercises 25 and 26, complete the table to determine the balance A for $10,000 invested at rate r for t years, compounded continuously.

t	1	10	20	30	40	50
A						

25. $r = 8\%$ **26.** $r = 3\%$

27. *Depreciation* After t years, the value of a car that costs $26,000 is modeled by $V(t) = 26,000\left(\frac{3}{4}\right)^t$.

    (a) Use a graphing utility to graph the function.

    (b) Find the value of the car 2 years after it was purchased.

    (c) According to the model, when does the car depreciate most rapidly? Is this realistic? Explain.

28. *Radioactive Decay* Let Q represent a mass, in grams, of plutonium 241 (^{241}Pu), whose half-life is 14 years. The quantity of plutonium present after t years is given by $Q = 100\left(\frac{1}{2}\right)^{t/14}$.

    (a) Determine the initial quantity (when $t = 0$).

    (b) Determine the quantity present after 10 years.

    (c) Use a graphing utility to graph the function over the interval $t = 0$ to $t = 100$.

4.2 In Exercises 29–42, write the logarithmic equation in exponential form or write the exponential equation in logarithmic form.

29. $\log_5 125 = 3$ **30.** $\log_6 36 = 2$

31. $\log_{64} 2 = \frac{1}{6}$ **32.** $\log_{10}\left(\frac{1}{100}\right) = -2$

33. $\ln e^4 = 4$ **34.** $\ln\sqrt{e^3} = \frac{3}{2}$

35. $4^3 = 64$ **36.** $3^5 = 243$

37. $25^{3/2} = 125$ **38.** $12^{-1} = \frac{1}{12}$

39. $\left(\frac{1}{2}\right)^{-3} = 8$ **40.** $\left(\frac{2}{3}\right)^{-2} = \frac{9}{4}$

41. $e^7 = 1096.6331\ldots$ **42.** $e^{-3} = 0.0497\ldots$

In Exercises 43–46, evaluate the function at the indicated value of x without using a calculator.

Function	Value
43. $f(x) = \log_6 x$	$x = 216$
44. $f(x) = \log_7 x$	$x = 1$
45. $f(x) = \log_4 x$	$x = \frac{1}{4}$
46. $f(x) = \log_{10} x$	$x = 0.001$

In Exercises 47–50, find the domain, vertical asymptote, and x-intercept of the logarithmic function, and sketch its graph by hand.

47. $g(x) = -\log_2 x + 5$ 48. $g(x) = \log_5(x - 3)$
49. $f(x) = \log_2(x - 1) + 6$ 50. $f(x) = \log_5(x + 2) - 3$

In Exercises 51–54, use a calculator to evaluate the function $f(x) = \ln x$ at the indicated value of x. Round your result to three decimal places, if necessary.

51. $x = 21.5$ 52. $x = 0.98$
53. $x = \sqrt{6}$ 54. $x = \frac{2}{5}$

In Exercises 55–58, solve the equation for x.

55. $\log_5 3 = \log_5 x$ 56. $\log_2 8 = x$
57. $\log_9 x = \log_9 3^{-2}$ 58. $\log_4 4^3 = x$

In Exercises 59–62, use a graphing utility to graph the logarithmic function. Determine the domain and identify any vertical asymptote and x-intercept.

59. $f(x) = \ln x + 3$ 60. $f(x) = \ln(x - 3)$
61. $h(x) = \frac{1}{2}\ln x$ 62. $f(x) = \frac{1}{4}\ln x$

63. **Climb Rate** The time t (in minutes) for a small plane to climb to an altitude of h feet is given by

$$t = 50 \log_{10}[18{,}000/(18{,}000 - h)]$$

where 18,000 feet is the plane's absolute ceiling.

(a) Determine the domain of the function appropriate for the context of the problem.

(b) Use a graphing utility to graph the function and identify any asymptotes.

(c) As the plane approaches its absolute ceiling, what can be said about the time required to further increase its altitude?

(d) Find the amount of time it will take for the plane to climb to an altitude of 4000 feet.

64. **Home Mortgage** The model

$$t = 12.542 \ln[x/(x - 1000)], \quad x > 1000$$

approximates the length of a home mortgage of $150,000 at 8% in terms of the monthly payment. In the model, t is the length of the mortgage in years and x is the monthly payment in dollars.

(a) Use the model to approximate the length of a $150,000 mortgage at 8% when the monthly payment is $1254.68.

(b) Approximate the total amount paid over the term of the mortgage with a monthly payment of $1254.68. What amount of the total is interest costs?

4.3 In Exercises 65–68, evaluate the logarithm using the change-of-base formula. Do each problem twice, once with common logarithms and once with natural logarithms. Round your results to three decimal places.

65. $\log_4 9$ 66. $\log_{1/2} 5$
67. $\log_{12} 200$ 68. $\log_3 0.28$

In Exercises 69–72, use the change-of-base formula and a graphing utility to graph the function.

69. $f(x) = \log_2(x - 1)$ 70. $f(x) = 2 - \log_3 x$
71. $f(x) = -\log_{1/2}(x + 2)$ 72. $f(x) = \log_{1/3}(x - 1) + 1$

In Exercises 73–76, approximate the logarithm using the properties of logarithms, given that $\log_b 2 \approx 0.3562$, $\log_b 3 \approx 0.5646$, and $\log_b 5 \approx 0.8271$.

73. $\log_b 9$ 74. $\log_b\left(\frac{4}{9}\right)$
75. $\log_b \sqrt{5}$ 76. $\log_b 50$

In Exercises 77–80, use the properties of logarithms to rewrite and simplify the logarithmic expression.

77. $\ln(5e^{-2})$ 78. $\ln \sqrt{e^5}$
79. $\log_{10} 200$ 80. $\log_{10} 0.002$

In Exercises 81–86, use the properties of logarithms to expand the expression as a sum, difference, and/or constant multiple of logarithms. (Assume all variables are positive.)

81. $\log_5 5x^2$ 82. $\log_4 3xy^2$
83. $\log_{10} \dfrac{5\sqrt{y}}{x^2}$ 84. $\ln \dfrac{\sqrt{x}}{4}$
85. $\ln\left(\dfrac{x + 3}{xy}\right)$ 86. $\ln \dfrac{xy^5}{\sqrt{z}}$

In Exercises 87–92, condense the expression to the logarithm of a single quantity.

87. $\log_2 5 + \log_2 x$
88. $\log_6 y - 2\log_6 z$
89. $\frac{1}{2}\ln(2x - 1) - 2\ln(x + 1)$
90. $5\ln(x - 2) - \ln(x + 2) - 3\ln(x)$
91. $\ln 3 + \frac{1}{3}\ln(4 - x^2) - \ln x$
92. $3[\ln x - 2\ln(x^2 + 1)] + 2\ln 5$

93. Snow Removal The number of miles s of roads cleared of snow is approximated by the model

$$s = 25 - \frac{13 \ln(h/12)}{\ln 3}, \quad 2 \le h \le 15$$

where h is the depth of the snow (in inches).

(a) Use a graphing utility to graph the function.

(b) Complete the table.

h	4	6	8	10	12	14
s						

(c) Using the graph of the function and the table, what conclusion can you make about the number of miles of roads cleared as the depth of the snow increases?

94. Human Memory Model Students in a sociology class were given an exam and then retested monthly with an equivalent exam. The average scores for the class are given by the human memory model $f(t) = 85 - 14 \log_{10}(t + 1)$, where t is the time in months and $0 \le t \le 10$. When will the average score decrease to 71?

4.4 In Exercises 95–108, solve the equation for x without using a calculator.

95. $8^x = 512$

96. $3^x = 729$

97. $6^x = \frac{1}{216}$

98. $6^{x-2} = 1296$

99. $2^{x+1} = \frac{1}{16}$

100. $4^{x/2} = 64$

101. $\log_7 x = 4$

102. $\log_x 243 = 5$

103. $\log_2(x - 1) = 3$

104. $\log_5(2x + 1) = 2$

105. $\ln x = 4$

106. $\ln x = -3$

107. $\ln(x - 1) = 2$

108. $\ln(2x + 1) = -4$

In Exercises 109–118, solve the exponential equation algebraically. Round your result to three decimal places.

109. $3e^{-5x} = 132$

110. $14e^{3x+2} = 560$

111. $2^x + 13 = 35$

112. $6^x - 28 = -8$

113. $-4(5^x) = -68$

114. $2(12^x) = 190$

115. $2e^{x-3} - 1 = 4$

116. $-e^{x/2} + 1 = \frac{1}{2}$

117. $e^{2x} - 7e^x + 10 = 0$

118. $e^{2x} - 6e^x + 8 = 0$

In Exercises 119–128, solve the logarithmic equation algebraically. Round your result to three decimal places.

119. $\ln 3x = 8.2$

120. $\ln 5x = 7.2$

121. $\ln x - \ln 3 = 2$

122. $\ln x - \ln 5 = 4$

123. $\ln \sqrt{x + 1} = 2$

124. $\ln \sqrt{x + 8} = 3$

125. $\log_4(x - 1) = \log_4(x - 2) - \log_4(x + 2)$

126. $\log_5(x + 2) - \log_5 x = \log_5(x + 5)$

127. $\log_{10}(1 - x) = -1$

128. $\log_{10}(-x - 4) = 2$

In Exercises 129–132, solve the equation algebraically. Round your result to three decimal places.

129. $xe^x + e^x = 0$

130. $2xe^{2x} + e^{2x} = 0$

131. $x \ln x + x = 0$

132. $\frac{1 - \ln x}{x^2} = 0$

133. Compound Interest You deposit $7550 in an account that pays 7.25% interest, compounded continuously. How long will it take for the money to triple?

134. Demand The demand x for a 32-inch television is modeled by $p = 500 - 0.5e^{0.004x}$. Find the demands x for prices of (a) $p = \$450$ and (b) $p = \$400$.

4.5 Library of Parent Functions In Exercises 135–140, match the function with its graph. [The graphs are labeled (a), (b), (c), (d), (e), and (f).]

(a)
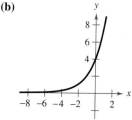

(b)
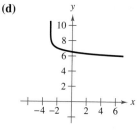

(c)
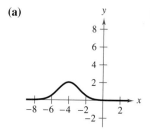

(d)
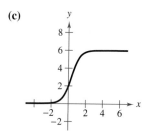

(e)
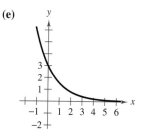

(f)
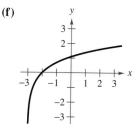

135. $y = 3e^{-2x/3}$

136. $y = 4e^{2x/3}$

137. $y = \ln(x + 3)$

138. $y = 7 - \log_{10}(x + 3)$

139. $y = 2e^{-(x+4)^2/3}$

140. $y = \dfrac{6}{1 + 2e^{-2x}}$

In Exercises 141–144, find the exponential model $y = ae^{bx}$ that fits the two points.

141. $(0, 2), (4, 3)$

142. $(0, 2), (5, 1)$

143. $\left(0, \frac{1}{2}\right), (5, 5)$

144. $(0, 4), \left(5, \frac{1}{2}\right)$

145. *Population* The population P (in thousands) of Colorado Springs, Colorado is given by

$$P = 361e^{kt}$$

where t represents the year, with $t = 0$ corresponding to 2000. In 1980, the population was 215,000. Find the value of k and use this result to predict the population in the year 2020. (Source: U.S. Census Bureau)

146. *Radioactive Decay* The half-life of radioactive uranium (^{234}U) is 245,500 years. What percent of the present amount of radioactive uranium will remain after 5000 years?

147. *Compound Interest* A deposit of $10,000 is made in a savings account for which the interest is compounded continuously. The balance will double in 12 years.

(a) What is the annual interest rate for this account?

(b) Find the balance after 1 year.

148. *Test Scores* The test scores for a biology test follow a normal distribution modeled by

$$y = 0.0499e^{-(x-74)^2/128}, \quad 40 \le x \le 100$$

where x is the test score.

(a) Use a graphing utility to graph the function.

(b) From the graph in part (a), estimate the average test score.

149. *Typing Speed* In a typing class, the average number of words per minute N typed after t weeks of lessons was found to be modeled by

$$N = \frac{158}{1 + 5.4e^{-0.12t}}.$$

Find the numbers of weeks necessary to type (a) 50 words per minute and (b) 75 words per minute.

150. *Geology* On the Richter scale, the magnitude R of an earthquake of intensity I is modeled by

$$R = \log_{10} \frac{I}{I_0}$$

where $I_0 = 1$ is the minimum intensity used for comparison. Find the intensities I of the following earthquakes measuring R on the Richter scale.

(a) $R = 8.4$ (b) $R = 6.85$ (c) $R = 9.1$

4.6 Library of Parent Functions **In Exercises 151–154, determine whether the scatter plot could best be modeled by a linear model, a quadratic model, an exponential model, a logarithmic model, or a logistic model.**

151. 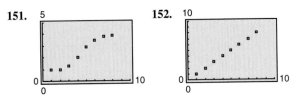 **152.**

153. 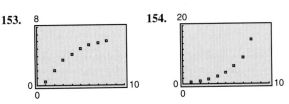 **154.**

155. *Fitness* The table shows the sales S (in millions of dollars) of exercise equipment in the United States from 1998 to 2004. (Source: National Sporting Goods Association)

Year	Sales, S (in millions of dollars)
1998	3233
1999	3396
2000	3610
2001	3889
2002	4378
2003	4727
2004	4869

(a) Use the *regression* feature of a graphing utility to find a linear model, a quadratic model, an exponential model, a logarithmic model, and a power model for the data and to identify the coefficient of determination for each model. Let t represent the year, with $t = 8$ corresponding to 1998.

(b) Use a graphing utility to graph each model with the original data.

(c) Determine which model best fits the data. Explain.

(d) Use the model you chose in part (c) to predict the sales of exercise equipment in 2010.

(e) Use the model you chose in part (c) to predict the year that sales will reach 5.25 billion dollars.

156. Sports The table shows the numbers of female partici-pants P (in thousands) in high school athletic programs from 1991 to 2004. (Source: National Federation of State High School Associations)

Year	Female participants, P (in thousands)
1991	1892
1992	1941
1993	1997
1994	2130
1995	2240
1996	2368
1997	2474
1998	2570
1999	2653
2000	2676
2001	2784
2002	2807
2003	2856
2004	2865

(a) Use the *regression* feature of a graphing utility to find a linear model, a quadratic model, an exponential model, a logarithmic model, and a power model for the data and to identify the coefficient of determination for each model. Let t represent the year, with $t = 1$ corresponding to 1991.

(b) Use a graphing utility to graph each model with the original data.

(c) Determine which model best fits the data. Explain.

(d) Use the model you chose in part (c) to predict the number of participants in 2010.

(e) Use the model you chose in part (c) to predict when the number of participants will exceed 3 million.

157. Wildlife A lake is stocked with 500 fish, and the fish population P increases every month. The local fish commission records this increase as shown in the table.

Month, x	Position, P
0	500
6	1488
12	3672
18	6583
24	8650
30	9550
36	9860

(a) Use the *regression* feature of a graphing utility to find a logistic model for the data. Let x represent the month.

(b) Use a graphing utility to graph the model with the original data.

(c) How closely does the model represent the data?

(d) What is the limiting size of the population?

158. Population The population P of Italy (in millions) from 1990 to 2005 can be modeled by $P = 56.8e^{0.001603t}$, $0 \le t \le 15$, where t is the year, with $t = 0$ corresponding to 1990. (Source: U.S. Census Bureau)

(a) Use the *table* feature of a graphing utility to create a table of the values of P for $0 \le t \le 15$.

(b) Use the first and last values in your table to create a linear model for the data.

(c) What is the slope of your linear model, and what does it tell you about the situation?

(d) Graph both models in the same viewing window. Explain any differences in the models.

Synthesis

True or False? In Exercises 159–164, determine whether the equation or statement is true or false. Justify your answer.

159. $\log_b b^{2x} = 2x$ **160.** $e^{x-1} = \dfrac{e^x}{e}$

161. $\ln(x + y) = \ln x + \ln y$ **162.** $\ln(x + y) = \ln(xy)$

163. The domain of the function $f(x) = \ln x$ is the set of all real numbers.

164. The logarithm of the quotient of two numbers is equal to the difference of the logarithms of the numbers.

165. Think About It Without using a calculator, explain why you know that $2^{\sqrt{2}}$ is greater than 2, but less than 4.

166. Pattern Recognition

(a) Use a graphing utility to compare the graph of the function $y = e^x$ with the graph of each function below. [$n!$ (read as "n factorial") is defined as $n! = 1 \cdot 2 \cdot 3 \cdots (n - 1) \cdot n$.]

$$y_1 = 1 + \frac{x}{1!}, \ y_2 = 1 + \frac{x}{1!} + \frac{x^2}{2!},$$

$$y_3 = 1 + \frac{x}{1!} + \frac{x^2}{2!} + \frac{x^3}{3!}$$

(b) Identify the pattern of successive polynomials given in part (a). Extend the pattern one more term and compare the graph of the resulting polynomial function with the graph of $y = e^x$. What do you think this pattern implies?

4 Chapter Test

See www.CalcChat.com for worked-out solutions to odd-numbered exercises.

Take this test as you would take a test in class. After you are finished, check your work against the answers given in the back of the book.

In Exercises 1–3, use a graphing utility to construct a table of values for the function. Then sketch a graph of the function. Identify any asymptotes and intercepts.

1. $f(x) = 10^{-x}$ **2.** $f(x) = -6^{x-2}$ **3.** $f(x) = 1 - e^{2x}$

In Exercises 4–6, evaluate the expression.

4. $\log_7 7^{-0.89}$ **5.** $4.6 \ln e^2$ **6.** $2 - \log_{10} 100$

In Exercises 7–9, use a graphing utility to graph the function. Determine the domain and identify any vertical asymptotes and x-intercepts.

7. $f(x) = -\log_{10} x - 6$ **8.** $f(x) = \ln(x - 4)$ **9.** $f(x) = 1 + \ln(x + 6)$

In Exercises 10–12, evaluate the logarithm using the change-of-base formula. Round your result to three decimal places.

10. $\log_7 44$ **11.** $\log_{2/5} 0.9$ **12.** $\log_{24} 68$

In Exercises 13–15, use the properties of logarithms to expand the expression as a sum, difference, and/or multiple of logarithms.

13. $\log_2 3a^4$ **14.** $\ln \dfrac{5\sqrt{x}}{6}$ **15.** $\ln \dfrac{x\sqrt{x+1}}{2e^4}$

In Exercises 16–18, condense the expression to the logarithm of a single quantity.

16. $\log_3 13 + \log_3 y$ **17.** $4 \ln x - 4 \ln y$ **18.** $\ln x - \ln(x + 2) + \ln(2x - 3)$

In Exercises 19–22, solve the equation for x.

19. $3^x = 81$ **20.** $5^{2x} = 2500$

21. $\log_7 x = 3$ **22.** $\log_{10}(x - 4) = 5$

In Exercises 23–26, solve the equation algebraically. Round your result to three decimal places.

23. $\dfrac{1025}{8 + e^{4x}} = 5$ **24.** $-xe^{-x} + e^{-x} = 0$

25. $\log_{10} x - \log_{10}(8 - 5x) = 2$ **26.** $2x \ln x - x = 0$

27. The half-life of radioactive actinium (^{227}Ac) is 22 years. What percent of a present amount of radioactive actinium will remain after 19 years?

28. The table at the right shows the mail revenues R (in billions of dollars) for the U.S. Postal Service from 1995 to 2004. (Source: U.S. Postal Service)

(a) Use the *regression* feature of a graphing utility to find a quadratic model, an exponential model, and a power model for the data. Let t represent the year, with $t = 5$ corresponding to 1995.

(b) Use a graphing utility to graph each model with the original data.

(c) Determine which model best fits the data. Use the model to predict the mail revenues in 2010.

Year	Revenues, R
1995	52.5
1996	54.5
1997	56.3
1998	58.0
1999	60.4
2000	62.3
2001	63.4
2002	63.8
2003	65.7
2004	65.9

Table for 28

Proofs in Mathematics

Each of the following three properties of logarithms can be proved by using properties of exponential functions.

Properties of Logarithms   (p. 358)

Let a be a positive number such that $a \neq 1$, and let n be a real number. If u and v are positive real numbers, the following properties are true.

	Logarithm with Base a	*Natural Logarithm*
1. Product Property:	$\log_a(uv) = \log_a u + \log_a v$	$\ln(uv) = \ln u + \ln v$
2. Quotient Property:	$\log_a \dfrac{u}{v} = \log_a u - \log_a v$	$\ln \dfrac{u}{v} = \ln u - \ln v$
3. Power Property:	$\log_a u^n = n \log_a u$	$\ln u^n = n \ln u$

Slide Rules

The slide rule was invented by William Oughtred (1574–1660) in 1625. The slide rule is a computational device with a sliding portion and a fixed portion. A slide rule enables you to perform multiplication by using the Product Property of logarithms. There are other slide rules that allow for the calculation of roots and trigonometric functions. Slide rules were used by mathematicians and engineers until the invention of the hand-held calculator in 1972.

Proof

Let

$$x = \log_a u \quad \text{and} \quad y = \log_a v.$$

The corresponding exponential forms of these two equations are

$$a^x = u \quad \text{and} \quad a^y = v.$$

To prove the Product Property, multiply u and v to obtain

$$uv = a^x a^y = a^{x+y}.$$

The corresponding logarithmic form of $uv = a^{x+y}$ is $\log_a(uv) = x + y$. So,

$$\log_a(uv) = \log_a u + \log_a v.$$

To prove the Quotient Property, divide u by v to obtain

$$\frac{u}{v} = \frac{a^x}{a^y} = a^{x-y}.$$

The corresponding logarithmic form of $u/v = a^{x-y}$ is $\log_a(u/v) = x - y$. So,

$$\log_a \frac{u}{v} = \log_a u - \log_a v.$$

To prove the Power Property, substitute a^x for u in the expression $\log_a u^n$, as follows.

$$\log_a u^n = \log_a (a^x)^n \qquad \text{Substitute } a^x \text{ for } u.$$
$$= \log_a a^{nx} \qquad \text{Property of exponents}$$
$$= nx \qquad \text{Inverse Property of logarithms}$$
$$= n \log_a u \qquad \text{Substitute } \log_a u \text{ for } x.$$

So, $\log_a u^n = n \log_a u.$

5.1 Solving Systems of Equations

The Methods of Substitution and Graphing

So far in this text, most problems have involved either a function of one variable or a single equation in two variables. However, many problems in science, business, and engineering involve two or more equations in two or more variables. To solve such problems, you need to find solutions of **systems of equations.** Here is an example of a system of two equations in two unknowns, x and y.

$$\begin{cases} 2x + y = 5 & \text{Equation 1} \\ 3x - 2y = 4 & \text{Equation 2} \end{cases}$$

A **solution** of this system is an ordered pair that satisfies each equation in the system. Finding the set of all such solutions is called **solving the system of equations.** For instance, the ordered pair $(2, 1)$ is a solution of this system. To check this, you can substitute 2 for x and 1 for y in *each* equation.

In this section, you will study two ways to solve systems of equations, beginning with the **method of substitution.**

> ### The Method of Substitution
>
> To use the **method of substitution** to solve a system of two equations in x and y, perform the following steps.
>
> 1. Solve one of the equations for one variable in terms of the other.
>
> 2. Substitute the expression found in Step 1 into the other equation to obtain an equation in one variable.
>
> 3. Solve the equation obtained in Step 2.
>
> 4. Back-substitute the value(s) obtained in Step 3 into the expression obtained in Step 1 to find the value(s) of the other variable.
>
> 5. Check that each solution satisfies *both* of the original equations.

When using the **method of graphing,** note that the solution of the system corresponds to the **point(s) of intersection** of the graphs.

> ### The Method of Graphing
>
> To use the **method of graphing** to solve a system of two equations in x and y, perform the following steps.
>
> 1. Solve both equations for y in terms of x.
>
> 2. Use a graphing utility to graph both equations in the same viewing window.
>
> 3. Use the *intersect* feature or the *zoom* and *trace* features of the graphing utility to approximate the point(s) of intersection of the graphs.
>
> 4. Check that each solution satisfies *both* of the original equations.

What you should learn

- Use the methods of substitution and graphing to solve systems of equations in two variables.

- Use systems of equations to model and solve real-life problems.

Why you should learn it

You can use systems of equations in situations in which the variables must satisfy two or more conditions. For instance, Exercise 76 on page 415 shows how to use a system of equations to compare two models for estimating the number of board feet in a 16-foot log.

Bruce Hands/Getty Images

STUDY TIP

When using the method of substitution, it does not matter which variable you choose to solve for first. Whether you solve for y first or x first, you will obtain the same solution. When making your choice, you should choose the variable and equation that are easier to work with.

Example 1   Solving a System of Equations

Solve the system of equations.

$$\begin{cases} x + y = 4 & \text{Equation 1} \\ x - y = 2 & \text{Equation 2} \end{cases}$$

Algebraic Solution

Begin by solving for y in Equation 1.

$y = 4 - x$ Solve for y in Equation 1.

Next, substitute this expression for y into Equation 2 and solve the resulting single-variable equation for x.

$x - y = 2$	Write Equation 2.
$x - (4 - x) = 2$	Substitute $4 - x$ for y.
$x - 4 + x = 2$	Distributive Property
$2x = 6$	Combine like terms.
$x = 3$	Divide each side by 2.

Finally, you can solve for y by *back-substituting* $x = 3$ into the equation $y = 4 - x$ to obtain

$y = 4 - x$	Write revised Equation 1.
$y = 4 - 3$	Substitute 3 for x.
$y = 1.$	Solve for y.

The solution is the ordered pair $(3, 1)$. Check this as follows.

Check $(3, 1)$ in Equation 1:

$x + y = 4$	Write Equation 1.
$3 + 1 \overset{?}{=} 4$	Substitute for x and y.
$4 = 4$	Solution checks in Equation 1. ✓

Check $(3, 1)$ in Equation 2:

$x - y = 2$	Write Equation 2.
$3 - 1 \overset{?}{=} 2$	Substitute for x and y.
$2 = 2$	Solution checks in Equation 2. ✓

✓CHECKPOINT   Now try Exercise 13.

Graphical Solution

Begin by solving both equations for y. Then use a graphing utility to graph the equations $y_1 = 4 - x$ and $y_2 = x - 2$ in the same viewing window. Use the *intersect* feature (see Figure 5.1) or the *zoom* and *trace* features of the graphing utility to approximate the point of intersection of the graphs.

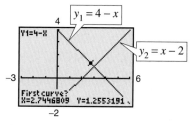

Figure 5.1

The point of intersection is $(3, 1)$, as shown in Figure 5.2.

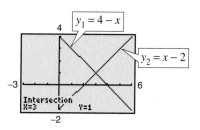

Figure 5.2

Check that $(3, 1)$ is the exact solution as follows.

Check $(3, 1)$ in Equation 1:

$3 + 1 \overset{?}{=} 4$	Substitute for x and y in Equation 1.
$4 = 4$	Solution checks in Equation 1. ✓

Check $(3, 1)$ in Equation 2:

$3 - 1 \overset{?}{=} 2$	Substitute for x and y in Equation 2.
$2 = 2$	Solution checks in Equation 2. ✓

In the algebraic solution of Example 1, note that the term *back-substitution* implies that you work *backwards*. First you solve for one of the variables, and then you substitute that value *back* into one of the equations in the system to find the value of the other variable.

Example 2 Solving a System by Substitution

A total of $12,000 is invested in two funds paying 9% and 11% simple interest. The yearly interest is $1180. How much is invested at each rate?

Solution

Verbal Model:

$$\boxed{\begin{array}{c} 9\% \\ \text{fund} \end{array}} + \boxed{\begin{array}{c} 11\% \\ \text{fund} \end{array}} = \boxed{\begin{array}{c} \text{Total} \\ \text{investment} \end{array}}$$

$$\boxed{\begin{array}{c} 9\% \\ \text{interest} \end{array}} + \boxed{\begin{array}{c} 11\% \\ \text{interest} \end{array}} = \boxed{\begin{array}{c} \text{Total} \\ \text{interest} \end{array}}$$

Labels: Amount in 9% fund $= x$ Amount in 11% fund $= y$ (dollars)
    Interest for 9% fund $= 0.09x$ Interest for 11% fund $= 0.11y$ (dollars)
    Total investment $= \$12,000$ Total interest $= \$1180$ (dollars)

System:
$$\begin{cases} x + \quad\; y = 12,000 & \text{Equation 1} \\ 0.09x + 0.11y = \;\; 1,180 & \text{Equation 2} \end{cases}$$

To begin, it is convenient to multiply each side of Equation 2 by 100. This eliminates the need to work with decimals.

$$9x + 11y = 118,000 \qquad \text{Revised Equation 2}$$

To solve this system, you can solve for x in Equation 1.

$$x = 12,000 - y \qquad \text{Revised Equation 1}$$

Next, substitute this expression for x into revised Equation 2 and solve the resulting equation for y.

$$9x + 11y = 118,000 \qquad \text{Write revised Equation 2.}$$
$$9(12,000 - y) + 11y = 118,000 \qquad \text{Substitute } 12,000 - y \text{ for } x.$$
$$108,000 - 9y + 11y = 118,000 \qquad \text{Distributive Property}$$
$$2y = 10,000 \qquad \text{Combine like terms.}$$
$$y = 5000 \qquad \text{Divide each side by 2.}$$

Finally, back-substitute the value $y = 5000$ to solve for x.

$$x = 12,000 - y \qquad \text{Write revised Equation 1.}$$
$$x = 12,000 - 5000 \qquad \text{Substitute 5000 for } y.$$
$$x = 7000 \qquad \text{Simplify.}$$

The solution is $(7000, 5000)$. So, $7000 is invested at 9% and $5000 is invested at 11% to yield yearly interest of $1180. Check this in the original system.

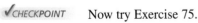 ✓CHECKPOINT   Now try Exercise 75.

The equations in Examples 1 and 2 are linear. Substitution and graphing can also be used to solve systems in which one or both of the equations are nonlinear.

TECHNOLOGY TIP

Remember that a good way to check the answers you obtain in this section is to use a graphing utility. For instance, enter the two equations in Example 2

$$y_1 = 12,000 - x$$

$$y_2 = \frac{1180 - 0.09x}{0.11}$$

and find an appropriate viewing window that shows where the lines intersect. Then use the *intersect* feature or the *zoom* and *trace* features to find the point of intersection.

Example 3 Substitution: Two-Solution Case

Solve the system of equations: $\begin{cases} x^2 + 4x - y = 7 & \text{Equation 1} \\ 2x - y = -1 & \text{Equation 2} \end{cases}$.

Algebraic Solution

Begin by solving for y in Equation 2 to obtain $y = 2x + 1$. Next, substitute this expression for y into Equation 1 and solve for x.

$$x^2 + 4x - y = 7 \qquad \text{Write Equation 1.}$$

$$x^2 + 4x - (2x + 1) = 7 \qquad \text{Substitute } 2x + 1 \text{ for } y.$$

$$x^2 + 4x - 2x - 1 = 7 \qquad \text{Distributive Property}$$

$$x^2 + 2x - 8 = 0 \qquad \text{Write in general form.}$$

$$(x + 4)(x - 2) = 0 \qquad \text{Factor.}$$

$$x + 4 = 0 \implies x = -4 \qquad \text{Set 1st factor equal to 0.}$$

$$x - 2 = 0 \implies x = 2 \qquad \text{Set 2nd factor equal to 0.}$$

Back-substituting these values of x into revised Equation 2 produces

$$y = 2(-4) + 1 = -7 \qquad \text{and} \qquad y = 2(2) + 1 = 5.$$

So, the solutions are $(-4, -7)$ and $(2, 5)$. Check these in the original system.

✔CHECKPOINT   Now try Exercise 23.

Graphical Solution

To graph each equation, first solve both equations for y. Then use a graphing utility to graph the equations in the same viewing window. Use the *intersect* feature or the *zoom* and *trace* features to approximate the points of intersection of the graphs. The points of intersection are $(-4, -7)$ and $(2, 5)$, as shown in Figure 5.3. Check that $(-4, -7)$ and $(2, 5)$ are the exact solutions by substituting *both* ordered pairs into *both* equations.

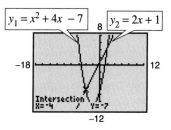

Figure 5.3

Example 4 Substitution: No-Solution Case

Solve the system of equations.

$$\begin{cases} -x + y = 4 & \text{Equation 1} \\ x^2 + y = 3 & \text{Equation 2} \end{cases}$$

Solution

Begin by solving for y in Equation 1 to obtain $y = x + 4$. Next, substitute this expression for y into Equation 2 and solve for x.

$$x^2 + y = 3 \qquad \text{Write Equation 2.}$$

$$x^2 + (x + 4) = 3 \qquad \text{Substitute } x + 4 \text{ for } y.$$

$$x^2 + x + 1 = 0 \qquad \text{Simplify.}$$

$$x = \frac{-1 \pm \sqrt{3}i}{2} \qquad \text{Quadratic Formula}$$

Because this yields two complex values, the equation $x^2 + x + 1 = 0$ has no *real* solution. So, the original system of equations has no *real* solution.

✔CHECKPOINT   Now try Exercise 25.

STUDY TIP

When using substitution, solve for the variable that is not raised to a power in either equation. For instance, in Example 4 it would not be practical to solve for x in Equation 2. Can you see why?

Exploration

Graph the system of equations in Example 4. Do the graphs of the equations intersect? Why or why not?

From Examples 1, 3, and 4, you can see that a system of two equations in two unknowns can have exactly one solution, more than one solution, or no solution. For instance, in Figure 5.4, the two equations in Example 1 graph as two lines with a *single point* of intersection. The two equations in Example 3 graph as a parabola and a line with *two points* of intersection, as shown in Figure 5.5. The two equations in Example 4 graph as a line and a parabola that have *no points* of intersection, as shown in Figure 5.6.

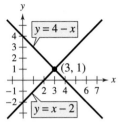

One Intersection Point
Figure 5.4

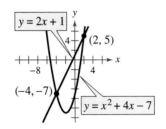

Two Intersection Points
Figure 5.5

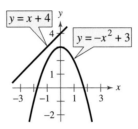

No Intersection Points
Figure 5.6

Example 5 shows the value of a graphical approach to solving systems of equations in two variables. Notice what would happen if you tried only the substitution method in Example 5. You would obtain the equation $x + \ln x = 1$. It would be difficult to solve this equation for x using standard algebraic techniques. In such cases, a graphical approach to solving systems of equations is more convenient.

Example 5 Solving a System of Equations Graphically

Solve the system of equations.

$$\begin{cases} y = \ln x & \text{Equation 1} \\ x + y = 1 & \text{Equation 2} \end{cases}$$

Solution

From the graphs of these equations, it is clear that there is only one point of intersection. Use the *intersect* feature or the *zoom* and *trace* features of a graphing utility to approximate the solution point as $(1, 0)$, as shown in Figure 5.7. You can confirm this by substituting $(1, 0)$ into *both* equations.

Check $(1, 0)$ *in Equation 1:*

$y = \ln x$ Write Equation 1.

$0 = \ln 1$ Equation 1 checks. ✓

Check $(1, 0)$ *in Equation 2:*

$x + y = 1$ Write Equation 2.

$1 + 0 = 1$ Equation 2 checks. ✓

✓**CHECKPOINT**   Now try Exercise 45.

TECHNOLOGY SUPPORT

For instructions on how to use the *intersect* feature and the *zoom* and *trace* features, see Appendix A; for specific keystrokes, go to this textbook's *Online Study Center*.

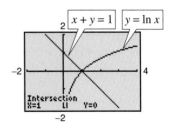

Figure 5.7

Points of Intersection and Applications

The total cost C of producing x units of a product typically has two components: the initial cost and the cost per unit. When enough units have been sold that the total revenue R equals the total cost C, the sales are said to have reached the **break-even point.** You will find that the break-even point corresponds to the point of intersection of the cost and revenue curves.

Example 6   Break-Even Analysis

A small business invests \$10,000 in equipment to produce a new soft drink. Each bottle of the soft drink costs \$0.65 to produce and is sold for \$1.20. How many bottles must be sold before the business breaks even?

Solution

The total cost of producing x bottles is

$$\begin{array}{ccccc} \text{Total} \\ \text{cost} \end{array} = \begin{array}{c} \text{Cost per} \\ \text{bottle} \end{array} \cdot \begin{array}{c} \text{Number} \\ \text{of bottles} \end{array} + \begin{array}{c} \text{Initial} \\ \text{cost} \end{array}$$

$$C = 0.65x + 10{,}000. \qquad \text{Equation 1}$$

The revenue obtained by selling x bottles is

$$\begin{array}{c} \text{Total} \\ \text{revenue} \end{array} = \begin{array}{c} \text{Price per} \\ \text{bottle} \end{array} \cdot \begin{array}{c} \text{Number} \\ \text{of bottles} \end{array}$$

$$R = 1.20x. \qquad \text{Equation 2}$$

Because the break-even point occurs when $R = C$, you have $C = 1.20x$, and the system of equations to solve is

$$\begin{cases} C = 0.65x + 10{,}000 \\ C = 1.20x \end{cases}.$$

Now you can solve by substitution.

$$1.20x = 0.65x + 10{,}000 \qquad \text{Substitute } 1.20x \text{ for } C \text{ in Equation 1.}$$

$$0.55x = 10{,}000 \qquad \text{Subtract } 0.65x \text{ from each side.}$$

$$x = \frac{10{,}000}{0.55} \approx 18{,}182 \text{ bottles.} \qquad \text{Divide each side by 0.55.}$$

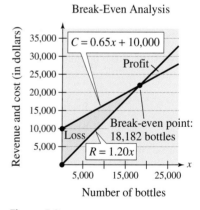

Break-Even Analysis

Figure 5.8

Note in Figure 5.8 that revenue less than the break-even point corresponds to an overall loss, whereas revenue greater than the break-even point corresponds to a profit. Verify the break-even point using the *intersect* feature or the *zoom* and *trace* features of a graphing utility.

✔CHECKPOINT   Now try Exercise 71.

Another way to view the solution in Example 6 is to consider the profit function $P = R - C$. The break-even point occurs when the profit is 0, which is the same as saying that $R = C$.

Example 7   State Populations

From 1998 to 2004, the population of Colorado increased more rapidly than the population of Alabama. Two models that approximate the populations P (in thousands) are

$$\begin{cases} P = 3488 + 81.9t & \text{Colorado} \\ P = 4248 + 19.9t & \text{Alabama} \end{cases}$$

where t represents the year, with $t = 8$ corresponding to 1998.   (Source: U.S. Census Bureau)

a. According to these two models, when would you expect the population of Colorado to have exceeded the population of Alabama?

b. Use the two models to estimate the populations of both states in 2010.

TECHNOLOGY SUPPORT
> **TECHNOLOGY SUPPORT**
>
> For instructions on how to use the *value* feature, see Appendix A; for specific keystrokes, go to this textbook's *Online Study Center.*

Algebraic Solution

a. Because the first equation has already been solved for P in terms of t, you can substitute this value into the second equation and solve for t, as follows.

$$3488 + 81.9t = 4248 + 19.9t$$

$$81.9t - 19.9t = 4248 - 3488$$

$$62.0t = 760$$

$$t \approx 12.26$$

So, from the given models, you would expect that the population of Colorado exceeded the population of Alabama after $t \approx 12.26$ years, which was sometime during 2002.

b. To estimate the populations of both states in 2010, substitute $t = 20$ into each model and evaluate, as follows.

$P = 3488 + 81.9t$	Model for Colorado
$= 3488 + 81.9(20)$	Substitute 20 for t.
$= 5126$	Simplify.
$P = 4248 + 19.9t$	Model for Alabama
$= 4248 + 19.9(20)$	Substitute 20 for t.
$= 4646$	Simplify.

So, according to the models, Colorado's population in 2010 will be 5,126,000 and Alabama's population in 2010 will be 4,646,000.

✓CHECKPOINT   Now try Exercise 77.

Graphical Solution

a. Use a graphing utility to graph $y_1 = 3488 + 81.9x$ and $y_2 = 4248 + 19.9x$ in the same viewing window. Use the *intersect* feature or the *zoom* and *trace* features of the graphing utility to approximate the point of intersection of the graphs. The point of intersection occurs at $x \approx 12.26$, as shown in Figure 5.9. So, it appears that the population of Colorado exceeded the population of Alabama sometime during 2002.

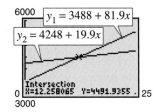

Figure 5.9

b. To estimate the populations of both states in 2010, use the *value* feature or the *zoom* and *trace* features of the graphing utility to find the value of y when $x = 20$. (Be sure to adjust your viewing window.) So, from Figure 5.10, you can see that Colorado's population in 2010 will be 5126 thousand, or 5,126,000, and Alabama's population in 2010 will be 4646 thousand, or 4,646,000.

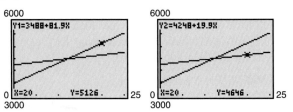

Figure 5.10

5.1 Exercises

See www.CalcChat.com for worked-out solutions to odd-numbered exercises.

Vocabulary Check

Fill in the blanks.

1. A set of two or more equations in two or more unknowns is called a _____ of _____ .

2. A _____ of a system of equations is an ordered pair that satisfies each equation in the system.

3. The first step in solving a system of equations by the _____ of _____ is to solve one of the equations for one variable in terms of the other variable.

4. Graphically, the solution to a system of equations is called the _____ of _____ .

5. In business applications, the _____ occurs when revenue equals cost.

In Exercises 1–4, determine whether each ordered pair is a solution of the system of equations.

1. $\begin{cases} 4x - y = 1 \\ 6x + y = -6 \end{cases}$
   (a) $(0, -3)$ (b) $(-1, -5)$ (c) $\left(-\frac{3}{2}, 3\right)$ (d) $\left(-\frac{1}{2}, -3\right)$

2. $\begin{cases} 4x^2 + y = 3 \\ -x - y = 11 \end{cases}$
   (a) $(2, -13)$ (b) $(-2, -9)$ (c) $\left(-\frac{3}{2}, 6\right)$ (d) $\left(-\frac{7}{4}, -\frac{37}{4}\right)$

3. $\begin{cases} y = -2e^x \\ 3x - y = 2 \end{cases}$
   (a) $(-2, 0)$ (b) $(0, -2)$ (c) $(0, -3)$ (d) $(-1, -5)$

4. $\begin{cases} -\log_{10} x + 3 = y \\ \frac{1}{9}x + y = \frac{28}{9} \end{cases}$
   (a) $(100, 1)$ (b) $(10, 2)$ (c) $(1, 3)$ (d) $(1, 1)$

In Exercises 5–12, solve the system by the method of substitution. Check your solution graphically.

5. $\begin{cases} 2x + y = 6 \\ -x + y = 0 \end{cases}$

6. $\begin{cases} x - y = -4 \\ x + 2y = 5 \end{cases}$

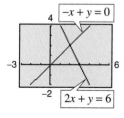

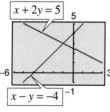

7. $\begin{cases} x - y = -4 \\ x^2 - y = -2 \end{cases}$

8. $\begin{cases} -2x + y = -5 \\ x^2 + y^2 = 25 \end{cases}$

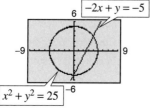
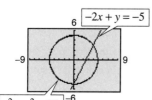

9. $\begin{cases} 3x + y = 2 \\ x^3 - 2 + y = 0 \end{cases}$

10. $\begin{cases} x + y = 0 \\ x^3 - 5x - y = 0 \end{cases}$

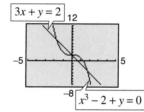
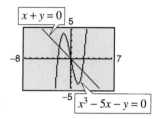

11. $\begin{cases} -\frac{7}{2}x - y = -18 \\ 8x^2 - 2y^3 = 0 \end{cases}$

12. $\begin{cases} y = x^3 - 3x^2 + 4 \\ y = -2x + 4 \end{cases}$

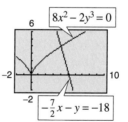
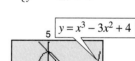

In Exercises 13–28, solve the system by the method of substitution. Use a graphing utility to verify your results.

13. $\begin{cases} x - y = 0 \\ 5x - 3y = 10 \end{cases}$

14. $\begin{cases} x + 2y = 1 \\ 5x - 4y = -23 \end{cases}$

15. $\begin{cases} 2x - y + 2 = 0 \\ 4x + y - 5 = 0 \end{cases}$

16. $\begin{cases} 6x - 3y - 4 = 0 \\ x + 2y - 4 = 0 \end{cases}$

17. $\begin{cases} 1.5x + 0.8y = 2.3 \\ 0.3x - 0.2y = 0.1 \end{cases}$

18. $\begin{cases} 0.5x + 3.2y = 9.0 \\ 0.2x - 1.6y = -3.6 \end{cases}$

19. $\begin{cases} \frac{1}{5}x + \frac{1}{2}y = 8 \\ x + y = 20 \end{cases}$

20. $\begin{cases} \frac{1}{2}x + \frac{3}{4}y = 10 \\ \frac{3}{4}x - y = 4 \end{cases}$

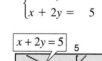

21. $\begin{cases} -\frac{5}{3}x + y = 5 \\ -5x + 3y = 6 \end{cases}$

22. $\begin{cases} -\frac{2}{3}x + y = 2 \\ 2x - 3y = 6 \end{cases}$

23. $\begin{cases} x^2 - 2x + y = 8 \\ x - y = -2 \end{cases}$

24. $\begin{cases} 2x^2 - 2x - y = 14 \\ 2x - y = -2 \end{cases}$

25. $\begin{cases} 2x^2 - y = 1 \\ x - y = 2 \end{cases}$

26. $\begin{cases} 2x^2 + y = 3 \\ x + y = 4 \end{cases}$

27. $\begin{cases} x^3 - y = 0 \\ x - y = 0 \end{cases}$

28. $\begin{cases} y = -x \\ y = x^3 + 3x^2 + 2x \end{cases}$

In Exercises 29–36, solve the system graphically. Verify your solutions algebraically.

29. $\begin{cases} -x + 2y = 2 \\ 3x + y = 15 \end{cases}$

30. $\begin{cases} x + y = 0 \\ 3x - 2y = 10 \end{cases}$

31. $\begin{cases} x - 3y = -2 \\ 5x + 3y = 17 \end{cases}$

32. $\begin{cases} -x + 2y = 1 \\ x - y = 2 \end{cases}$

33. $\begin{cases} x^2 + y = 1 \\ x + y = 2 \end{cases}$

34. $\begin{cases} x^2 - y = 4 \\ x - y = 2 \end{cases}$

35. $\begin{cases} -x + y = 3 \\ x^2 + y^2 - 6x - 27 = 0 \end{cases}$

36. $\begin{cases} y^2 - 4x + 11 = 0 \\ -\frac{1}{2}x + y = -\frac{1}{2} \end{cases}$

In Exercises 37–50, use a graphing utility to approximate all points of intersection of the graph of the system of equations. Round your results to three decimal places. Verify your solutions by checking them in the original system.

37. $\begin{cases} 7x + 8y = 24 \\ x - 8y = 8 \end{cases}$

38. $\begin{cases} x - y = 0 \\ 5x - 2y = 6 \end{cases}$

39. $\begin{cases} x - y^2 = -1 \\ x - y = 5 \end{cases}$

40. $\begin{cases} x - y^2 = -2 \\ x - 2y = 6 \end{cases}$

41. $\begin{cases} x^2 + y^2 = 8 \\ y = x^2 \end{cases}$

42. $\begin{cases} x^2 + y^2 = 25 \\ (x - 8)^2 + y^2 = 41 \end{cases}$

43. $\begin{cases} y = e^x \\ x - y + 1 = 0 \end{cases}$

44. $\begin{cases} y = -4e^{-x} \\ y + 3x + 8 = 0 \end{cases}$

45. $\begin{cases} x + 2y = 8 \\ y = 2 + \ln x \end{cases}$

46. $\begin{cases} y = -2 + \ln(x - 1) \\ 3y + 2x = 9 \end{cases}$

47. $\begin{cases} y = \sqrt{x} + 4 \\ y = 2x + 1 \end{cases}$

48. $\begin{cases} x - y = 3 \\ \sqrt{x} - y = 1 \end{cases}$

49. $\begin{cases} x^2 + y^2 = 169 \\ x^2 - 8y = 104 \end{cases}$

50. $\begin{cases} x^2 + y^2 = 4 \\ 2x^2 - y = 2 \end{cases}$

In Exercises 51–64, solve the system graphically or algebraically. Explain your choice of method.

51. $\begin{cases} 2x - y = 0 \\ x^2 - y = -1 \end{cases}$

52. $\begin{cases} x + y = 4 \\ x^2 + y = 2 \end{cases}$

53. $\begin{cases} 3x - 7y = -6 \\ x^2 - y^2 = 4 \end{cases}$

54. $\begin{cases} x^2 + y^2 = 25 \\ 2x + y = 10 \end{cases}$

55. $\begin{cases} x^2 + y^2 = 1 \\ x + y = 4 \end{cases}$

56. $\begin{cases} x^2 + y^2 = 4 \\ x - y = 5 \end{cases}$

57. $\begin{cases} y = 2x + 1 \\ y = \sqrt{x + 2} \end{cases}$

58. $\begin{cases} y = 2x - 1 \\ y = \sqrt{x + 1} \end{cases}$

59. $\begin{cases} y - e^{-x} = 1 \\ y - \ln x = 3 \end{cases}$

60. $\begin{cases} 2 \ln x + y = 4 \\ e^x - y = 0 \end{cases}$

61. $\begin{cases} y = x^3 - 2x^2 + 1 \\ y = 1 - x^2 \end{cases}$

62. $\begin{cases} y = x^3 - 2x^2 + x - 1 \\ y = -x^2 + 3x - 1 \end{cases}$

63. $\begin{cases} xy - 1 = 0 \\ 2x - 4y + 7 = 0 \end{cases}$

64. $\begin{cases} xy - 2 = 0 \\ 3x - 2y + 4 = 0 \end{cases}$

Break-Even Analysis **In Exercises 65–68, use a graphing utility to graph the cost and revenue functions in the same viewing window. Find the sales x necessary to break even $(R = C)$ and the corresponding revenue R obtained by selling x units. (Round to the nearest whole unit.)**

Cost	*Revenue*
65. $C = 8650x + 250,000$	$R = 9950x$
66. $C = 2.65x + 350,000$	$R = 4.15x$
67. $C = 5.5\sqrt{x} + 10,000$	$R = 3.29x$
68. $C = 7.8\sqrt{x} + 18,500$	$R = 12.84x$

69. ***DVD Rentals*** The daily DVD rentals of a newly released animated film and a newly released horror film from a movie rental store can be modeled by the equations

$\begin{cases} N = 360 - 24x & \text{Animated film} \\ N = 24 + 18x & \text{Horror film} \end{cases}$

where N is the number of DVDs rented and x represents the week, with $x = 1$ corresponding to the first week of release.

(a) Use the *table* feature of a graphing utility to find the numbers of rentals of each movie for each of the first 12 weeks of release.

(b) Use the results of part (a) to determine the solution to the system of equations.

(c) Solve the system of equations algebraically.

(d) Compare your results from parts (b) and (c).

(e) Interpret the results in the context of the situation.

70. *Sports* The points scored during each of the first 12 games by two players on a girl's high school basketball team can be modeled by the equations

$$\begin{cases} P_S = 24 - 2x & \text{Sofia} \\ P_P = 12 + 2x & \text{Paige} \end{cases}$$

where P represents the points scored by each player and x represents the number of games played, with $x = 1$ corresponding to the first game.

(a) Use the *table* feature of a graphing utility to find the numbers of points scored by each player for each of the first 12 games.

(b) Use the results of part (a) to determine the solution to the system of equations.

(c) Solve the system of equations algebraically.

(d) Compare your results from parts (b) and (c).

(e) Interpret the results in the context of the situation.

71. *Break-Even Analysis* A small software company invests $16,000 to produce a software package that will sell for $55.95. Each unit can be produced for $35.45.

(a) Write the cost and revenue functions for x units produced and sold.

(b) Use a graphing utility to graph the cost and revenue functions in the same viewing window. Use the graph to approximate the number of units that must be sold to break even, and verify the result algebraically.

72. *Break-Even Analysis* A small fast food restaurant invests $5000 to produce a new food item that will sell for $3.49. Each item can be produced for $2.16.

(a) Write the cost and revenue functions for x items produced and sold.

(b) Use a graphing utility to graph the cost and revenue functions in the same viewing window. Use the graph to approximate the number of items that must be sold to break even, and verify the result algebraically.

73. *Choice of Two Jobs* You are offered two different jobs selling dental supplies. One company offers a straight commission of 6% of sales. The other company offers a salary of $350 per week plus 3% of sales. How much would you have to sell in a week in order to make the straight commission offer the better offer?

74. *Choice of Two Jobs* You are offered two jobs selling college textbooks. One company offers an annual salary of $25,000 plus a year-end bonus of 1% of your total sales. The other company offers an annual salary of $20,000 plus a year-end bonus of 2% of your total sales. How much would you have to sell in a year to make the second offer better offer?

75. *Investment* A total of $20,000 is invested in two funds paying 6.5% and 8.5% simple interest. The 6.5% investment has a lower risk. The investor wants a yearly interest check of $1600 from the investments.

(a) Write a system of equations in which one equation represents the total amount invested and the other equation represents the $1600 required in interest. Let x and y represent the amounts invested at 6.5% and 8.5%, respectively.

(b) Use a graphing utility to graph the two equations in the same viewing window. As the amount invested at 6.5% increases, how does the amount invested at 8.5% change? How does the amount of interest change? Explain.

(c) What amount should be invested at 6.5% to meet the requirement of $1600 per year in interest?

76. *Log Volume* You are offered two different rules for estimating the number of board feet in a 16-foot log. (A board foot is a unit of measure for lumber equal to a board 1 foot square and 1 inch thick.) One rule is the *Doyle Log Rule* and is modeled by

$$V = (D - 4)^2, \quad 5 \le D \le 40$$

and the other rule is the *Scribner Log Rule* and is modeled by

$$V = 0.79D^2 - 2D - 4, \quad 5 \le D \le 40$$

where D is the diameter (in inches) of the log and V is its volume in (board feet).

(a) Use a graphing utility to graph the two log rules in the same viewing window.

(b) For what diameter do the two rules agree?

(c) You are selling large logs by the board foot. Which rule would you use? Explain your reasoning.

77. *Population* The populations (in thousands) of Missouri M and Tennessee T from 1990 to 2004 can by modeled by the system

$$\begin{cases} M = 47.4t + 5104 & \text{Missouri} \\ T = 76.5t + 4875 & \text{Tennessee} \end{cases}$$

where t is the year, with $t = 0$ corresponding to 1990. (Source: U.S. Census Bureau)

(a) Record in a table the populations of the two states for the years 1990, 1994, 1998, 2002, 2006, and 2010.

(b) According to the table, over what period of time does the population of Tennessee exceed that of Missouri?

(c) Use a graphing utility to graph the models in the same viewing window. Estimate the point of intersection of the models.

(d) Find the point of intersection algebraically.

(e) Summarize your findings of parts (b) through (d).

78. *Tuition* The table shows the average costs (in dollars) of one year's tuition for public and private universities in the United States from 2000 to 2004. (Source: U.S. National Center for Education Statistics)

Year	Public universities	Private universities
2000	2506	14,081
2001	2562	15,000
2002	2700	15,742
2003	2903	16,383
2004	3313	17,442

(a) Use the *regression* feature of a graphing utility to find a quadratic model T_{public} for tuition at public universities and a linear model $T_{private}$ for tuition at private universities. Let x represent the year, with $x = 0$ corresponding to 2000.

(b) Use a graphing utility to graph the models with the original data in the same viewing window.

(c) Use the graph in part (b) to determine the year after 2004 in which tuition at public universities will exceed tuition at private universities.

(d) Algebraically determine the year in which tuition at public universities will exceed tuition at private universities.

(e) Compare your results from parts (c) and (d).

Geometry **In Exercises 79 and 80, find the dimensions of the rectangle meeting the specified conditions.**

79. The perimeter is 30 meters and the length is 3 meters greater than the width.

80. The perimeter is 280 centimeters and the width is 20 centimeters less than the length.

81. *Geometry* What are the dimensions of a rectangular tract of land if its perimeter is 40 miles and its area is 96 square miles?

82. *Geometry* What are the dimensions of an isosceles right triangle with a two-inch hypotenuse and an area of 1 square inch?

Synthesis

True or False? **In Exercises 83 and 84, determine whether the statement is true or false. Justify your answer.**

83. In order to solve a system of equations by substitution, you must always solve for y in one of the two equations and then back-substitute.

84. If a system consists of a parabola and a circle, then it can have at most two solutions.

85. *Think About It* When solving a system of equations by substitution, how do you recognize that the system has no solution?

86. *Writing* Write a brief paragraph describing any advantages of substitution over the graphical method of solving a system of equations.

87. *Exploration* Find the equations of lines whose graphs intersect the graph of the parabola $y = x^2$ at (a) two points, (b) one point, and (c) no points. (There are many correct answers.)

88. *Exploration* Create systems of two linear equations in two variables that have (a) no solution, (b) one distinct solution, and (c) infinitely many solutions. (There are many correct answers.)

89. *Exploration* Create a system of linear equations in two variables that has the solution $(2, -1)$ as its only solution. (There are many correct answers.)

90. *Conjecture* Consider the system of equations.

$$\begin{cases} y = b^x \\ y = x^b \end{cases}$$

(a) Use a graphing utility to graph the system of equations for $b = 2$ and $b = 4$.

(b) For a fixed value of $b > 1$, make a conjecture about the number of points of intersection of the graphs in part (a).

Skills Review

In Exercises 91–96, find the general form of the equation of the line passing through the two points.

91. $(-2, 7), (5, 5)$ **92.** $(3, 4), (10, 6)$

93. $(6, 3), (10, 3)$ **94.** $(4, -2), (4, 5)$

95. $\left(\frac{3}{5}, 0\right), (4, 6)$ **96.** $\left(-\frac{7}{3}, 8\right), \left(\frac{5}{2}, \frac{1}{2}\right)$

In Exercises 97–102, find the domain of the function and identify any horizontal or vertical asymptotes.

97. $f(x) = \dfrac{5}{x - 6}$ **98.** $f(x) = \dfrac{2x - 7}{3x + 2}$

99. $f(x) = \dfrac{x^2 + 2}{x^2 - 16}$ **100.** $f(x) = 3 - \dfrac{2}{x^2}$

101. $f(x) = \dfrac{x + 1}{x^2 + 1}$ **102.** $f(x) = \dfrac{x - 4}{x^2 + 16}$

5.2 Systems of Linear Equations in Two Variables

The Method of Elimination

In Section 5.1, you studied two methods for solving a system of equations: substitution and graphing. Now you will study the **method of elimination** to solve a system of linear equations in two variables. The key step in this method is to obtain, for one of the variables, coefficients that differ only in sign so that *adding* the equations eliminates the variable.

$$
\begin{aligned}
3x + 5y &= 7 \qquad &\text{Equation 1}\\
-3x - 2y &= -1 \qquad &\text{Equation 2}\\
\hline
3y &= 6 \qquad &\text{Add equations.}
\end{aligned}
$$

Note that by adding the two equations, you eliminate the x-terms and obtain a single equation in y. Solving this equation for y produces $y = 2$, which you can then back-substitute into one of the original equations to solve for x.

Example 1 Solving a System by Elimination

Solve the system of linear equations.

$$
\begin{cases}
3x + 2y = 4 \qquad & \text{Equation 1}\\
5x - 2y = 8 \qquad & \text{Equation 2}
\end{cases}
$$

Solution

You can eliminate the y-terms by adding the two equations.

$$
\begin{aligned}
3x + 2y &= 4 \qquad & \text{Write Equation 1.}\\
5x - 2y &= 8 \qquad & \text{Write Equation 2.}\\
\hline
8x &= 12 \qquad & \text{Add equations.}
\end{aligned}
$$

So, $x = \frac{3}{2}$. By back-substituting into Equation 1, you can solve for y.

$$
\begin{aligned}
3x + 2y &= 4 \qquad & \text{Write Equation 1.}\\
3\left(\tfrac{3}{2}\right) + 2y &= 4 \qquad & \text{Substitute } \tfrac{3}{2} \text{ for } x.\\
y &= -\tfrac{1}{4} \qquad & \text{Solve for } y.
\end{aligned}
$$

The solution is $\left(\frac{3}{2}, -\frac{1}{4}\right)$. You can check the solution *algebraically* by substituting into the original system, or graphically as shown in Section 5.1.

Check

$$
\begin{aligned}
3\left(\tfrac{3}{2}\right) + 2\left(-\tfrac{1}{4}\right) &\overset{?}{=} 4 \qquad & \text{Substitute into Equation 1.}\\
\tfrac{9}{2} - \tfrac{1}{2} &= 4 \qquad & \text{Equation 1 checks. } \checkmark\\
5\left(\tfrac{3}{2}\right) - 2\left(-\tfrac{1}{4}\right) &\overset{?}{=} 8 \qquad & \text{Substitute into Equation 2.}\\
\tfrac{15}{2} + \tfrac{1}{2} &= 8 \qquad & \text{Equation 2 checks. } \checkmark
\end{aligned}
$$

✓CHECKPOINT   Now try Exercise 7.

What you should learn

- Use the method of elimination to solve systems of linear equations in two variables.
- Graphically interpret the number of solutions of a system of linear equations in two variables.
- Use systems of linear equations in two variables to model and solve real-life problems.

Why you should learn it

You can use systems of linear equations to model many business applications. For instance, Exercise 76 on page 425 shows how to use a system of linear equations to compare sales of two competing companies.

Spencer Platt/Getty Images

Exploration

Use the method of substitution to solve the system given in Example 1. Which method is easier?

> ### The Method of Elimination
>
> To use the **method of elimination** to solve a system of two linear equations in x and y, perform the following steps.
>
>   1. Obtain coefficients for x (or y) that differ only in sign by multiplying all terms of one or both equations by suitably chosen constants.
>
>   2. Add the equations to eliminate one variable; solve the resulting equation.
>
>   3. Back-substitute the value obtained in Step 2 into either of the original equations and solve for the other variable.
>
>   4. Check your solution in both of the original equations.

Example 2   Solving a System by Elimination

Solve the system of linear equations.

$$\begin{cases} 5x + 3y = 9 & \text{Equation 1} \\ 2x - 4y = 14 & \text{Equation 2} \end{cases}$$

Algebraic Solution

You can obtain coefficients of y that differ only in sign by multiplying Equation 1 by 4 and multiplying Equation 2 by 3.

$5x + 3y = 9$ ⟹ $20x + 12y = 36$ Multiply Equation 1 by 4.

$\underline{2x - 4y = 14}$ ⟹ $\underline{6x - 12y = 42}$ Multiply Equation 2 by 3.

$26x \qquad = 78$ Add equations.

From this equation, you can see that $x = 3$. By back-substituting this value of x into Equation 2, you can solve for y.

$2x - 4y = 14$ Write Equation 2.

$2(3) - 4y = 14$ Substitute 3 for x.

$-4y = 8$ Combine like terms.

$y = -2$ Solve for y.

The solution is $(3, -2)$. You can check the solution algebraically by substituting into the original system.

Graphical Solution

Solve each equation for y. Then use a graphing utility to graph $y_1 = 3 - \frac{5}{3}x$ and $y_2 = -\frac{7}{2} + \frac{1}{2}x$ in the same viewing window. Use the *intersect* feature or the *zoom* and *trace* features to approximate the point of intersection of the graphs. The point of intersection is $(3, -2)$, as shown in Figure 5.11. You can determine that this is the exact solution by checking $(3, -2)$ in both equations.

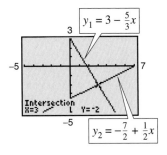

Figure 5.11

✓CHECKPOINT   Now try Exercise 9.

In Example 2, the original system and the system obtained by multiplying by constants are called **equivalent systems** because they have precisely the same solution set. The operations that can be performed on a system of linear equations to produce an equivalent system are (1) interchanging any two equations, (2) multiplying an equation by a nonzero constant, and (3) adding a multiple of one equation to any other equation in the system.

Graphical Interpretation of Two-Variable Systems

It is possible for any system of equations to have exactly one solution, two or more solutions, or no solution. If a system of *linear* equations has two different solutions, it must have an *infinite* number of solutions. To see why this is true, consider the following graphical interpretations of a system of two linear equations in two variables.

Graphical Interpretation of Solutions

For a system of two linear equations in two variables, the number of solutions is one of the following.

Number of Solutions	*Graphical Interpretation*
1. Exactly one solution	The two lines intersect at one point.
2. Infinitely many solutions	The two lines are coincident (identical).
3. No solution	The two lines are parallel.

A system of linear equations is **consistent** if it has at least one solution. It is **inconsistent** if it has no solution.

Example 3   Recognizing Graphs of Linear Systems

Match each system of linear equations (a, b, c) with its graph (i, ii, iii) in Figure 5.12. Describe the number of solutions. Then state whether the system is consistent or inconsistent.

a. $\begin{cases} 2x - 3y = 3 \\ -4x + 6y = 6 \end{cases}$ **b.** $\begin{cases} 2x - 3y = 3 \\ x + 2y = 5 \end{cases}$ **c.** $\begin{cases} 2x - 3y = 3 \\ -4x + 6y = -6 \end{cases}$

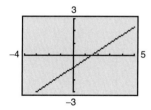   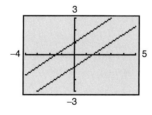   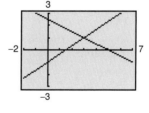

i.   **ii.**   **iii.**

Figure 5.12

Solution

a. The graph is a pair of parallel lines (ii). The lines have no point of intersection, so the system has no solution. The system is inconsistent.

b. The graph is a pair of intersecting lines (iii). The lines have one point of intersection, so the system has exactly one solution. The system is consistent.

c. The graph is a pair of lines that coincide (i). The lines have infinitely many points of intersection, so the system has infinitely many solutions. The system is consistent.

✔CHECKPOINT   Now try Exercises 17–20.

> ### Exploration
>
> Rewrite each system of equations in slope-intercept form and use a graphing utility to graph each system. What is the relationship between the slopes of the two lines and the number of points of intersection?
>
> **a.** $\begin{cases} y = 5x + 1 \\ y - x = -5 \end{cases}$
>
> **b.** $\begin{cases} 3y = 4x - 1 \\ -8x + 2 = -6y \end{cases}$
>
> **c.** $\begin{cases} 2y = -x + 3 \\ -4 = y + \frac{1}{2}x \end{cases}$

> ### Prerequisite Skills
>
> If you have difficulty with this example, review graphing of linear equations in Section 1.2.

In Examples 4 and 5, note how you can use the method of elimination to determine that a system of linear equations has no solution or infinitely many solutions.

Example 4   The Method of Elimination: No–Solution Case

Solve the system of linear equations.

$$\begin{cases} x - 2y = 3 & \text{Equation 1} \\ -2x + 4y = 1 & \text{Equation 2} \end{cases}$$

Algebraic Solution

To obtain coefficients that differ only in sign, multiply Equation 1 by 2.

$$x - 2y = 3 \implies 2x - 4y = 6$$

$$\underline{-2x + 4y = 1} \implies \underline{-2x + 4y = 1}$$

$$0 = 7$$

By adding the equations, you obtain $0 = 7$. Because there are no values of x and y for which $0 = 7$, this is a false statement. So, you can conclude that the system is inconsistent and has no solution.

Graphical Solution

Solving each equation for y yields $y_1 = -\frac{3}{2} + \frac{1}{2}x$ and $y_2 = \frac{1}{4} + \frac{1}{2}x$. Notice that the lines have the same slope and different y-intercepts, so they are parallel. You can use a graphing utility to verify this by graphing both equations in the same viewing window, as shown in Figure 5.13. Then try using the *intersect* feature to find a point of intersection. Because the graphing utility cannot find a point of intersection, you will get an error message. Therefore, the system has no solution.

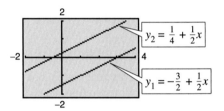

Figure 5.13

✓CHECKPOINT   Now try Exercise 23.

Example 5   The Method of Elimination: Infinitely Many Solutions Case

Solve the system of linear equations: $\begin{cases} 2x - y = 1 & \text{Equation 1} \\ 4x - 2y = 2 & \text{Equation 2} \end{cases}$.

Solution

To obtain coefficients that differ only in sign, multiply Equation 1 by -2.

$$2x - y = 1 \implies -4x + 2y = -2 \qquad \text{Multiply Equation 1 by } -2.$$

$$\underline{4x - 2y = 2} \implies \underline{4x - 2y = 2} \qquad \text{Write Equation 2.}$$

$$0 = 0 \qquad \text{Add equations.}$$

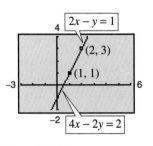

Because $0 = 0$ for all values of x and y, the two equations turn out to be equivalent (have the same solution set). You can conclude that the system has infinitely many solutions. The solution set consists of all points (x, y) lying on the line $2x - y = 1$, as shown in Figure 5.14.

Figure 5.14

✓CHECKPOINT   Now try Exercise 25.

In Example 4, note that the occurrence of the false statement $0 = 7$ indicates that the system has no solution. In Example 5, note that the occurrence of a statement that is true for all values of the variables—in this case, $0 = 0$—indicates that the system has infinitely many solutions.

Example 6 illustrates a strategy for solving a system of linear equations that has decimal coefficients.

Example 6   A Linear System Having Decimal Coefficients

Solve the system of linear equations.

$$\begin{cases} 0.02x - 0.05y = -0.38 & \text{Equation 1} \\ 0.03x + 0.04y = 1.04 & \text{Equation 2} \end{cases}$$

Solution

Because the coefficients in this system have two decimal places, you can begin by multiplying each equation by 100 to produce a system with integer coefficients.

$$\begin{cases} 2x - 5y = -38 & \text{Revised Equation 1} \\ 3x + 4y = 104 & \text{Revised Equation 2} \end{cases}$$

Now, to obtain coefficients that differ only in sign, multiply revised Equation 1 by 3 and multiply revised Equation 2 by -2.

$$2x - 5y = -38 \quad \Longrightarrow \quad 6x - 15y = -114 \qquad \text{Multiply revised Equation 1 by 3.}$$

$$\underline{3x + 4y = 104} \quad \Longrightarrow \quad \underline{-6x - 8y = -208} \qquad \text{Multiply revised Equation 2 by } -2.$$

$$-23y = -322 \qquad \text{Add equations.}$$

So, you can conclude that $y = \dfrac{-322}{-23} = 14$. Back-substituting this value into revised Equation 2 produces the following.

$$3x + 4y = 104 \qquad \text{Write revised Equation 2.}$$

$$3x + 4(14) = 104 \qquad \text{Substitute 14 for } y.$$

$$3x = 48 \qquad \text{Combine like terms.}$$

$$x = 16 \qquad \text{Solve for } x.$$

The solution is $(16, 14)$. Check this as follows in the original system.

Check $(16, 14)$ in Equation 1:

$$0.02x - 0.05y = -0.38 \qquad \text{Write Equation 1.}$$

$$0.02(16) - 0.05(14) \overset{?}{=} -0.38 \qquad \text{Substitute for } x \text{ and } y.$$

$$-0.38 = 0.38 \qquad \text{Solution checks in Equation 1.}$$

Check $(16, 14)$ in Equation 2:

$$0.03x + 0.04y = 1.04 \qquad \text{Write Equation 2.}$$

$$0.03(16) + 0.04(14) \overset{?}{=} 1.04 \qquad \text{Substitute for } x \text{ and } y.$$

$$1.04 = 1.04 \qquad \text{Solution checks in Equation 2.}$$

✔CHECKPOINT   Now try Exercise 33.

Application

At this point, you may be asking the question "How can I tell which application problems can be solved using a system of linear equations?" The answer comes from the following considerations.

1. Does the problem involve more than one unknown quantity?

2. Are there two (or more) equations or conditions to be satisfied?

If one or both of these conditions are met, the appropriate mathematical model for the problem may be a system of linear equations.

Example 7   An Application of a Linear System

An airplane flying into a headwind travels the 2000-mile flying distance between Cleveland, Ohio and Fresno, California in 4 hours and 24 minutes. On the return flight, the same distance is traveled in 4 hours. Find the airspeed of the plane and the speed of the wind, assuming that both remain constant.

Solution

The two unknown quantities are the speeds of the wind and the plane. If r_1 is the speed of the plane and r_2 is the speed of the wind, then

$r_1 - r_2 =$ speed of the plane *against* the wind

$r_1 + r_2 =$ speed of the plane *with* the wind

as shown in Figure 5.15. Using the formula distance = (rate)(time) for these two speeds, you obtain the following equations.

$$2000 = (r_1 - r_2)\left(4 + \frac{24}{60}\right)$$

$$2000 = (r_1 + r_2)(4)$$

These two equations simplify as follows.

$$\begin{cases} 5000 = 11r_1 - 11r_2 & \text{Equation 1} \\ 500 = r_1 + r_2 & \text{Equation 2} \end{cases}$$

Original flight

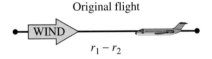

$r_1 - r_2$

Return flight

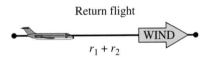

$r_1 + r_2$

Figure 5.15

To solve this system by elimination, multiply Equation 2 by 11.

$5000 = 11r_1 - 11r_2$ ⟹ $5000 = 11r_1 - 11r_2$ Write Equation 1.

$\underline{500 = r_1 + r_2}$ ⟹ $\underline{5500 = 11r_1 + 11r_2}$ Multiply Equation 2 by 11.

$10{,}500 = 22r_1$ Add equations.

So,

$$r_1 = \frac{10{,}500}{22} = \frac{5250}{11} \approx 477.27 \text{ miles per hour} \qquad \text{Speed of plane}$$

$$r_2 = 500 - \frac{5250}{11} = \frac{250}{11} \approx 22.73 \text{ miles per hour.} \qquad \text{Speed of wind}$$

Check this solution in the original statement of the problem.

✓CHECKPOINT   Now try Exercise 71.

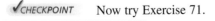

5.2 Exercises

See www.CalcChat.com for worked-out solutions to odd-numbered exercises.

Vocabulary Check

Fill in the blanks.

1. The first step in solving a system of equations by the _____ of _____ is to obtain coefficients for x (or y) that differ only in sign.

2. Two systems of equations that have the same solution set are called _____ systems.

3. A system of linear equations that has at least one solution is called _____ , whereas a system of linear equations that has no solution is called _____ .

In Exercises 1–6, solve the system by the method of elimination. Label each line with its equation.

1. $\begin{cases} 2x + y = 5 \\ x - y = 1 \end{cases}$ 2. $\begin{cases} x + 3y = 1 \\ -x + 2y = 4 \end{cases}$

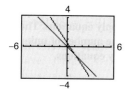

3. $\begin{cases} x + y = 0 \\ 3x + 2y = 1 \end{cases}$ 4. $\begin{cases} 2x - y = 3 \\ 4x + 3y = 21 \end{cases}$

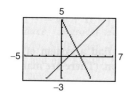   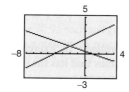

5. $\begin{cases} x - y = 2 \\ -2x + 2y = 5 \end{cases}$ 6. $\begin{cases} 3x - 2y = 5 \\ -6x + 4y = -10 \end{cases}$

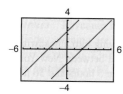   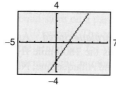

Exercises 7–16, solve the system by the method of elimination and check any solutions algebraically.

7. $\begin{cases} x + 2y = 4 \\ x - 2y = 1 \end{cases}$ 8. $\begin{cases} 3x - 2y = 5 \\ x + 2y = 7 \end{cases}$

9. $\begin{cases} 2x + 3y = 18 \\ 5x - y = 11 \end{cases}$ 10. $\begin{cases} x + 7y = 12 \\ 3x - 5y = 10 \end{cases}$

11. $\begin{cases} 3r + 2s = 10 \\ 2r + 5s = 3 \end{cases}$ 12. $\begin{cases} 2r + 4s = 5 \\ 16r + 50s = 55 \end{cases}$

13. $\begin{cases} 5u + 6v = 24 \\ 3u + 5v = 18 \end{cases}$ 14. $\begin{cases} 3u + 11v = 4 \\ -2u - 5v = 9 \end{cases}$

15. $\begin{cases} 1.8x + 1.2y = 4 \\ 9x + 6y = 3 \end{cases}$ 16. $\begin{cases} 3.1x - 2.9y = -10.2 \\ 31x - 12y = 34 \end{cases}$

In Exercises 17–20, match the system of linear equations with its graph. Give the number of solutions. Then state whether the system is consistent or inconsistent. [The graphs are labeled (a), (b), (c), and (d).]

(a)   (b)

(c)   (d)

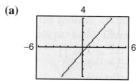   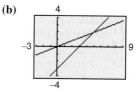

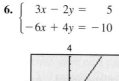   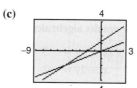

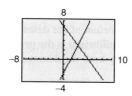   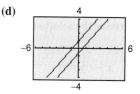

17. $\begin{cases} 2x - 5y = 0 \\ x - y = 3 \end{cases}$ 18. $\begin{cases} -7x + 6y = -4 \\ 14x - 12y = 8 \end{cases}$

19. $\begin{cases} 2x - 5y = 0 \\ 2x - 3y = -4 \end{cases}$ 20. $\begin{cases} 7x - 6y = -6 \\ -7x + 6y = -4 \end{cases}$

In Exercises 21–40, solve the system by the method of elimination and check any solutions using a graphing utility.

21. $\begin{cases} 4x + 3y = 3 \\ 3x + 11y = 13 \end{cases}$ 22. $\begin{cases} 2x + 5y = 8 \\ 5x + 8y = 10 \end{cases}$

84. *Data Analysis*   A candy store manager wants to know the demand y for a candy bar as a function of the price x. The daily sales for different prices of the product are shown in the table.

Price, x	Demand, y
$1.00	45
$1.20	37
$1.50	23

(a) Find the least squares regression line $y = ax + b$ for the data by solving the system for a and b.

$$\begin{cases} 3.00b + 3.70a = 105.00 \\ 3.70b + 4.69a = 123.90 \end{cases}$$

(b) Use the *regression* feature of a graphing utility to confirm the result in part (a).

(c) Use a graphing utility to plot the data and graph the linear model from part (a) in the same viewing window.

(d) Use the linear model from part (a) to predict the demand when the price is $1.75.

Synthesis

True or False?   In Exercises 85 and 86, determine whether the statement is true or false. Justify your answer.

85. If a system of linear equations has two distinct solutions, then it has an infinite number of solutions.

86. If a system of linear equations has no solution, then the lines must be parallel.

Think About It   In Exercises 87 and 88, the graphs of the two equations appear to be parallel. Yet, when the system is solved algebraically, it is found that the system does have a solution. Find the solution and explain why it does not appear on the portion of the graph that is shown.

87. $\begin{cases} 100y - x = 200 \\ 99y - x = -198 \end{cases}$ **88.** $\begin{cases} 21x - 20y = 0 \\ 13x - 12y = 120 \end{cases}$

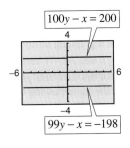

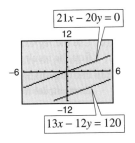

89. *Writing*   Briefly explain whether or not it is possible for a consistent system of linear equations to have exactly two solutions.

90. *Think About It*   Give examples of (a) a system of linear equations that has no solution and (b) a system of linear equations that has an infinite number of solutions.

In Exercises 91 and 92, find the value of k such that the system of equations is inconsistent.

91. $\begin{cases} 4x - 8y = -3 \\ 2x + ky = 16 \end{cases}$

92. $\begin{cases} 15x + 3y = 6 \\ -10x + ky = 9 \end{cases}$

∫ *Advanced Applications*   In Exercises 93 and 94, solve the system of equations for u and v. While solving for these variables, consider the transcendental functions as constants. (Systems of this type are found in a course in differential equations.)

93. $\begin{cases} ue^x + vxe^x = 0 \\ ue^x + v(x + 1)e^x = e^x \ln x \end{cases}$

94. $\begin{cases} ue^{2x} + vxe^{2x} = 0 \\ u(2e^{2x}) + v(2x + 1)e^{2x} = \dfrac{e^{2x}}{x} \end{cases}$

Skills Review

In Exercises 95–100, solve the inequality and graph the solution on a real number line.

95. $-11 - 6x \geq 33$ **96.** $-6 \leq 3x - 10 < 6$

97. $|x - 8| < 10$ **98.** $|x + 10| \geq -3$

99. $2x^2 + 3x - 35 < 0$ **100.** $3x^2 + 12x > 0$

In Exercises 101–106, write the expression as the logarithm of a single quantity.

101. $\ln x + \ln 6$ **102.** $\ln x - 5\ln(x + 3)$

103. $\log_9 12 - \log_9 x$ **104.** $\frac{1}{4}\log_6 3 + \frac{1}{4}\log_6 x$

105. $2\ln x - \ln(x + 2)$ **106.** $\frac{1}{2}\ln(x^2 + 4) - \ln x$

107. *Make a Decision*   To work an extended application analyzing the average undergraduate tuition, room, and board charges at private colleges in the United States from 1985 to 2004, visit this textbook's *Online Study Center.* (Data Source: U.S. Census Bureau)

5.3 Multivariable Linear Systems

Row-Echelon Form and Back-Substitution

The method of elimination can be applied to a system of linear equations in more than two variables. When elimination is used to solve a system of linear equations, the goal is to rewrite the system in a form to which back-substitution can be applied. To see how this works, consider the following two systems of linear equations.

System of Three Linear Equations in Three Variables (See Example 2):

$$\begin{cases} x - 2y + 3z = 9 \\ -x + 3y + z = -2 \\ 2x - 5y + 5z = 17 \end{cases}$$

Equivalent System in Row-Echelon Form (See Example 1):

$$\begin{cases} x - 2y + 3z = 9 \\ y + 4z = 7 \\ z = 2 \end{cases}$$

The second system is said to be in **row-echelon form,** which means that it has a "stair-step" pattern with leading coefficients of 1. After comparing the two systems, it should be clear that it is easier to solve the system in row-echelon form, using back-substitution.

Example 1 Using Back-Substitution in Row-Echelon Form

Solve the system of linear equations.

$$\begin{cases} x - 2y + 3z = 9 & \text{Equation 1} \\ y + 4z = 7 & \text{Equation 2} \\ z = 2 & \text{Equation 3} \end{cases}$$

Solution

From Equation 3, you know the value of z. To solve for y, substitute $z = 2$ into Equation 2 to obtain

$$y + 4(2) = 7 \qquad \text{Substitute 2 for } z.$$
$$y = -1. \qquad \text{Solve for } y.$$

Finally, substitute $y = -1$ and $z = 2$ into Equation 1 to obtain

$$x - 2(-1) + 3(2) = 9 \qquad \text{Substitute } -1 \text{ for } y \text{ and 2 for } z.$$
$$x = 1. \qquad \text{Solve for } x.$$

The solution is $x = 1$, $y = -1$, and $z = 2$, which can be written as the **ordered triple** $(1, -1, 2)$. Check this in the original system of equations.

✓**CHECKPOINT**   Now try Exercise 5.

What you should learn

- Use back-substitution to solve linear systems in row-echelon form.
- Use Gaussian elimination to solve systems of linear equations.
- Solve nonsquare systems of linear equations.
- Graphically interpret three-variable linear systems.
- Use systems of linear equations to write partial fraction decompositions of rational expressions.
- Use systems of linear equations in three or more variables to model and solve real-life problems.

Why you should learn it

Systems of linear equations in three or more variables can be used to model and solve real-life problems. For instance, Exercise 105 on page 440 shows how to use a system of linear equations to analyze the numbers of par-3, par-4, and par-5 holes on a golf course.

AP/Wide World Photos

Gaussian Elimination

Two systems of equations are *equivalent* if they have the same solution set. To solve a system that is not in row-echelon form, first convert it to an *equivalent* system that *is* in row-echelon form by using one or more of the elementary row operations shown below. This process is called **Gaussian elimination,** after the German mathematician Carl Friedrich Gauss (1777–1855).

> **Elementary Row Operations for Systems of Equations**
>
> **1.** Interchange two equations.
>
> **2.** Multiply one of the equations by a nonzero constant.
>
> **3.** Add a multiple of one equation to another equation.

Example 2 Using Gaussian Elimination to Solve a System

Solve the system of linear equations.

$$\begin{cases} x - 2y + 3z = 9 & \text{Equation 1} \\ -x + 3y + z = -2 & \text{Equation 2} \\ 2x - 5y + 5z = 17 & \text{Equation 3} \end{cases}$$

Solution

Because the leading coefficient of the first equation is 1, you can begin by saving the x at the upper left and eliminating the other x-terms from the first column.

$$\begin{cases} x - 2y + 3z = 9 \\ y + 4z = 7 \\ 2x - 5y + 5z = 17 \end{cases}$$

Adding the first equation to the second equation produces a new second equation.

$$\begin{cases} x - 2y + 3z = 9 \\ y + 4z = 7 \\ -y - z = -1 \end{cases}$$

Adding -2 times the first equation to the third equation produces a new third equation.

Now that all but the first x have been eliminated from the first column, go to work on the second column. (You need to eliminate y from the third equation.)

$$\begin{cases} x - 2y + 3z = 9 \\ y + 4z = 7 \\ 3z = 6 \end{cases}$$

Adding the second equation to the third equation produces a new third equation.

Finally, you need a coefficient of 1 for z in the third equation.

$$\begin{cases} x - 2y + 3z = 9 \\ y + 4z = 7 \\ z = 2 \end{cases}$$

Multiplying the third equation by $\frac{1}{3}$ produces a new third equation.

This is the same system that was solved in Example 1. As in that example, you can conclude that the solution is $x = 1$, $y = -1$, and $z = 2$, written as $(1, -1, 2)$.

✓CHECKPOINT   Now try Exercise 15.

STUDY TIP

Arithmetic errors are often made when elementary row operations are performed. You should note the operation performed in each step so that you can go back and check your work.

The goal of Gaussian elimination is to use elementary row operations on a system in order to isolate one variable. You can then solve for the value of the variable and use back-substitution to find the values of the remaining variables.

The next example involves an inconsistent system—one that has no solution. The key to recognizing an inconsistent system is that at some stage in the elimination process, you obtain a false statement such as $0 = -2$.

Example 3   An Inconsistent System

Solve the system of linear equations.

$$\begin{cases} x - 3y + z = 1 & \text{Equation 1} \\ 2x - y - 2z = 2 & \text{Equation 2} \\ x + 2y - 3z = -1 & \text{Equation 3} \end{cases}$$

Solution

$$\begin{cases} x - 3y + z = 1 \\ 5y - 4z = 0 \\ x + 2y - 3z = -1 \end{cases}$$

Adding -2 times the first equation to the second equation produces a new second equation.

$$\begin{cases} x - 3y + z = 1 \\ 5y - 4z = 0 \\ 5y - 4z = -2 \end{cases}$$

Adding -1 times the first equation to the third equation produces a new third equation.

$$\begin{cases} x - 3y + z = 1 \\ 5y - 4z = 0 \\ 0 = -2 \end{cases}$$

Adding -1 times the second equation to the third equation produces a new third equation.

Because $0 = -2$ is a false statement, you can conclude that this system is inconsistent and so has no solution. Moreover, because this system is equivalent to the original system, you can conclude that the original system also has no solution.

✓CHECKPOINT   Now try Exercise 21.

As with a system of linear equations in two variables, the number of solutions of a system of linear equations in more than two variables must fall into one of three categories.

The Number of Solutions of a Linear System

For a system of linear equations, exactly one of the following is true.

1. There is exactly one solution.

2. There are infinitely many solutions.

3. There is no solution.

A system of linear equations is called *consistent* if it has at least one solution. A consistent system with exactly one solution is **independent.** A consistent system with infinitely many solutions is **dependent.** A system of linear equations is called *inconsistent* if it has no solution.

Example 4 A System with Infinitely Many Solutions

Solve the system of linear equations.

$$\begin{cases} x + y - 3z = -1 & \text{Equation 1} \\ y - z = 0 & \text{Equation 2} \\ -x + 2y = 1 & \text{Equation 3} \end{cases}$$

Solution

$$\begin{cases} x + y - 3z = -1 \\ y - z = 0 \\ 3y - 3z = 0 \end{cases}$$

Adding the first equation to the third equation produces a new third equation.

$$\begin{cases} x + y - 3z = -1 \\ y - z = 0 \\ 0 = 0 \end{cases}$$

Adding -3 times the second equation to the third equation produces a new third equation.

This result means that Equation 3 depends on Equations 1 and 2 in the sense that it gives us no additional information about the variables. So, the original system is equivalent to the system

$$\begin{cases} x + y - 3z = -1 \\ y - z = 0 \end{cases}.$$

In the last equation, solve for y in terms of z to obtain $y = z$. Back-substituting for y in the previous equation produces $x = 2z - 1$. Finally, letting $z = a$, where a is a real number, the solutions to the original system are all of the form

$$x = 2a - 1, \qquad y = a, \qquad \text{and} \qquad z = a.$$

So, every ordered triple of the form

$$(2a - 1, a, a), \qquad a \text{ is a real number}$$

is a solution of the system.

✓**CHECKPOINT** Now try Exercise 25.

In Example 4, there are other ways to write the same infinite set of solutions. For instance, the solutions could have been written as

$$\left(b, \tfrac{1}{2}(b + 1), \tfrac{1}{2}(b + 1)\right), \qquad b \text{ is a real number.}$$

This description produces the same set of solutions, as shown below.

Substitution	*Solution*	
$a = 0$	$(2(0) - 1, 0, 0) = (-1, 0, 0)$	Same solution
$b = -1$	$\left(-1, \tfrac{1}{2}(-1 + 1), \tfrac{1}{2}(-1 + 1)\right) = (-1, 0, 0)$	
$a = 1$	$(2(1) - 1, 1, 1) = (1, 1, 1)$	Same solution
$b = 1$	$\left(1, \tfrac{1}{2}(1 + 1), \tfrac{1}{2}(1 + 1)\right) = (1, 1, 1)$	
$a = 2$	$(2(2) - 1, 2, 2) = (3, 2, 2)$	Same solution
$b = 3$	$\left(3, \tfrac{1}{2}(3 + 1), \tfrac{1}{2}(3 + 1)\right) = (3, 2, 2)$	

STUDY TIP

There are an infinite number of solutions to Example 4, but they are all of a specific form. By selecting, for example, a-values of 0, 1, and 3, you can verify that $(-1, 0, 0)$, $(1, 1, 1)$, and $(5, 3, 3)$ are specific solutions. It is incorrect to say simply that the solution to Example 4 is "infinite." You must also specify the form of the solutions.

Nonsquare Systems

So far, each system of linear equations you have looked at has been *square*, which means that the number of equations is equal to the number of variables. In a **nonsquare system of equations,** the number of equations differs from the number of variables. A system of linear equations cannot have a unique solution unless there are at least as many equations as there are variables in the system.

Example 5   A System with Fewer Equations than Variables

Solve the system of linear equations.

$$\begin{cases} x - 2y + z = 2 & \text{Equation 1} \\ 2x - y - z = 1 & \text{Equation 2} \end{cases}$$

Solution

Begin by rewriting the system in row-echelon form.

$$\begin{cases} x - 2y + z = 2 \\ 3y - 3z = -3 \end{cases}$$

> Adding -2 times the first equation to the second equation produces a new second equation.

$$\begin{cases} x - 2y + z = 2 \\ y - z = -1 \end{cases}$$

> Multiplying the second equation by $\frac{1}{3}$ produces a new second equation.

Solve for y in terms of z to obtain $y = z - 1$. By back-substituting into Equation 1, you can solve for x as follows.

$$x - 2(z - 1) + z = 2 \qquad \text{Substitute for } y \text{ in Equation 1.}$$

$$x - 2z + 2 + z = 2 \qquad \text{Distributive Property}$$

$$x = z \qquad \text{Solve for } x.$$

Finally, by letting $z = a$ where a is a real number, you have the solution $x = a$, $y = a - 1$, and $z = a$. So, every ordered triple of the form

$$(a, a - 1, a), \qquad a \text{ is a real number}$$

is a solution of the system.

✓CHECKPOINT   Now try Exercise 37.

In Example 5, try choosing some values of a to obtain different solutions of the system, such as $(1, 0, 1)$, $(2, 1, 2)$, and $(3, 2, 3)$. Then check each of the solutions in the original system, as follows.

Check: $(1, 0, 1)$ *Check:* $(2, 1, 2)$ *Check:* $(3, 2, 3)$

$$1 - 2(0) + 1 \overset{?}{=} 2 \qquad 2 - 2(1) + 2 \overset{?}{=} 2 \qquad 3 - 2(2) + 3 \overset{?}{=} 2$$
$$2 = 2 \checkmark \qquad\qquad 2 = 2 \checkmark \qquad\qquad 2 = 2 \checkmark$$

$$2(1) - 0 - 1 \overset{?}{=} 1 \qquad 2(2) - 1 - 2 \overset{?}{=} 1 \qquad 2(3) - 2 - 3 \overset{?}{=} 1$$
$$1 = 1 \checkmark \qquad\qquad 1 = 1 \checkmark \qquad\qquad 1 = 1 \checkmark$$

Graphical Interpretation of Three-Variable Systems

Solutions of equations in three variables can be pictured using a **three-dimensional coordinate system.** To construct such a system, begin with the xy-coordinate plane in a horizontal position. Then draw the z-axis as a vertical line through the origin.

Every ordered triple (x, y, z) corresponds to a point on the three-dimensional coordinate system. For instance, the points corresponding to

$$(-2, 5, 4), \quad (2, -5, 3), \quad \text{and} \quad (3, 3, -2)$$

are shown in Figure 5.16.

The **graph of an equation in three variables** consists of all points (x, y, z) that are solutions of the equation. The graph of a linear equation in three variables is a *plane*. Sketching graphs on a three-dimensional coordinate system is difficult because the sketch itself is only two-dimensional.

One technique for sketching a plane is to find the three points at which the plane intersects the axes. For instance, the plane

$$3x + 2y + 4z = 12$$

intersects the x-axis at the point $(4, 0, 0)$, the y-axis at the point $(0, 6, 0)$, and the z-axis at the point $(0, 0, 3)$. By plotting these three points, connecting them with line segments, and shading the resulting triangular region, you can sketch a portion of the graph, as shown in Figure 5.17.

The graph of a system of three linear equations in three variables consists of *three* planes. When these planes intersect in a single point, the system has exactly one solution (see Figure 5.18). When the three planes have no point in common, the system has no solution (see Figures 5.19 and 5.20). When the three planes intersect in a line or a plane, the system has infinitely many solutions (see Figures 5.21 and 5.22).

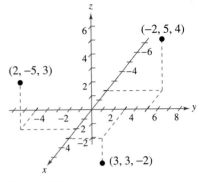

Figure 5.16

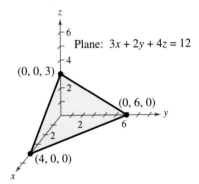

Figure 5.17

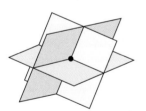

Solution: One point
Figure 5.18

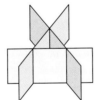

Solution: None
Figure 5.19

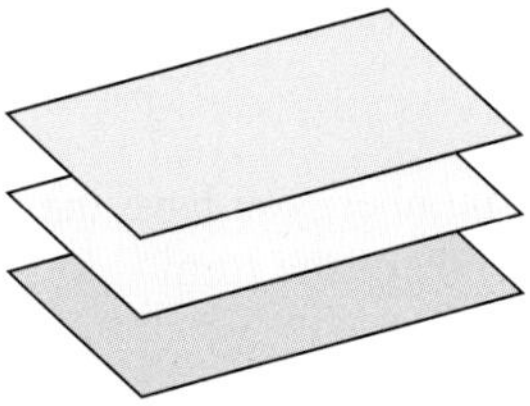

Solution: None
Figure 5.20

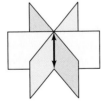

Solution: One line
Figure 5.21

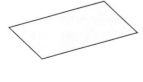

Solution: One plane
Figure 5.22

TECHNOLOGY TIP

Three-dimensional graphing utilities and computer algebra systems, such as *Derive* and *Mathematica*, are very efficient in producing three-dimensional graphs. They are good tools to use while studying calculus. If you have access to such a utility, try reproducing the plane shown in Figure 5.17.